TEACHER'S EDITION

STUDY GUIDES FOR

SOLVING
ALGEBRAIC
WORD
PROBLEMS

Andrewdelle R. Hensley
Deerfield Beach High School
Deerfield Beach, Florida

Copyright © 1987
by South-Western Publishing Co.
Cincinnati, Ohio

All Rights Reserved

The text of this publication, or any part thereof, may be reproduced for use in classes for which *Study Guides for Solving Algebraic Word Problems* is the adopted text. It may not be reproduced in any manner whatsoever for any other purpose without permission in writing from the publisher.

ISBN: 0-538-28136-7

Published by

M38TE **SOUTH-WESTERN PUBLISHING CO.**

CINCINNATI   WEST CHICAGO, IL   DALLAS   LIVERMORE, CA

Printed in the United States of America   123456789H432109876

CONTENTS

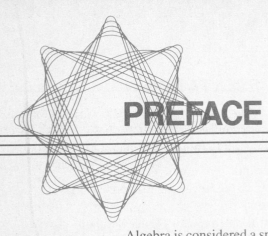

PREFACE

Algebra is considered a springboard for continuing the study of mathematics. Each student deserves a high quality of instruction in algebra. The overall objective of *Study Guides for Solving Algebraic Word Problems* is to help students overcome fears or despair associated with solving algebraic word problems. At the same time, students can gain insight and perspective in algebra and its applications.

FEATURES

Study Guides for Solving Algebraic Word Problems is a text-workbook with these features:

LEVELS OF COMPREHENSION—SIMPLE TO COMPLEX

Study Guides for Solving Algebraic Word Problems emphasizes skills for use in translating English sentences into mathematical sentences. This is accomplished by moving from the simple to the complex in a developmental manner. The thinking required to fully comprehend a word problem, set up an equation for it, solve the equation, and then check the solution has been organized into a single approach called levels of comprehension.

SCHEMATICS AND/OR TABULAR ARRANGEMENTS

To further enhance learning and comprehension and to supplement the text, schematics and/or tabular arrangements are included.

GROUP INSTRUCTION OR INDIVIDUALIZATION

Each study guide is designed to allow the student to progress according to individual ability. Allowance is made for class instruction as well as individual progression through each study guide.

CHALLENGE PROBLEMS

Each set of word problems ends with an advanced complex problem.

FLEXIBILITY

The format and design of *Study Guides for Solving Algebraic Word Problems* allows much flexibility. You may require the students to solve selected problems or all problems of each study guide. In addition, *Study Guides for Solving Algebraic Word Problems* is designed so that you may assign similar problems from any accompanying algebra text.

PLAN OF PRESENTATION

Study Guides for Solving Algebraic Word Problems is organized into an overview and 17 study guides that cover the basic topics of algebraic word problems. Each study guide follows this plan of presentation:

Terms and Concepts
Model Problems Using Levels of Comprehension
Activity Extension
Algebraic Word Problems with Partial Solutions Given
Algebraic Word Problems without Help Given

METHOD OF INSTRUCTION

Each study guide in *Study Guides for Solving Algebraic Word Problems* uses the same developmental approach and includes the following:

TERMS AND CONCEPTS

Fundamental, introductory precepts, which will usually already be meaningful to students, are presented for each particular type of algebraic word problem.

LEVELS OF COMPREHENSION

The levels of comprehension are five steps for solving any type of algebraic word problem.

STEP 1: Read the problem.
STEP 2: Choose the variable(s).
STEP 3: Form the equation.
STEP 4: Solve the equation.
STEP 5: Check the equation.

MODEL PROBLEMS

Model problems are presented as samples, guiding the student through each of the five levels of comprehension with student participation at all levels of comprehension. The guided approach is a deliberate attempt to build student confidence through competence.

The first level of comprehension is a *literal level* where facts about the algebraic word problem are stated. Then the text-workbook progresses to the *interpretive level,* which goes one step beyond the factual information. The meaning of the facts and their relations are explored as the variable is chosen. The *application level* involves translating the English sentences into mathematical sentences, solving the equation, and checking the equation. To be successful, the student must follow the sequence of levels of comprehension. The *activity extension* poses questions to test the students' understanding not only of the model problems but also of a closely allied problem.

ALGEBRAIC WORD PROBLEMS

Two sets of algebraic word problems are included with each study guide. The first set uses a guided approach with partial solutions and hints for solving the problems. The second set of problems requires a student to apply the five levels of comprehension independently.

TEACHER'S EDITION

The following features of the *Teacher's Edition* of *Study Guides for Solving Algebraic Word Problems* will help you in developing students' skills for solving algebraic word problems:

- *Detailed solutions* are given for all model problems and for each algebraic word problem.

- *Marginal notes* provide helpful teaching suggestions.

- A *study guide supplement* is included for each study guide. These supplements provide additional teaching suggestions, problems (with solutions) for individual and/or class discussions, and space for any relevant teacher notes regarding instruction and/or assignments. Transparency masters are included for use with the overview unit.

- A *cumulative test master* and *solutions* are included. The test master has one algebraic word problem for each of the 17 types of word problems discussed in the text-workbook.

- *Individual and class assessment sheets* provide evaluation guidelines for solving algebraic word problems using the levels of comprehension.

Study Guides for Solving Algebraic Word Problems is the result of many years of experience during which concept-building and this unique approach to solving algebraic word problems were analyzed thoroughly.

Andrewdelle R. Hensley

TEACHING SUGGESTIONS

The degree to which solving algebraic word problems is perplexing varies from problem to problem, student to student, text to text, teacher to teacher, and class to class. These teaching suggestions will help you to use *Study Guides for Solving Algebraic Word Problems* successfully:

1. Realize that the student's grade level is insignificant if the student is ready for algebra.

2. The study guides enhance instruction for *any* accompanying algebra text.

3. Use Transparency Master 1 and Transparency Master 2 to discuss the overview unit. To convert these masters into transparencies, use a thermocopier. On many thermocopiers, you merely place the plastic transparency sheet on top of the master (or a photocopy of the master) and feed both sheets through the thermocopier. Use colored pens to highlight material on the transparency.

4. First present each type of word problem using the material in the accompanying algebra text. Follow the text presentation with the levels-of-comprehension approach used in *Study Guides for Solving Algebraic Word Problems*.

5. Be sure to emphasize that students should follow the levels of comprehension in *written* form. Verify that each student is participating in the development levels.

6. Be familiar with all terminology and word problems *before* presenting them.

7. Before introducing each study guide topic, review the related study guide supplement (pages TE8–TE16) for additional teaching suggestions and problems (with solutions) for individual and/or class discussions. Record your teaching notes regarding instruction and/or assignments on the study guide supplements.

8. Make sure students always round off their answers using the $\frac{5}{4}$ rule unless they are instructed otherwise.

   Example: $0.85 = 0.9$ (to nearest tenth) and $0.84 = 0.8$ (to nearest tenth)

9. Group-pace your students while they solve the model problems unless you are individualizing instruction with an honors class. Assist students

individually as they do the first set of problems or pace the entire group, as the class requires. The students should work independently on the second set of word problems. Encourage all students to try the challenge problems.

10. Discuss the evaluation method for the study guides. You may develop your own evaluation standards, or you may assign ten points for each word problem in the second set of word problems. Then, to emphasize the importance of the levels of comprehension, assign partial credit for each word problem as follows: two points for successful completion of the statement and/or schematic levels, three points for correct equation formation, three points for solving the equation correctly, and two points for checking the equation correctly. You may photocopy the assessment sheets (pages TE31–TE32) to record the evaluation of each student's problems. You may also use the assessment sheet to determine mastery and weaknesses for each type of word problem on an individual basis (page TE31) or on a group basis (page TE32).

CUMULATIVE TEST

The cumulative test master (pages TE19–TE23) has one algebraic word problem for each of the 17 types of word problems discussed in *Study Guides for Solving Algebraic Word Problems*. The number of each word problem is correlated with the study guide number. For instance, problem 1 is related to Study Guide 1. You may photocopy this test to use as a final test. The solutions for the test are given on pages TE24–TE30. You may use the Class Assessment Sheet to determine mastery and weaknesses for each type of word problem on an individual basis (page TE31) or on a group basis (page TE32).

STUDY GUIDE SUPPLEMENTS

OVERVIEW

The overview unit is designed to give the students an overview of *Study Guides for Solving Algebraic Word Problems*.

It is important to note that $\frac{1}{3}n = 10$ is more simply stated as $n = 30$. Also, the equations $2n = 80$, $4n = 160$, and $8n = 320$ may be stated more simply as $n = 40$.

The overview emphasizes use of basic properties to simplify problems. Use Transparency Masters 1 and 2 (pages TE17–TE18) to discuss the classification of numbers and their properties.

Simplify each of the following expressions.

1. $999 + 17 + 1 = $ ___1017___
2. $98 + 6 + 2 + 500 = $ ___606___
3. $\dfrac{3}{4} + \dfrac{7}{8} + \dfrac{1}{4} + \dfrac{1}{8} + \dfrac{9}{10} = $ ___$2\frac{9}{10}$___
4. $0.98 + 0.17 + 0.02 + 0.83 + 2.5 = $ ___4.5___
5. $98 + (-2) + 100 + 2 + 2 = $ ___200___

Teacher's Notes:

STUDY GUIDE 1: NUMBER (ELEMENTARY)

Make sure students understand fraction, decimal, and percent equivalents.

1. Common fractions

$\dfrac{1}{4} = 0.25 = 25$ percent $\dfrac{2}{10} = \dfrac{1}{5} = 0.20 = 20$ percent $\dfrac{6}{10} = \dfrac{3}{5} = 0.60 = 60$ percent

$\dfrac{1}{2} = 0.50 = 50$ percent $\dfrac{3}{10} = 0.30 = 30$ percent $\dfrac{7}{10} = 0.70 = 70$ percent

$\dfrac{3}{4} = 0.75 = 75$ percent $\dfrac{4}{10} = \dfrac{2}{5} = 0.40 = 40$ percent $\dfrac{8}{10} = \dfrac{4}{5} = 0.80 = 80$ percent

$\dfrac{1}{10} = 0.10 = 10$ percent $\dfrac{5}{10} = \dfrac{1}{2} = 0.50 = 50$ percent $\dfrac{9}{10} = 0.90 = 90$ percent

2. Other fractions

$$\frac{1}{3} = 0.33\frac{1}{3} = 33\frac{1}{3} \text{ percent}$$

$$\frac{2}{3} = 0.66\frac{2}{3} = 66\frac{2}{3} \text{ percent}$$

$$\frac{5}{8} = 0.62\frac{1}{2} = 62\frac{1}{2} \text{ percent}$$

$$\frac{7}{8} = 0.87\frac{1}{2} = 87\frac{1}{2} \text{ percent}$$

$$\frac{1}{6} = 0.16\frac{2}{3} = 16\frac{2}{3} \text{ percent}$$

$$\frac{5}{6} = 0.83\frac{1}{3} = 83\frac{1}{3} \text{ percent}$$

3. Fractions less than 1 are less than 100 percent.

$$\frac{3}{4} = \frac{75}{100} = 75 \text{ percent}$$

4. Fractions equal to 1 are equal to 100 percent.

$$\frac{8}{8} = 1.00 = 100 \text{ percent}$$

5. Fractions greater than 1 are greater than 100 percent.

$$\frac{5}{2} = \frac{250}{100} = 250 \text{ percent}$$

6. Percents less than 1 percent

$$0.8 \text{ percent} = 0.008 = \frac{8}{1000} = \frac{1}{125}$$

$$\frac{1}{2} \text{ percent} = 0.5 \text{ percent} = 0.005 = \frac{5}{1000} = \frac{1}{200}$$

Teacher's Notes:

STUDY GUIDE 2: RATIOS

A ratio is an indicated quotient: 3:4 means $4\overline{)3}$, and 4:3 means $3\overline{)4}$.

Solve the following equations.

1. $\dfrac{7}{x} = \dfrac{8}{16}$ $x = \underline{\ 14\ }$

2. $\dfrac{3}{5} = \dfrac{6}{x}$ $x = \underline{\ 10\ }$

3. $\dfrac{81}{27} = \dfrac{x}{3}$ $x = \underline{\ 9\ }$

4. $\dfrac{8}{100} = \dfrac{16}{x}$ $x = \underline{\ 200\ }$

5. $\dfrac{74}{6} = \dfrac{37}{x}$ $x = \underline{\ 3\ }$

Teacher's Notes:

STUDY GUIDE 3: PROPORTIONS

$\frac{8}{4}$ means $4\overline{)8}^{2}$ and implies that $4 \times 2 = 8$. $\frac{0}{4}$ means $4\overline{)0}^{0}$ and implies that $4 \times 0 = 0$. $\frac{4}{0}$ means $0\overline{)4}^{?}$, but $0 \times$ (what?) $= 4$? If a number is placed as the quotient, then $N \cdot 0$ should equal 4, but is there a number times zero whose product is 4? *No.* This would contradict the property of zero in multiplication: $N \cdot 0 = 0$.

Solve for the unknown.

1. $\dfrac{3}{3 - n} = \dfrac{7}{10}$ $n = -\dfrac{9}{7} = -1\dfrac{2}{7}$

2. $\dfrac{4}{10 + n} = \dfrac{3}{10}$ $n = \dfrac{10}{3} = 3\dfrac{1}{3}$

3. $\dfrac{8}{16} = \dfrac{4}{2 + n}$ $n = 6$

4. $\dfrac{15}{75} = \dfrac{n}{100}$ $n = 20$

5. $\dfrac{1}{10 - 5n} = \dfrac{20}{700}$ $n = -5$

Teacher's Notes:

STUDY GUIDE 4: THE LEVER

All students tend to recall playing on a seesaw. They should be able to apply the principles they learned there to this study guide.

Solve for the unknown.

1. $80(5) = 40(n - 5)$ $n = \underline{15}$

2. $90(10) = 50(n - 10)$ $n = \underline{28}$

3. $20(6) = 30(n - 6)$ $n = \underline{10}$

4. $120(8) = 60(n + 8)$ $n = \underline{8}$

5. $100(7) = 50(n + 2)$ $n = \underline{12}$

Teacher's Notes:

STUDY GUIDE 5: AVERAGES

Understanding how to find an average should enable students to better understand evaluation of the requirements in this course.

Solve for the unknown.

1. $\dfrac{60 + 80 + 50 + 50}{4} = a$ $\underline{\quad a = 60 \quad}$

2. $\dfrac{70 + n}{2} = 70$ $\underline{\quad n = 70 \quad}$

3. $\dfrac{n + n + n}{3} = 60$ $\underline{\quad n = 60 \quad}$

4. $\dfrac{90 + 80 + 70}{3} = a$ $\underline{\quad a = 80 \quad}$

5. $\dfrac{50 + 60 + n}{3} = 70$ $\underline{\quad n = 100 \quad}$

Teacher's Notes:

STUDY GUIDE 6: DIGITS

1. Complete these statements:

   In 26, 2 is the tens digit and $\underline{\quad 6 \quad}$ is the units digit. In 48, 4 is the $\underline{\quad\text{tens}\quad}$ digit and $\underline{\quad 8 \quad}$ is the units digit. In 98, $\underline{\quad 9 \quad}$ is the tens digit and $\underline{\quad 8 \quad}$ is the units digit. The number 26 becomes $\underline{\quad 62 \quad}$ if the tens digit and the units digit are interchanged.

2. Solve for t and u.

   $t + u = 6$ (where $t > u$)

   $10t + u - (10u + t) = 18$

   1. $t + u = 6$

   2. $\underline{10t + u - 10u - t = 18}$

1. $t + u = 6$
2. $9t - 9u = 18$

$\overline{}$

1. $9t + 9u = 54$
2. $+9t - 9u = 18$

$\overline{}$

$18t = 72$

$t = 4$

$t + u = 6$

$4 + u = 6$

$u = 2$

$$\underline{t = 4, u = 2}$$

Teacher's Notes:

STUDY GUIDE 7: INTEGERS

Proof is important in mathematics. Please use marginal proof in this study guide.

Solve for the unknown:

1. $n + (n + 2) = 78$

$2n + 2 = 78$

$2n = 76$

$n = 38$

2. $n + (n + 2) + (n + 4) = 96$

$3n + 6 = 96$

$3n = 90$

$n = 30$

3. $n + (n + 1) + (n + 2) = 123$

$3n + 3 = 123$

$3n = 120$

$n = 40$

4. $n + (n - 2) = 50$

$2n - 2 = 50$

$2n = 52$

$n = 26$

5. $(n + 1) + (n + 2) - (n + 4) = 79$

$2n + 3 - n - 4 = 79$

$n - 1 = 79$

$n = 80$

Teacher's Notes:

STUDY GUIDE 8: AGE

Complete these statements:

1. If Jane is 42 years old now, then four years ago she was ___38___ years old. Four years from she will be ___46___ years old.

2. If Jon is 82 years old now, then ___20___ years ago he was 62 years old. Twenty years from now, Jon will be ___102___ years old.

3. If you are 14 years old now, then someone half your age is ___seven___ years old.

4. If you are 40 years old now, then two years from now, you will be ___42___ years old.

5. If James is 80 years old now, ___x___ years from now, James will be $80 + x$ years old. James was ___$80 - x$___ years old x years ago.

Teacher's Notes:

STUDY GUIDE 9: DISTANCE, RATE, TIME

Let's consider the speed of a car—60 miles per hour. Every student knows that you do not enter a car already traveling 60 miles per hour, stay in the car for three hours traveling at a rate of 60 miles per hour, and jump out at your grandmother's house while the car is still traveling 60 miles per hour! If you could do this, the average rate of speed is 60 miles per hour.

On the contrary, you travel three hours to reach your grandmother's house. The speed fluctuates as you stop, start, slow down, pass other cars, etc. Divide distance by time to determine the rate of speed. Divide distance by rate to determine the time. Distance is equal to rate times time.

Of interest to most high school students is the rate of speed in auto racing. Qualifying time is usually around 200 miles per hour.

Teacher's Notes:

STUDY GUIDE 10: AIR TRAVEL

Air travel involves many factors—air speed, wind speed, ground speed, tail wind, and head wind. A tail wind *increases* speed. A head wind *decreases* speed. Make sure that the problems about air travel are presented as elementary problems. Pilots must know a great deal about trigonometry, also.

Teacher's Notes:

STUDY GUIDE 11: MIXTURES

Concrete is a mixture of cement, sand, and water. The parts associated with each could just as well be mentioned as proportions. See if some students can find out how many parts cement, water, and sand go into the pouring of a concrete patio.

Have students solve two equations in two unknowns. Here's a sample problem:

1. $m - t = 12$
2. $3m + t = 4$

$4m = 16$

$m = 4$

$m - t = 12$

$4 - t = 12$

$-t = 8$

$t = -8$

$m = 4, t = -8$

Teacher's Notes:

STUDY GUIDE 12: SOLUTIONS

Solve these problems.

1. If 12 pounds of rose water are used in a solution and six pounds of glycerine are added to the rose water, then the rose water–glycerine solution would weigh __18__ pounds. Rose water is 12 pounds of the 18 pounds, or __$66\frac{2}{3}$ percent__ of the solution. Six pounds of glycerine is $\frac{6}{18}$ or __$33\frac{1}{3}$ percent__ of the solution.

2. Iodine is added to baby oil for suntan purposes. Ann uses two parts of iodine to ten parts of baby oil. If she uses two tablespoons of iodine and ten tablespoons of baby oil, the solution will contain __12 tablespoons__. The iodine represents $\frac{2}{12}$ or $\frac{1}{6}$ = __$16\frac{2}{3}$ percent__ of the solution. The baby oil represents $\frac{10}{12}$ or $\frac{5}{6}$ = __$83\frac{1}{3}$ percent__ of the solution. The percent of iodine + the percent of baby oil should equal __100 percent__.

Teacher's Notes:

STUDY GUIDE 13: GEOMETRY

Students are interested in the five Platonic solids—tetrahedron, cube, octahedron, dodecahedron, and icosahedron. Your school's Media Center may have information on how to make these, and on what their historical value is.

Recognition of the basic three-dimensional figures and the plane figures will aid their next step into geometry.

Teacher's Notes:

STUDY GUIDE 14: COINS

Students who participate in money-making projects understand coins and rolls of money. One thing that all students must understand is that 0.50¢ is not fifty cents but $\frac{1}{2}$ of a cent. Discuss millage (1 mill is $\frac{1}{10}$ of a cent) as a part of tax levying.

Teacher's Notes:

STUDY GUIDE 15: INVESTMENT

Students should be aware that the higher the risk involved in an investment, the higher the interest rate is. Emphasize the difference between simple interest and compound interest.

Teacher's Notes:

STUDY GUIDE 16: WORK

Complete these statements:

1. If Tom paints $\frac{1}{5}$ of a fence, then _____$\frac{4}{5}$_____ remains to be painted.

2. If Jane sells $\frac{1}{8}$ of the magazines sold at school and John sells $\frac{3}{8}$ of the magazines sold, then _____$\frac{1}{2}$_____ of the magazines are sold by salespeople other than Jane and John.

Discuss the complex fraction, using this example:

$$\frac{\dfrac{a}{b}}{\dfrac{c}{d}} = \frac{ad}{bc}$$

Example: $\dfrac{\dfrac{3}{4}}{\dfrac{7}{8}} = \dfrac{24}{28} = \dfrac{6}{7}$

Solve these equations.

1. $\dfrac{1}{2} + \dfrac{1}{3} = \dfrac{1}{x}$ $x = \dfrac{6}{5}$

2. $\dfrac{x}{4} + \dfrac{x}{2} = 1$ $x = \dfrac{4}{3}$

3. $\dfrac{x}{10} + \dfrac{x}{5} + \dfrac{x}{2} = 1$ $x = \dfrac{10}{8}$

4. $\dfrac{1}{4} + \dfrac{1}{10} = \dfrac{1}{x}$ $x = \dfrac{20}{7}$

5. $\dfrac{1}{8} + \dfrac{3}{8} + \dfrac{1}{x} = 1$ $x = 2$

Teacher's Notes:

STUDY GUIDE 17: SOLVING EQUATIONS FOR ONE VARIABLE IN TERMS OF OTHER VARIABLES

Solve each equation for x.

1. $y = mx + b$

$mx + b = y$

$mx = y - b$

$x = \dfrac{y - b}{m}$ $x = \dfrac{y - b}{m}$

2. $a + x + y = z$

$x = z - y - a$ $x = z - y - a$

3. $y - y_1 = m(x - x_1)$

$y - y_1 = mx - mx_1$

$mx - mx_1 = y - y_1$

$mx = y - y_1 + mx_1$

$x = \dfrac{y - y_1 + mx_1}{m}$ $x = \dfrac{y - y_1 + mx_1}{m}$

Teacher's Notes:

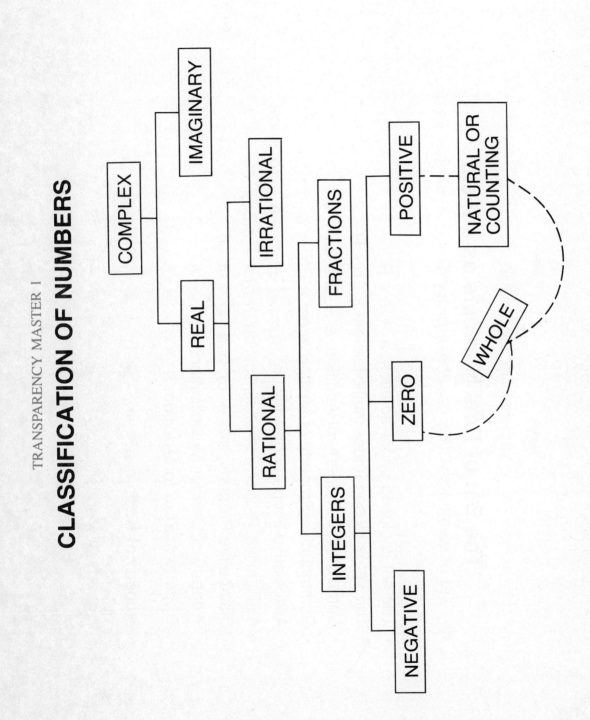

TRANSPARENCY MASTER 1

CLASSIFICATION OF NUMBERS

The Set of Real Numbers as a Field

Any set of elements which has these properties is a number field:

- The set is closed under addition: $a + b \in R$
- The set is closed under multiplication: $a \cdot b \in R$
- Commutative Property of Addition: $a + b = b + a$
- Commutative Property of Multiplication: $a \cdot b = b \cdot a$
- Associative Property of Addition: $(a + b) + c = a + (b + c)$
- Associative Property of Multiplication: $(ab)c = a(bc)$
- Distributive Property: $a(b + c) = a \cdot b + a \cdot c$
- Property of One for Multiplication: $a \cdot 1 = a$
- Property of Zero for Addition: $a + 0 = a$
- Property of Reciprocals: $a \cdot \dfrac{1}{a} = 1, \quad a \neq 0$
- Property of Opposites: $a + (-a) = 0$

Name _____ Period _____

Teacher _____ Date _____ Grade _____

Cumulative Test: Solving Algebraic Word Problems

1. Jane has 40 more necklaces than Donna. Together they have 188 necklaces. How many necklaces does each girl have?

Let n = the number of necklaces Donna owns.

Donna : _____

Jane: _____

2. In a store's Christmas decorating department, there are red and green ornaments in a barrel in the ratio of 7:2. If there are 999 ornaments in the barrel, how many ornaments are red and how many are green?

Let x = the number by which 7 and 2 are to be multiplied.

Red: _____

Green: _____

3. A farmers' market sold watermelons and honeydews in the ratio of 25 to 12. If the market sold 48 honeydews, how many watermelons did the market sell?

Let n = the number of watermelons.

4. Joe weighs 70 pounds and sits six feet from the fulcrum of a seesaw. Jack weighs 42 pounds. How many feet from the fulcrum must Jack sit in order to balance Joe?

   Let n = the number of feet Jack sits from fulcrum.

   _____

5. Mary has three test grades of 70, 80 and 90. Beth has two test grades of 60 and 90. What grade must Beth make on her third test in order to have the same average as Mary?

   Let g = the grade Beth must make on third test.

   _____

6. Rita and Jamie live next door to each other. The sum of Rita's house number and Jamie's house number is 70 and the difference of Rita's house number and Jamie's house number is 10. (Rita's number is greater than Jamie's number.) Find the number of each house.

   Let r = Rita's house number.
   Let j = Jamie's house number.

   Rita:
   Jamie:
   _____

7. The sum of three consecutive seat numbers is 354. Find the three numbers.

   Let n = the first seat number.

   First seat:
   Second seat:
   Third seat:
   _____

8. Mame is now ten years older than Jane. The sum of their ages 20 years ago was 50. What is the sum of their ages now?

   Let m = Jane's age now (in years).

   _____

9. Mrs. Smith travels due east at 60 miles per hour. Her daughter, who lives 800 miles due east from her, travels due west at 40 miles per hour in a disabled car. If both travel the same number of hours, how many miles does Mrs. Smith's daughter travel in the disabled car before they meet?

   Let t = the time Mrs. Smith and daughter travel (in hours).

Traveler	Distance	Rate	Time
Mrs. Smith			t
Daughter			t

   _____

10. The air speed of an evacuation plane was 400 miles per hour. If the plane could travel the same distance in four hours with the wind as it flew in six hours against the wind, what was the wind speed?

    Let w = the wind speed (in miles/hour).

Wind direction	Ground speed	Time	Distance
Tail wind			
Head wind			

    _____

11. Chocolate truffles sell for $20 per pound. Raspberry creams sell for $15 per pound. How many pounds of each should be placed in a ten-pound box retailing for $180?

    Let t = the number of pounds of truffles.

Ingredient	Number of pounds	Price per pound	Value in dollars
Truffles			
Raspberry			
Mixture			

Truffles: _____

Raspberries: _____

12. Dr. Abel has a grant for research. In one project he uses two ounces of plutonium. How many ounces of another unknown chemical testing one percent plutonium must he use in order for the final solution to test two percent plutonium?

Let n = the number of ounces of the mystery chemical.

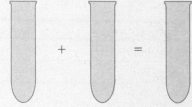

_____

13. A highway department employee must find the area of the shaded region in the figure below this problem in order to know the amount of blacktop to be poured to resurface a road. Using the figure, how many square feet of blacktop will be used for a turn from one street to another? The area of the circle equals πr^2, where r = 10 feet and $\pi \cong 3.14$. One s equals 20 feet.

Let a = the area of the shaded region (in square feet).

_____

14. A bag contained 1,000 more nickels than quarters and 500 more dimes than quarters. If the total was $500, how many coins of each kind were in the bag?

Let n = the number of quarters.

Coins	Number	Value of each (in dollars)	Total value (in dollars)
Quarters			
Nickels			
Dimes			
Total			

Quarters:
Nickels:
Dimes:

15. James invested $10,000 in municipal bonds paying ten percent interest per year. How much should he invest in municipal bonds paying 12 percent interest per year in order for his yearly income to be $3,400 from these two investments?

Let n = the amount of investment paying 12 percent interest (in dollars).

Investment	Dollars	Rate	Interest for one year, in dollars
Ten percent bonds			
Twelve percent bonds			

16. Miss Smith can grade 500 papers in 10 hours. Mr. Ezra can grade 500 papers in 8 hours. All papers are the same. How long would it take them, working together, to grade 500 papers?

Let x = the number of hours it would take Miss Smith and Mr. Ezra to grade papers by working together.

17. Solve the following equation for b_2:

$$A = \frac{1}{2}h\,(b_1 + b_2)$$

Solutions for Cumulative Test, Pages TE19–TE23

1. Let n = the number of necklaces Donna owns.

$n + 40$ = number of necklaces Jane owns
$n + (n + 40) = 188$
$n + n + 40 = 188$
$2n + 40 = 188$
$2n = 148$
$n = 74$ (number of necklaces Donna has)
$n + 40 = 114$ (number of necklaces Jane has)

Donna: 74
Jane: 114

Check: $n + (n + 40) = 188$
$74 + (74 + 40) = 188$
$74 + 114 = 188$
$188 = 188$

2. Let x = the number by which 7 and 2 are to be multiplied.

$7x$ = number of red ornaments
$2x$ = number of green ornaments
$7x + 2x = 999$
$9x = 999$
$x = 111$ (number by which 7 and 2 are to be multiplied)
$7 \cdot 111 = 777$ (number of red ornaments)
$2 \cdot 111 = 222$ (number of green ornaments)

Red: 777
Green: 222

Check: $7x + 2x = 999$
$7 \cdot 111 + 2 \cdot 111 = 999$
$999 = 999$

3. Let n = the number of watermelons.

$\dfrac{25}{12} = \dfrac{n}{48}$
$12n = 1{,}200$
$n = 100$ (number of watermelons)

100 watermelons

Check: $\dfrac{25}{12} = \dfrac{n}{48}$
$\dfrac{25}{12} = \dfrac{100}{48}$
$1{,}200 = 1{,}200$

4. Let n = the number of feet Jack sits from fulcrum.

$42n = 70 \cdot 6$
$42n = 420$
$n = 10$ (number of feet Jack sits from fulcrum)

10 feet

Check: $42n = 70 \cdot 6$
$42 \cdot 10 = 420$
$420 = 420$

5. Let g = the grade Beth must make on third test.

$$\frac{70 + 80 + 90}{3} = \frac{60 + 90 + g}{3}$$

$$\frac{240}{3} = \frac{150 + g}{3}$$

$240 = 150 + g$
$g = 90$ (grade Beth must make on third test)

          90
          _____

Check: $\dfrac{70 + 80 + 90}{3} = \dfrac{60 + 90 + g}{3}$

$$\frac{70 + 80 + 90}{3} = \frac{60 + 90 + 90}{3}$$

$$\frac{240}{3} = \frac{240}{3}$$

$80 = 80$

6. Let r = Rita's house number; j = Jamie's house number.

1. $r + j = 70$
2. $+r - j = 10$
      $2r$ $=$ 80
     $r = 40$ (Rita's number)
     $r + j = 70$
     $40 + j = 70$
     $j = 30$ (Jamie's number)

Rita: 40
Jamie: 30
_____

Check 1: $r + j = 70$
           $40 + 30 = 70$
           $70 = 70$

Check 2: $r - j = 10$
           $40 - 30 = 10$
           $10 = 10$

7. Let n = the first seat number.

$n + 1$ = second seat number
$n + 2$ = third seat number
$n + (n + 1) + (n + 2) = 354$
$n + n + 1 + n + 2 = 354$
$3n + 3 = 354$
$3n = 351$
$n = 117$ (first seat number)
$n + 1 = 118$ (second seat number)
$n + 2 = 119$ (third seat number)

First seat: 117
Second seat: 118
Third seat: 119
_____

Check: $n + (n + 1) + (n + 2) = 354$
        $117 + (117 + 1) + (117 + 2) = 354$
        $117 + 118 + 119 = 354$
        $354 = 354$

8. Let m = Jane's age now (in years).

$m + 10$ = Mame's age now
$m - 20$ = Jane's age 20 years ago
$m + 10 - 20$ = Mame's age 20 years ago
$m - 20 + (m + 10 - 20) = 50$
$m - 20 + m + 10 - 20 = 50$
$2m - 30 = 50$
$2m = 80$
$m = 40$ (Jane's age now)
$m + 10 = 50$ (Mame's age now)
$50 + 40 = 90$ (sum of ages now)

**90 years**

Check: $m - 20 + (m + 10 - 20) = 50$
$40 - 20 + (40 + 10 - 20) = 50$
$20 + 30 = 50$
$50 = 50$

9.

Traveler	Distance	Rate	Time
Mrs. Smith	$60t$	60	t
Daughter	$40t$	40	t

$60t + 40t = 800$
$100t = 800$
$t = 8$ hours
$40t = 320$ miles (distance traveled by daughter)

**320 miles**

Check: $60t + 40t = 800$
$60 \cdot 8 + 40 \cdot 8 = 800$
$480 + 320 = 800$
$800 = 800$

10. Let w = the wind speed (in miles/hour).

400 miles/hour = air speed

Wind direction	Ground speed	Time	Distance
Tail wind	$400 + w$	4	$4(400 + w)$
Head wind	$400 - w$	6	$6(400 - w)$

$4(400 + w) = 6(400 - w)$
$1{,}600 + 4w = 2{,}400 - 6w$
$10w = 800$
$w = 80$ miles/hour

**80 miles/hour**

Check: $4(400 + w) = 6(400 - w)$
$4(400 + 80) = 6(400 - 80)$
$4(480) = 6(320)$
$1{,}920 = 1{,}920$

11. Let t = the number of pounds of truffles.

Ingredient	Number of pounds	Price per pound	Value in dollars
Truffles	t	$20	$20t$
Raspberry	$10 - t$	$15	$15(10 - t)$
Mixture	10	$18	$18(10)$

$20t + 15(10 - t) = 18(10)$
$20t + 150 - 15t = 180$
$5t + 150 = 180$
$5t = 30$
$t = 6$ (pounds of truffles)
$10 - t = 4$ (pounds of raspberry)

Truffles: **6 pounds**
Raspberries: **4 pounds**

Check: $20t + 15(10 - t) = 18(10)$
$20(6) + 15(10 - 6) = 18(10)$
$120 + 15(4) = 180$
$120 + 60 = 180$
$180 = 180$

12. Let n = the number of ounces of the mystery chemical.

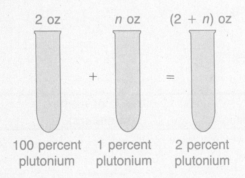

2 oz n oz $(2 + n)$ oz

100 percent plutonium   1 percent plutonium   2 percent plutonium

$1.00(2) + 0.01(n) = 0.02(2 + n)$
$100(2) + 1n = 2(2 + n)$
$200 + n = 4 + 2n$
$-n = -196$
$n = 196$ (number of ounces of mystery chemical)

196 ounces of the mystery chemical

Check: $1.00(2) + 0.01(n) = 0.02(2 + n)$
$1.00(2) + 0.01(196) = 0.02(2 + 196)$
$2 + 1.96 = 0.02(198)$
$3.96 = 3.96$

13. Let a = the area of the shaded region (in square feet).

$$a = \frac{s^2 - \pi r^2}{4}$$

$$a = \frac{20^2 - \pi \, 10^2}{4}$$

$$a = \frac{400 - 100\,\pi}{4}$$

$$a \cong \frac{400 - 100(3.14)}{4}$$

$$a \cong \frac{400 - 314}{4}$$

$$a \cong \frac{86}{4}$$

$$a \cong 21.5 \text{ square feet}$$

Approximately 21.5 square feet

Check: $a = \dfrac{s^2 - \pi r^2}{4}$

$$a = \frac{20^2 - \pi \, 10^2}{4}$$

$$21.5 \cong \frac{400 - 100\,\pi}{4}$$

$$21.5 \cong \frac{400 - 100(3.14)}{4}$$

$$21.5 \cong \frac{400 - 314}{4}$$

$$21.5 \cong \frac{86}{4}$$

$$21.5 \cong 21.5$$

14. Let $n =$ the number of quarters.

Coins	Number	Value of each (in dollars)	Total value (in dollars)
Quarters	n	$\dfrac{1}{4}$	$\dfrac{1}{4}n$
Nickels	$n + 1{,}000$	$\dfrac{1}{20}$	$\dfrac{1}{20}(n + 1{,}000)$
Dimes	$n + 500$	$\dfrac{1}{10}$	$\dfrac{1}{10}(n + 500)$
Total	—	—	

$$\frac{1}{4}n + \frac{1}{20}(n + 1{,}000) + \frac{1}{10}(n + 500) = 500$$

$$5n + n + 1{,}000 + 2(n + 500) = 10{,}000$$

$$5n + n + 1{,}000 + 2n + 1{,}000 = 10{,}000$$

$$8n + 2{,}000 = 10{,}000$$

$$8n = 8{,}000$$

$n = 1,000$ (number of quarters)
$n + 1,000 = 2,000$ (number of nickels)
$n + 500 = 1,500$ (number of dimes)

Quarters: 1,000
Nickels: 2,000
Dimes: 1,500

Check: $\frac{1}{4}n + \frac{1}{20}(n + 1,000) + \frac{1}{10}$ $500) = 500$

$\frac{1}{4}(1,000) + \frac{1}{20}(1,000 + 1,000) + \frac{1}{10}(1,000 + 500) = 500$

$250 + \frac{1}{20}(2,000) + \frac{1}{10}(1,500) = 500$

$250 + 100 + 150 = 500$

$500 = 500$

15. Let n = the amount of investment paying 12 percent interest (in dollars).

Investment	Dollars	Rate	Interest for one year, in dollars
Ten percent bonds	10,000	10 percent	0.10(1,000)
Twelve percent bonds	n	12 percent	0.12n

$0.10(10,000) + 0.12n = 3,400$
$1,000 + 0.12n = 3,400$
$0.12n = 2,400$
$n = 20,000$ (investment at 12 percent)

$20,000

Check: $0.10(10,000) + 0.12n = 3,400$
$0.10(10,000) + 0.12(20,000) = 3,400$
$1,000 + 2,400 = 3,400$
$3,400 = 3,400$

16. Let x = the number of hours it would take Miss Smith and Mr. Ezra to grade papers by working together.

$\frac{x}{10} + \frac{x}{8} = 1$
$4x + 5x = 40$
$9x = 40$
$x = 4\frac{4}{9}$ (hours to grade papers by working together)

$4\frac{4}{9}$ hours

Check: $\frac{x}{10} + \frac{x}{8} = 1$

$\frac{4\frac{4}{9}}{10} + \frac{4\frac{4}{9}}{8} = 1$

$\frac{\frac{40}{9}}{10} + \frac{\frac{40}{9}}{8} = 1$

$$\frac{40}{90} + \frac{40}{72} = 1$$

$$\frac{4}{9} + \frac{5}{9} = 1$$

$$1 = 1$$

17. $A = \frac{1}{2}h\,(b_1 + b_2)$

$2A = h(b_1 + b_2)$

$2A = b_1h + b_2h$

$2A - b_1h = b_2h$

$\dfrac{2A - b_1h}{h} = b_2$

$$b_2 = \frac{2A - b_1h}{h}$$

Check: $A = \frac{1}{2}h\,(b_1 + b_2)$

$A = \frac{1}{2}h\left(b_1 + \dfrac{2A - b_1h}{h}\right)$

$A = \frac{1}{2}h\left(\dfrac{b_1h}{h} + \dfrac{2A}{h} - \dfrac{b_1h}{h}\right)$

$A = \frac{1}{2}h\left(\dfrac{b_1h + 2A - b_1h}{h}\right)$

$A = \frac{1}{2}h\left(\dfrac{2A}{h}\right)$

$A = A$

Student's Name _____

Study Guide No. _____   Date _____

Individual Assessment Sheet

Problem	Statement and/or Schematic (2 points)	Equation (3 points)	Solving (3 points)	Checking (2 points)
1	_____	_____	_____	_____
2	_____	_____	_____	_____
3	_____	_____	_____	_____
4	_____	_____	_____	_____
5	_____	_____	_____	_____
6	_____	_____	_____	_____
7	_____	_____	_____	_____
8	_____	_____	_____	_____
9	_____	_____	_____	_____
10	_____	_____	_____	_____
11	_____	_____	_____	_____
Individual Scores	_____	_____	_____	_____
TOTAL SCORE	_____			

Class _____

Study Guide No. _____ or Cumulative Test   Date _____

Class Assessment Sheet

Problem	Statement and/or Schematic (2 points)	Equation (3 points)	Solving (3 points)	Checking (2 points)
1	_____	_____	_____	_____
2	_____	_____	_____	_____
3	_____	_____	_____	_____
4	_____	_____	_____	_____
5	_____	_____	_____	_____
6	_____	_____	_____	_____
7	_____	_____	_____	_____
8	_____	_____	_____	_____
9	_____	_____	_____	_____
10	_____	_____	_____	_____
11	_____	_____	_____	_____
12	_____	_____	_____	_____
13	_____	_____	_____	_____
14	_____	_____	_____	_____
15	_____	_____	_____	_____
16	_____	_____	_____	_____
17	_____	_____	_____	_____
Individual Scores	_____	_____	_____	_____
TOTAL SCORE	_____	_____	_____	_____
Number Tested	_____	_____	_____	_____
Average Points	_____	_____	_____	_____
Percent Correct	_____	_____	_____	_____

Numerical Average for Class: _____

STUDY GUIDES FOR

SOLVING
ALGEBRAIC
WORD
PROBLEMS

Andrewdelle R. Hensley
Deerfield Beach High School
Deerfield Beach, Florida

Published by

M38 **SOUTH-WESTERN PUBLISHING CO.**

CINCINNATI   WEST CHICAGO, IL   DALLAS   LIVERMORE, CA

ISBN: 0-538-13381-3

Library of Congress Catalog Card Number: 86-61844

1 2 3 4 5 6 7 8 9 H 4 3 2 1 0 9 8 7 6

Printed in the United States of America

CONTENTS

PREFACE

Algebra is considered a springboard for continuing the study of mathematics. You deserve a high quality of instruction in algebra. The overall objective of *Study Guides for Solving Algebraic Word Problems* is to help you overcome fears or despair associated with solving algebraic word problems. At the same time, you can gain insight and perspective in algebra and its applications.

FEATURES

Study Guides for Solving Algebraic Word Problems is a text-workbook with these features:

LEVELS OF COMPREHENSION—SIMPLE TO COMPLEX

Study Guides for Solving Algebraic Word Problems emphasizes skills for use in translating English sentences into mathematical sentences. This is accomplished by moving from the simple to the complex in a developmental manner. The thinking required to fully comprehend a word problem, set up an equation for it, solve the equation, and then check the solution has been organized into a single approach called levels of comprehension.

SCHEMATICS AND/OR TABULAR ARRANGEMENTS

To further enhance learning and comprehension and to supplement the text, schematics and/or tabular arrangements are included.

GROUP INSTRUCTION OR INDIVIDUALIZATION

Each study guide is designed to allow you to progress according to your own ability. Allowance is made for class instruction as well as individual progression through each study guide.

CHALLENGE PROBLEMS

Each set of word problems ends with an advanced complex problem.

FLEXIBILITY

The format and design of *Study Guides for Solving Algebraic Word Problems* allows much flexibility. Your teacher may require you to solve selected problems or all problems of each study guide. In addition, *Study Guides for Solving Algebraic Word Problems* is designed so that your teacher may assign similar problems from your accompanying algebra text.

PLAN OF PRESENTATION

Study Guides for Solving Algebraic Word Problems is organized into an overview and 17 study guides that cover the basic topics of algebraic word problems. Each study guide follows this plan of presentation:

Terms and Concepts
Model Problems Using Levels of Comprehension
Activity Extension
Algebraic Word Problems with Partial Solutions Given
Algebraic Word Problems without Help Given

METHOD OF INSTRUCTION

Each study guide in *Study Guides for Solving Algebraic Word Problems* uses the same developmental approach and includes the following:

TERMS AND CONCEPTS

Fundamental, introductory precepts, which will usually already be meaningful to you, are presented for each particular type of algebraic word problem.

LEVELS OF COMPREHENSION

The levels of comprehension are five steps for solving any type of algebraic word problem.

STEP 1: Read the problem.
STEP 2: Choose the variable(s).
STEP 3: Form the equation.
STEP 4: Solve the equation.
STEP 5: Check the equation.

MODEL PROBLEMS

Model problems are presented as samples, guiding you through each of the five levels of comprehension with your participation at all levels of comprehension. The guided approach is a deliberate attempt to build your confidence through increased competence.

The first level of comprehension is a *literal level,* where facts about the algebraic word problem are stated. Then the text-workbook progresses to the *interpretive level,* which goes one step beyond the factual information. The meaning of the facts and their relations are explored as the variable is chosen. The *application level* involves translating English sentences into mathematical sentences, solving the equation, and checking the equation. To be successful, you must follow the sequence of levels of comprehension. The *activity extension* poses questions to test your understanding not only of the model problems but also of a closely allied problem.

ALGEBRAIC WORD PROBLEMS

Two sets of algebraic word problems are included with each study guide. The first set uses a guided approach with partial solutions and hints for solving the problems. The second set of problems requires you to apply the five levels of comprehension independently.

Study Guides for Solving Algebraic Word Problems is the result of many years of experience during which concept-building and this unique approach to solving algebraic word problems were analyzed thoroughly. May the insights you gain in this course assist you in your study of mathematics.

Andrewdelle R. Hensley

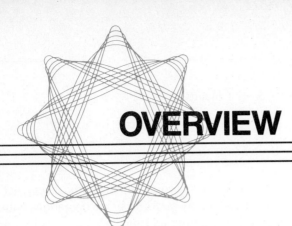

OVERVIEW

Punctuation in English
Punctuation in Algebra

TERMS AND CONCEPTS

Sets of words written in the same order can have entirely different meanings because of the sentence structure and its punctuation. In the following sentences, the punctuation allows two interpretations of the same set of words.

Example: The comedian said the teacher gets no respect.

    1. "The comedian," said the teacher, "gets no respect."

    2. The comedian said, "The teacher gets no respect."

Example: John said the teacher is not smart.

    1. "John," said the teacher, "is not smart."

    2. John said, "The teacher is not smart."

    In English, you should learn to say what you mean and to mean what you say. Make every effort to convey the correct meaning.

    In algebra, you must also concentrate on conveying the correct meaning. You must translate English sentences into mathematical sentences by following specific guidelines for the order of operations. When no grouping symbols (parentheses or brackets) are used in a mathematical sentence, do the multiplication first followed by the division, addition, and then subtraction. These guidelines for the order of operations are expressed in the following:

Examples: $8 + 3 \times 4$ means $8 + (3 \times 4) = 8 + 12 = 20$

              $7 \times 4 + 8$ means $(7 \times 4) + 8 = 28 + 8 = 36$

              $\dfrac{40}{8} - 3$ means $\left(\dfrac{40}{8}\right) - 3 = 5 - 3 = 2$

              $7 \times 8 - 6 \times 2$ means $(7 \times 8) - (6 \times 2)$
                                          $= 56 - 12 = 44$

Perhaps the students can top these. Misplaced modifiers are also intriguing. Examples: The house was painted red by the river. The child was spanked by the tree. Would you rather have a pit bull chase you or a ferocious teacher?

$$8 - 3 - 1 \text{ means } (8 - 3) - 1 = 4$$
$$8 + 3 \times (6 - 2) \text{ means } 8 + [3(6 - 2)]$$
$$= 8 + 3(4)$$
$$= 8 + 12 = 20$$

When grouping symbols are used in a mathematical sentence, the value of the expression is determined by performing the operations within brackets first, followed by the parentheses, and then all else, in this order: multiplication, division, addition, and subtraction.

Examples: Compare each entry in the lefthand column with its counterpart in the righthand column:

$(8 + 3) \times 4 = 44$	$8 + (3 \times 4) = 8 + 12 = 20$
$7 \times (4 + 8) = 84$	$(7 \times 4) + 8 = 36$
$\dfrac{40}{(8 - 3)} = 8$	$\left(\dfrac{40}{8}\right) - 3 = 2$
$[7 \times (8 - 6)] \times 2 = 28$	$(7 \times 8) - (6 \times 2) = 44$
$8 - (3 - 1) = 8 - 2 = 6$	$(8 - 3) - 1 = 4$
$(8 + 3)(6 - 2) = 11 \times 4 = 44$	$8 + 3(6 - 2) = 8 + 12 = 20$

In order to translate English sentences to mathematical sentences, you must apply these mathematical properties:

A. Commutative property of addition

$$3 + 8 = 11 \qquad 8 + 3 = 11$$

B. Commutative property of multiplication

$$3 \times 8 = 24 \qquad 8 \times 3 = 24$$

C. Associative property of addition

$$(6 + 2) + 8 = 16 \qquad 6 + (2 + 8) = 16$$

D. Associative property of multiplication

$$(3 \times 5) \times 2 = 30 \qquad 3 \times (5 \times 2) = 30$$

E. Distributive property of multiplication over addition

$$3 \times (6 + 4) = 30 \qquad 3(6 + 4) = 3(6) + 3(4)$$
$$= 18 + 12$$
$$= 30$$

F. Closure for addition

$$2 + 4 = 6$$

The numeral 6 is an element of the set of numbers called the real numbers.

G. Closure for multiplication

$2 \times 4 = 8$

The numeral 8 is an element of the set of numbers called the real numbers.

H. Identity element in addition, or additive identity

$3 + 0 = 3$

The numeral 0 is the identity element in addition.

I. Identity element in multiplication, or multiplicative identity

$3 \times 1 = 3$

The numeral 1 is the identity element in multiplication.

J. Property of opposites, or property of additive inverses

$3 + (-3) = 0$

The sum of a number and its opposite is zero.

K. Property of reciprocals, or property of multiplicative inverses

$3 \times \dfrac{1}{3} = 1$

The product of a number and its reciprocal is 1. Zero has no reciprocal.

When all eleven properties (A–K) are true for a set of numbers, the set is a *field*.

Explore the properties that hold true for the various classifications of numbers (integers, rationals, reals, irrationals, etc.)

THINKING WITH VARIABLES

Your primary task in solving a mathematical word problem will be to translate English sentences into mathematical sentences. An easy way to do this is to make up an arithmetic example to which you know the answer. Then use the same reasoning process to set up the algebraic sentence.

Example: A certain number is increased by a number that is 10 more than this number. The sum of the two numbers is 150. Find the numbers.

To solve the problem, make up an arithmetic example. For instance, 40 is 10 more than 30 and their sum is 70. Think: $30 + (30 + 10) = 70$. The algebra problem is related to this process and equation. Let $n =$ the certain number for which you are looking; n is also the variable about which you know the least. A number that is 10 more than this number can be represented by $n + 10$. The sum of these two numbers is 150. The equation is now easy to determine.

Example:

A certain number increased by 10 more than the number is 150.

$$n + (n + 10) = 150$$

A *variable* holds the place for a number. Using a letter or symbol for a variable is common practice. In elementary school, you provided answers to statements such as $3 + \square = 15$. You gave the answer 12. The box was your introduction to variables!

Remember these major principles when solving any equation for a variable:

1. You may *add* the same quantity to both members of an equation.

2. You may *subtract* the same quantity from both members of an equation.

3. You may *multiply* both members of an equation by the same quantity.

4. You may *divide* both members of an equation by the same quantity.

SKILL BUILDERS

For each of the following statements, choose the answer that *best* translates the English statement into a mathematical statement. Write your answers in the blanks at the right.

This exercise is equivalent to "say what you mean and mean what you say."

1. Ten more than x:

   $x + 10,$ $10 + x,$ $10x,$ $10 - x$ $\underline{x + 10}$

2. y more than x:

   $y + x,$ $x + y,$ $xy,$ $x - y$ $\underline{x + y}$

3. Eight decreased by 6:

   $6 + 8,$ $8 - 6,$ $6 - 8,$ 6×8 $\underline{8 - 6}$

4. z decreased by 6:

   $z - 6,$ $6 - z,$ $z + 6,$ $6z$ $\underline{z - 6}$

5. Ten times a plus four:

   $10(a) + 4,$ $10a - 4,$ $10(4 + a),$
   $10 \times a \times 4$ $\underline{10(a) + 4}$

6. Ten times the sum of a and four:

   $10(a + 4),$ $10a - 4,$ $10(4 + a),$
   $10 \times a \times 4$ $\underline{10(a + 4)}$

7. Six decreased by 2:

   $6 - 2,$ $2 - 6,$ $6 + 2,$ $2 + 6$ $\underline{6 - 2}$

8. z decreased by 3:

$z + 3,$ $3 - z,$ $z - 3,$

$z - 1 + 2$

$z - 3$

9. z times x plus eight:

$zx + 8,$ $z(x + 8),$ $zx - 8,$

$zx + 6 - 2$

$zx + 8$

10. z times the sum of x and eight:

$z(x - 8),$ $zx + 8,$ $zx + 8x,$

$z(x + 8)$

$z(x + 8)$

Translate the following English sentences into mathematical sentences. After forming the equation, solve and check the equation. Some of the work has been done for you. After reading each problem, continue to complete the process by supplying the necessary information.

11. Gary and Harold collected 100 pounds of aluminum cans for a school drive. Gary said, "Ten pounds more than the amount I collected is exactly the amount Harold collected." How much did each boy collect?

Let p = number of pounds collected by Gary (you know the least about this). Then $100 - p$ = number of pounds collected by Harold.

$$\underbrace{\text{Ten more than Gary's collection}}_{p + 10} \text{ is } \underbrace{\text{Harold's collection}}_{= \quad (100 - p)}.$$

$$\underbrace{\text{Gary's collection}}_{p} + 10 = \underbrace{\text{Harold's collection}}_{(100 - p)}.$$

$p + 10 = 100 - p$

$\dfrac{2p}{\rule{1cm}{0.4pt}} = 90$

$p = \dfrac{45}{\rule{1cm}{0.4pt}}$ (Gary's collection)

$\dfrac{100 - p}{\rule{1.5cm}{0.4pt}} = 100 - 45 = 55$ (Harold's collection)

Gary's collection: $\quad$ 45
Harold's collection: $\quad$ 55

Check: $p + 10 = 100 - p$

$\dfrac{45}{\rule{1cm}{0.4pt}} + 10 = 100 - \dfrac{45}{\rule{1cm}{0.4pt}}$

$55 = \dfrac{55}{\rule{1cm}{0.4pt}}$

12. A baseball team won ten times as many games as it lost. It won 40 games. How many did it lose?

Let n = number of games lost (you know the least about this).

In terms of this variable, $\underline{10n}$ = number of games won. The number of games won is 40. Therefore,

$10n = 40$

$n = \underline{\quad 4 \quad}$ games

4 games

Check: $10n = 40$

$\qquad 10(4) = \underline{\quad 40 \quad}$

$\qquad \underline{\quad 40 \quad} = 40$

13. A man traveled a certain number of miles by car and ten times as far by plane. His total trip was 330 miles. How far did he travel by car?

Let a = number of miles traveled by car (you know the least about this).

In terms of the variable a, $\underline{10a}$ = number of miles traveled by plane.

The number of miles by car plus the number of miles by plane is equal to 330 miles. Therefore,

$a + 10a = \underline{\quad 330 \quad}$

$\underline{\quad 11a \quad} = 330$

$a = 30$ miles

30 miles

Check: $a + 10a = 330$

$\qquad \underline{\quad 30 \quad} + 10 \cdot \underline{\quad 30 \quad} = 330$

$\qquad 30 + 300 = 330$

$\qquad \underline{\quad 330 \quad} = 330$

Remind students that the raised dot ($\cdot$) is also used as a multiplication sign. ($10 \cdot 30 = 10 \times 30$)

14. Petula's age is five years less than four times that of her sister Pansy. If the sum of their ages is 15, how old is Pansy?

Let p = Pansy's age in years (you know the least about this).

Then $4p - 5$ = Petula's age (in years).

$\underbrace{\text{Pansy's age}} + \underbrace{\text{Petula's age}}$ is 15.

$\qquad p \qquad + \underline{\quad (4p - 5) \quad} = 15$

$5p - 5 = 15$

$5p = \underline{\quad 20 \quad}$

$p = \underline{\quad 4 \quad}$ years (Pansy's age)

4 years

Check: $p + (4p - 5) = 15$

$$\underline{\quad 4 \quad} + (4 \cdot 4 - 5) = 15$$

$$4 + \underline{\quad (16 - 5) \quad} = 15$$

$$4 + \underline{\quad 11 \quad} = 15$$

$$\underline{\quad 15 \quad} = 15$$

15. The length of a rectangle is three more than five times its width. If the perimeter is 150 inches, find the dimensions.

Let w = width of rectangle in inches (you know the least about this).

Then $5w + 3$ = length of rectangle (in inches).

The sum of all sides is 150 inches.

$$w + (5w + 3) + w + (5w + 3) = \underline{\quad 150 \quad}$$

$$\underline{\quad 12w \quad} + 6 = 150$$

$$12w = \underline{\quad 144 \quad}$$

$$w = \underline{\quad 12 \quad} \text{ inches (width of rectangle)}$$

$$5w + 3 = \underline{\quad 63 \quad} \text{ inches (length of rectangle)}$$

Length: **63 inches**
Width: **12 inches**

Check: $w + (5w + 3) + w + (5w + 3) = 150$

$$12 + (5 \cdot \underline{\quad 12 \quad} + 3) + 12 + (5 \cdot \underline{\quad 12 \quad} + 3) = 150$$

$$12 + (\underline{\quad 60 \quad} + 3) + 12 + (\underline{\quad 60 \quad} + 3) = 150$$

$$12 + \underline{\quad 63 \quad} + 12 + \underline{\quad 63 \quad} = 150$$

$$\underline{\quad 150 \quad} = 150$$

16. An observation tower that is 100 feet high is built on the top of a mountain. If the observer, at the highest point, is 3,100 feet above ground level, how high is the mountain?

Let h = the height of the mountain in feet (you know the least about this).

The height of the observation tower is 100 feet.

Height of mountain + height of tower is 3,100 feet.

$$h \qquad + \qquad 100 \qquad = \qquad \underline{\quad 3,100 \quad}$$

$$h + 100 = 3,100$$

$$h = \underline{\quad 3,000 \quad} \text{ feet}$$

3,000 feet

Check: $h + 100 = 3,100$

$$\underline{\quad 3,000 \quad} + 100 = 3,100$$

$$\underline{\quad 3,100 \quad} = 3,100$$

17. The temperature in an orange grove is 28° Fahrenheit. If fires in smudge pots increase the temperature two degrees per hour, how many hours are required to raise the temperature to 36° Fahrenheit?

Let n = number of hours smudge pots must burn.

Then $2 \cdot n$ = increase in temperature, by degrees, that will result.

If the present temperature is increased by $2n$, the temperature will be 36° Fahrenheit.

$$28 + \underline{\quad 2n \quad} = 36$$

$$2n = 8$$

$$n = \underline{\quad 4 \quad} \text{ hours (number of hours}$$
$$\text{smudge pots must burn)}$$

$$\underline{\text{4 hours}}$$

Check: $28 + \underline{\quad 2n \quad} = 36$

$\quad\quad\quad\quad 28 + 2 \cdot \underline{\quad 4 \quad} = 36$

$\quad\quad\quad\quad 28 + \underline{\quad 8 \quad} = 36$

$\quad\quad\quad\quad \underline{\quad 36 \quad} = 36$

LEVELS OF COMPREHENSION

The previous Skill Builder problems were simple, and perhaps you did some of them mentally. However, you had to know certain basic terms and concepts before attacking each problem. You also had to read each problem for the facts and what they meant. You had to choose a variable. You then applied this information to form an equation, which you solved and immediately checked. This five-step approach, called *levels of comprehension*, will be helpful in solving all algebraic word problems.

Even though some examples are easily solved, stress the fact that the more difficult problems require a structured approach. Process is all-important.

In the teacher's edition throughout the study guides, the levels of comprehension will be classified as literal, interpretive, or application. The *literal level* states the facts. The *interpretive level* tells what the facts mean. The *application level* makes use of the previous levels to translate from the English sentence to the mathematical sentence—the formation of the equation. The remaining steps involve the mechanics of solving the equation and checking the equation.

LEVELS OF COMPREHENSION

STEP 1   Read the problem.

STEP 2   Choose the variable(s).

STEP 3   Form the equation.

STEP 4   Solve the equation.

STEP 5   Check the equation.

Using the levels of comprehension, let's solve the following problem.

MODEL PROBLEM

Christina has nine more coins than Yvette. Yvette has ten more coins than Andres. Together, they have 143 coins. How many coins does each have?

READ THE PROBLEM

After reading the problem, give the answers to the following statements in the spaces provided.

Literal Level

Three coin collectors, Christina, Yvette, and ___Andres___ , have ___143___ coins. You know the least about the number ___Andres___ has. Yvette has ___ten___ more coins than Andres. Christina has ___nine___ more coins than Yvette. You are to find the number of coins ___each___ collector has.

After reading a word problem, you must always determine the facts and the relationships. Then, you are ready to go to the next step of the levels of comprehension.

CHOOSE THE VARIABLE(S)

Interpretive Level

Let n = number of coins Andres has (you know the least about this). Then ___$n + 10$___ = number of coins Yvette has. And $(n + 10) +$ ___9___ = number of coins Christina has.

FORM THE EQUATION

Application Level

The number of coins Andres has	+	The number of coins Yvette has	+	The number of coins Christina has	= 143
n	+	$(n + 10)$	+	$(n + 10) + 9$	= 143

The equation is $n + (n + 10) + [(n + 10) + 9] =$ ___143___ .

SOLVE THE EQUATION

$n + n + 10 + n + 10 + 9 = 143$

___$3n + 29$___ $= 143$

$3n = 114$

$n =$ ___38___ coins (number of coins Andres has)

$n + 10 = \underline{\quad 48 \quad}$ coins (number of coins Yvette has)

$(n + 10) + 9 = \underline{\quad 57 \quad}$ coins (number of coins Christina has)

Andres: **38 coins**
Yvette: **48 coins**
Christina: **57 coins**

CHECK THE EQUATION

$n + (n + 10) + (n + 10) + 9 = 143$

$38 + (38 + 10) + (\underline{\quad 38 + 10 + 9 \quad}) = 143$

$38 + 48 + \underline{\quad 57 \quad} = 143$

$\underline{\quad 143 \quad} = 143$

CONCLUSION

Follow the levels of comprehension to solve algebraic word problems, and you will be successful.

STUDY GUIDE 1

Number (Elementary)

TERMS AND CONCEPTS

Introductory Precepts

Introductory Precepts are principles or general rules that have evolved in the education process. Ability to deal with these predict topical readiness.

There are many kinds of number problems. The topics for number problems cover all ranges and phases of human interest. The guidelines for solving number problems are stated here for you.

LEVELS OF COMPREHENSION

STEP 1   Read the problem.

STEP 2   Choose the variable(s).

STEP 3   Form the equation.

STEP 4   Solve the equation.

STEP 5   Check the equation.

MODEL PROBLEM 1

Helen has five stamps more than Lionel. They have 45 stamps together. How many stamps does each have?

READ THE PROBLEM

After reading the problem, give the answers to the following statements in the spaces provided.

Literal Level

Helen has ___five___ more stamps than ___Lionel___ . They have ___45___ stamps together. The sum of Helen's stamps and Lionel's stamps is ___45___ .

CHOOSE THE VARIABLE(S)

Interpretive Level

Let n = number of stamps Lionel has. Then ___$n + 5$___ = number of stamps Helen has.

FORM THE EQUATION

Application Level

$n + (n + 5) = $ ___45___

SOLVE THE EQUATION

$n + (n + 5) = 45$

___$2n$___ $+ 5 = 45$

$2n = 40$

$n = $ ___20___ (number of stamps Lionel has)

___$n + 5$___ $= 25$ (number of stamps Helen has)

Lionel: **20**
Helen: **25**

CHECK THE EQUATION

$n + (n + 5) = 45$

$20 + ($ ___20___ $+ 5) = 45$

$20 + $ ___25___ $ = 45$

___45___ $ = 45$

ACTIVITY EXTENSION

If you let n = number of stamps Helen has, then ___$n - 5$___ = number of stamps Lionel has.

MODEL PROBLEM 2

On a family trip of 600 miles, Sonja drove five times as far as Estelle. How many miles did each person drive?

READ THE PROBLEM

After reading the problem, give the answers to the following statements in the spaces provided.

Literal Level

Sonja drove ____five____ times the distance Estelle drove. Together, they drove ___600___ miles.

CHOOSE THE VARIABLE(S)

Interpretive Level

Let n = number of miles Estelle drove.

___5n___ = number of miles Sonja drove.

FORM THE EQUATION

Application Level

$n + $ ___5n___ $ = 600$

SOLVE THE EQUATION

$n + 5n = 600$

$6n = 600$

$n = $ ___100___ (number of miles Estelle drove)

$5n = $ ___500___ (number of miles Sonja drove)

Estelle: **100 miles**
Sonja: **500 miles**

CHECK THE EQUATION

$n + 5n = 600$

___100___ $ + 5(100) = 600$

$100 + $ ___500___ $ = 600$

___600___ $ = $ ___600___

ACTIVITY EXTENSION

Activity extensions pose questions which, if answered correctly, document the students' understanding of not only the problem at hand, but also the closely allied problems. Perspective enters the process.

If you let n = number of miles Sonja drove, then ___$\frac{n}{5}$___ = number of miles Estelle drove.

MODEL PROBLEM 3

Craig, Tom, and Harry sold tickets to the carnival. Tom sold five more than twice the number Harry sold. Craig sold five less than four times the number Harry sold. If together they sold 140 tickets, how many tickets did each sell?

READ THE PROBLEM

After reading the problem, answer the following statements in the spaces provided.

The person about whom you have the least information is ___Harry___.

The number of tickets sold by Tom and Craig are stated in terms of the number ___Harry___ sold.

CHOOSE THE VARIABLE(S)

Let n = number of tickets Harry sold.

___$2n + 5$___ = number of tickets Tom sold

$4n - 5$ = ___number of tickets Craig sold___

FORM THE EQUATION

$n + (2n + 5) + (4n - 5) =$ ___140___

SOLVE THE EQUATION

$n + (2n + 5) + (4n - 5) = 140$

$7n = 140$

n = ___20___ (number of tickets Harry sold)

$2n + 5 =$ ___45___ (number of tickets Tom sold)

$4n - 5 =$ ___75___ (number of tickets Craig sold)

Harry: **20**
Tom: **45**
Craig: **75**

CHECK THE EQUATION

$n + (2n + 5) + (4n - 5) = 140$

$20 + (2 \cdot$ ___20___ $+ 5) + (4 \cdot$ ___20___ $- 5) = 140$

$20 + ($ ___40___ $+ 5) + ($ ___80___ $- 5) = 140$

$20 +$ ___45___ $+ 75 = 140$

___140___ $= 140$

ACTIVITY EXTENSION

Emphasize to students
that as long as the facts of
the problem have the
same relationship, the solution will be the same.
Some equations are more
easily solved than others.
The more simply stated,
the better!

Would it be correct to state and solve Model Problem 3 this way?

Let $2n$ = number of tickets Harry sold.

$2 \cdot 2n + 5$ = number of tickets Tom sold

___$4 \cdot 2n - 5$___ = number of tickets Craig sold

___$2n$___ $+ (2 \cdot 2n + 5) + (4 \cdot 2n - 5) = 140$

$2n + 4n + 5 + 8n - 5 = 140$

___$14n$___ $= 140$

$n =$ ___10___

$2n =$ ___20___ (number of tickets Harry sold)

$2 \cdot 2n + 5 =$ ___45___ (number of tickets Tom sold)

$4 \cdot 2n - 5 =$ ___75___ (number of tickets Craig sold) ___Yes___

MODEL PROBLEM 4

Mr. Traister left a tax-free estate of $2,300,000. His lifelong secretary received $300,000. Half of the remainder of his estate was left to his favorite charity, and the other half was given to his immediate family. The wife received $100,000 more than five times the son's share. The daughter received $100,000 more than twice the son's share. How much did each family member receive? (No provisions were made for the poodle.)

READ THE PROBLEM

After reading the problem, give the answers to the following statements or questions in the spaces provided.

Literal Level

Mr. Traister left ___$1,000,000___ to his immediate family. The wife received ___$100,000___ more than five times the son's share. The daughter received ___$100,000___ more than twice the son's share.

Interpretive Level

1. Which member of the immediate family received the largest share? ___The wife___

2. The share about which you know the least is the share received by (whom?): ___The son___

3. If x represents the son's share, then the daughter's share is equal to: ___$2x + \$100,000$___

4. The sum of the shares received by the wife, son, and daughter is equal to: ___$1,000,000___

CHOOSE THE VARIABLE(S)

Let $x =$ son's share (in dollars)

$5x + 100,000 =$ wife's share (in dollars)

___$2x + 100,000$___ $=$ daughter's share (in dollars)

FORM THE EQUATION

Application Level

$x + (5x + 100,000) + (2x + 100,000) =$ ___1,000,000___

SOLVE THE EQUATION

$x + (5x + 100,000) + (2x + 100,000) = 1,000,000$

$8x + 200,000 = 1,000,000$

$8x = \underline{800,000}$

$x = \underline{100,000}$ (son's share in dollars)

$\underline{5x + 100,000} = \$600,000$ (wife's share in dollars)

$2x + 100,000 = \underline{\$300,000}$ (daughter's share in dollars)

CHECK THE EQUATION

$x + (5x + 100,000) + (2x + 100,000) = 1,000,000$

$100,000 + (500,000 + 100,000) + [2(100,000) +$

$100,000] = \underline{1,000,000}$

$100,000 + 600,000 + (200,000 + 100,000) = 1,000,000$

$\underline{700,000} + 300,000 = 1,000,000$

$\underline{1,000,000} = 1,000,000$

ACTIVITY EXTENSION

1. Could Mr. Traister have divided the family estate of $1,000,000 into the fractional parts the wife, son, and daughter should receive?

   Yes

2. What fractional part of the family estate would each have received?

   wife: **3/5**
   son: **1/10**
   daughter: **3/10**

3. Could Mr. Traister have divided the family estate by designating the percent the wife, son, and daughter would receive?

   Yes

4. What percent of the estate would have been received by each?

   wife: **60** percent
   son: **10** percent
   daughter: **30** percent

5. The percent received by the wife, son, and daughter is **100** percent of the family estate.

Name _____ Period _____

Teacher _____ Date _____ Grade _____

Number Problems with Help

DIRECTIONS: Each of the following problems has been given a partial solution. Solve the problem by completing the solution.

1. Janice picked a total of 160 boxes of oranges on five days of school. On Monday and Thursday, she picked half as many boxes as on Wednesday. On Tuesday, she picked ten fewer boxes than on Wednesday. On Friday, she picked 10 boxes more than on Wednesday. How many boxes did she pick on Friday?

Let x = number of boxes picked on Wednesday.

$\frac{1}{2}x$ = number of boxes picked on Monday

$\underline{\frac{1}{2}x}$ = number of boxes picked on Thursday

$\underline{x - 10}$ = number of boxes picked on Tuesday

$x + 10 =$ __number of boxes picked on Friday__

$x + \left(\frac{1}{2}x\right) + \left(\frac{1}{2}x\right) + (x - 10) + (x + 10) = \underline{160}$

$\underline{4x = 160}$ (above equation in simple form)

$x = \underline{40}$ (number of boxes picked on Wednesday)

$x + 10 = \underline{50}$ (number of boxes picked on Friday)

__50 boxes__

Check: $x + \left(\frac{1}{2}x\right) + \left(\frac{1}{2}x\right) + (x - 10) + (x + 10) = 160$

$40 + \underline{\left(\frac{1}{2} \cdot 40\right)} + \left(\frac{1}{2} \cdot 40\right) + \underline{(40 - 10)} +$

$(40 + 10) = \underline{160}$

$40 + \underline{20} + 20 + \underline{30} + 50 = 160$

$\underline{160} = 160$

2. The four classes at a school used streamers to decorate the assembly hall for American Education Week. The freshman class used 250 yards fewer than the senior class used. The sophomore class used as many yards as the seniors used. The juniors used 22 yards fewer than the

seniors used. If the four classes used 900 yards, how many yards did each class use?

Let s = number of yards used by seniors.

$\underline{\quad s - 250 \quad}$ = number of yards used by freshmen

$\underline{\quad s \quad}$ = number of yards used by sophomores

$\underline{\quad s - 22 \quad}$ = number of yards used by juniors

$s + (s - 250) + s + (s - 22) = \underline{\quad 900 \quad}$

$\underline{\quad 4s - 272 \quad}$ = 900 (above equation in simple form)

$4s = \underline{\quad 1,172 \quad}$

$s = \underline{\quad 293 \quad}$ (number of yards used by seniors)

$s - \underline{\quad 250 \quad} = \underline{\quad 43 \quad}$ (number of yards used by freshmen)

$s = \underline{\quad 293 \quad}$ (number of yards used by sophomores)

$s - \underline{\quad 22 \quad} = \underline{\quad 271 \quad}$ (number of yards used by juniors)

Seniors:	293
Freshmen:	43
Sophomores:	293
Juniors:	271

Check: $s + (s - 250) + s + (s - 22) = \underline{\quad 900 \quad}$

$293 + \underline{\quad (293 - 250) \quad} + 293 + \underline{\quad (293 - 22) \quad} = 900$

$293 + \underline{\quad 43 \quad} + 293 + \underline{\quad 271 \quad} = 900$

$\underline{\quad 900 \quad} = 900$

3. Leonardo puts $300 per month in his savings account for the first eleven months of the year. How much does he deposit in December if at the end of the year he has a principal of $3,800?

Let d = December's deposit (in dollars).

$\underline{\quad d + 11 \cdot 300 \quad} = 3,800$

$d + 3,300 = \underline{\quad 3,800 \quad}$

$d = \underline{\quad \$500 \quad}$ (December's deposit) $\underline{\quad \$500 \quad}$

Check: $d + 11 \cdot 300 = 3,800$

$500 + \underline{\quad 3,300 \quad} = 3,800$

$3,800 = 3,800$

4. Mr. Hernandez earned $1,600 one month. He budgeted 37.5 percent for rent, 25 percent for food, and equal amounts for utilities, transportation,

and miscellaneous expenses. How much did Mr. Hernandez spend for each item in his budget?

This is a good time for percent, fraction, and decimal review.

Mr. Hernandez's salary (s) = $1,600

Let n = money spent for utilities (in dollars).

n = money spent for transportation (in dollars)

n = money spent for miscellaneous expenses (in dollars)

$$0.375(1,600) + 0.25(1,600) + \underline{\ n + n + n\ } = 1,600$$

$$\frac{3}{8}\ \underline{(1,600)\ } + \frac{1}{4}\ \underline{(1,600)\ } + 3n = 1,600$$

$$600 + 400 + 3n = 1,600$$

$$\underline{\ 3n\ } = 600 \text{ (in dollars)}$$

$n = \underline{\ \$200\ }$ (money spent for utilities)

$n = \underline{\ \$200\ }$ (money spent for transportation)

$n = \underline{\ \$200\ }$ (money spent for miscellaneous expenses)

$\frac{3}{8}s = \$600$ (money spent for rent)

$\frac{1}{4}s = \underline{\ \$400\ }$ (money spent for food)

Utilities: **$200**
Transportation: **$200**
Miscellaneous: **$200**
Rent: **$600**
Food: **$400**

Check: $0.375(1,600) + 0.25(1,600) + \underline{\ n\ } + \underline{\ n\ } +$

$\underline{\ n\ } = 1,600$

$600 + 400 + 3(200) = 1,600$

$1,000 + \underline{\ 600\ } = 1,600$

$\$1,600 = \$1,600$

Challenge

The better student is sometimes not addressed in regular assignments. The Challenge problems in each study guide are designed as invitations to competition.

5. Three sisters, Nan, Lois, and Marlene, inherited $900,000 tax-free. Lois received $20,000 more than five times Nan's share. Marlene received $40,000 more than Nan's share. How much did each receive?

Let x = Nan's share (in dollars).

$5x + \underline{\ 20,000\ }$ = Lois' share (in dollars)

$\underline{x + 40,000\ }$ = Marlene's share (in dollars)

$\underline{x + (5x + 20,000) + (x + 40,000) = 900,000\ }$ (All shares: an equation)

$7x +$ _60,000 = 900,000_ (Summarize terms)

$7x =$ _840,000_

$x =$ _$120,000_ (Nan's share)

_5x + 20,000 = $620,000_ (Lois's share)

_x + 40,000 = $160,000_ (Marlene's share)

Nan: **$120,000**
Lois: **$620,000**
Marlene: **$160,000**

Check: $x + (5x + 20,000) +$ _(x + 40,000)_ $= 900,000$

_120,000_ $+ [5(120,000) + 20,000] + (120,000 +$
$40,000) = 900,000$

$120,000 + ($600,000 + 20,000) +$ _160,000_ $= 900,000$

$120,000 + 620,000 + 160,000 =$ _900,000_

$900,000 = 900,000$

Name _____ Period _____

Teacher _____ Date _____ Grade _____

Number Problems

DIRECTIONS: Use the five levels of comprehension to solve each of the problems in the space provided. Write your answers in the blank to the right after each problem.

1. Rhett sold 50 boxes of candy after school on Monday for the benefit of the band. On Tuesday and Wednesday, he sold 75 boxes each day. On Thursday, he sold 100 boxes. On Friday, he sold 200 boxes. How many boxes of candy will he need to sell on Saturday to make a total of 600 boxes?

   Let n = number of boxes sold on Saturday.

   $n + 50 + 75 + 75 + 100 + 200 = 600$

   $n + 500 = 600$

   $n = 100$ (number sold on Saturday)   <u>**100 boxes**</u>

   Check: $n + 50 + 75 + 75 + 100 + 200 = 600$

   $100 + 50 + 75 + 75 + 100 + 200 = 600$

   $600 = 600$

2. Each class spent hours to make floats for homecoming. The seniors spent nine times the number of hours spent by the freshmen. The juniors spent six times the number of hours spent by the freshmen. The sophomores, the winners, spent twelve times as long as the freshmen. If the total number of hours spent by the four classes was 2,800, how many hours were spent by the freshmen?

   Let n = number of hours spent by freshmen.

   $9n$ = number of hours spent by seniors

   $6n$ = number of hours spent by juniors

   $12n$ = number of hours spent by sophomores

   $n + 9n + 6n + 12n = 2,800$

   $28n = 2,800$

   $n = 100$ (number of hours spent by freshmen on floats)

   <u>**100 hours**</u>

Check: $n + 9n + 6n + 12n = 2{,}800$

$100 + 9(100) + 6(100) + 12(100) = 2{,}800$

$100 + 900 + 600 + 1{,}200 = 2{,}800$

$2{,}800 = 2{,}800$

3. Roberta made a deposit in her savings account. Blake deposited five-sixths of the amount that Roberta deposited. If they deposited a total of $1,650, how much did each deposit?

Let n = Roberta's deposit (in dollars).

$\frac{5}{6}n$ = Blake's deposit

$n + \frac{5}{6}n = 1{,}650$

$1\frac{5}{6}n = 1{,}650$

$\frac{11}{6}n = 1{,}650$

$\frac{6}{11} \cdot \frac{11}{6}n = \frac{6}{11} \cdot 1{,}650$

$n = \$900$

$\underline{\qquad \$900 \qquad}$

Check: $n + \frac{5}{6}n = 1{,}650$

$900 + \frac{5}{6}(900) = 1{,}650$

$900 + 750 = 1{,}650$

$1{,}650 = 1{,}650$

4. Toby and Warren were hired to pick fruit after school. Together they picked 20 more boxes of oranges than tangerines. They picked 30 more boxes of grapefruit than tangerines. How many boxes of each fruit did they pick if they picked a total of 650 boxes?

Let n = number of boxes of tangerines.

$n + 30$ = number of boxes of grapefruit

$n + 20$ = number of boxes of oranges

$n + (n + 30) + (n + 20) = 650$

$3n + 50 = 650$

$3n = 600$

$n = 200$ (number of boxes of tangerines)

$n + 30 = 230$ (number of boxes of grapefruit)

$n + 20 = 220$ (number of boxes of oranges)

Tangerines: **200 boxes**
Grapefruit: **230 boxes**
Oranges: **220 boxes**

Check: $n + (n + 30) + (n + 20) = 650$

$200 + (200 + 30) + (200 + 20) = 650$

$200 + 230 + 220 = 650$

$650 = 650$

5. Mrs. Mason bought an oceanfront lot. She sold it a year later for 50 percent more than she paid for it. What was the original price if the selling price one year later was $1,500,000?

Let n = original price of lot (in dollars).

$n + 0.50n = 1,500,000$

$1.50n = 1,500,000$

$150n = 150,000,000$

$n = \$1,000,000$

$1,000,000

Check: $n + 0.50n = 1,500,000$

$1,000,000 + 0.50(1,000,000) = 1,500,000$

$1,000,000 + 500,000 = 1,500,000$

$1,500,000 = 1,500,000$

Challenge

6. Mrs. Hanson found a fortune in jewels in the trunk of a rental car. She notified the police, and when the jewels were never claimed, the police eventually returned the jewels to Mrs. Hanson. She sold the jewels for $1,800,000. She gave some of this money to charity but invested in municipal bonds $1,000,000 more than that given to charity, and she deposited in a bank $80,000 more than that given to charity. What fractional part did she designate for each purpose? What percent did she designate for each purpose?

Let n = amount given to charity (in dollars).

$n + 80,000 =$ amount (dollars) deposited in a bank

$n + 1,000,000 =$ amount (dollars) invested in municipal bonds

$n + (n + 80,000) + (n + 1,000,000) = 1,800,000$

$3n + 1,080,000 = 1,800,000$

$$3n = 720,000$$

$$n = \$240,000 \text{ (amount given to charity)}$$

$$n + 80,000 = \$320,000 \text{ (amount deposited in bank)}$$

$$n + 1,000,000 = \$1,240,000 \text{ (amount invested in municipal bonds)}$$

Check: $n + (n + 80,000) + (n + 1,000,000) = 1,800,000$

$$240,000 + (240,000 + 80,000) + (240,000 + 1,000,000) = 1,800,000$$

$$240,000 + 320,000 + 1,240,000 = 1,800,000$$

$$1,800,000 = 1,800,000$$

Fractional Parts (For each use, express the dollar amount in fraction form and then reduce to lowest terms):

Percent (Express each fraction as a fractional percent and then as a decimal percent, for example):

$$\left(\frac{1}{6} = 16\frac{2}{3} \text{ percent} \cong 16.67 \text{ percent}\right):$$

Charity	$\dfrac{240,000}{1,800,000}$	$=$	$\dfrac{2}{15}$	$13\frac{1}{3}\%$ $\cong$	13.33%
Bank	$\dfrac{320,000}{1,800,000}$	$=$	$\dfrac{8}{45}$	$17\frac{7}{9}\%$ $\cong$	17.78%
Bonds	$\dfrac{1,240,000}{1,800,000}$	$=$	$\dfrac{31}{45}$	$68\frac{8}{9}\%$ $\cong$	68.89%

STUDY GUIDE 2

Ratios

TERMS AND CONCEPTS

Introductory Precepts

Numbers may be compared by division. When numbers are compared by division, the result is a quotient. A quotient may be expressed in words, as a number, as a fraction, or as a ratio.

A *ratio* compares two numbers.

Make sure the students are familiar with all notations for ratios.

Examples: **1.** The ratio of 3 to 4 is written 3 to 4, 3:4, or $\frac{3}{4}$.

2. The ratio of 4 to 3 is written 4 to 3, 4:3, or $\frac{4}{3}$.

3. The ratio of 3 to 3 is written 3 to 3, 3:3, or $\frac{3}{3}$.

The ratio of a small number to a larger number is always a proper fraction.

Example: 2:5 or $\frac{2}{5}$.

The ratio of a larger number to a smaller number is always an improper fraction.

Example: 7:3 or $\frac{7}{3}$.

The ratio of like quantities is 1:1.

Example: 5:5 = 1:1.

The ratio of 3 to 4 ≠ the ratio of 4 to 3!

Heretofore, you worked some examples a certain way in order to get the correct answer. You didn't know why this way worked. Now you are in a position to understand why.

Example: $\frac{7 \cdot 5}{8 \cdot 5} = \frac{35}{40} = \frac{7}{8}$ and $\frac{7}{8} \cdot \frac{5}{5}$ is also $\frac{7 \cdot 5}{8 \cdot 5}$.

Cancellation is used frequently.

Hence,

$$\frac{7}{8} \cdot 1 = \frac{7 \cdot 5}{8 \cdot 5} = \frac{7}{8}.$$

25

The underlying principle is that the numeral 1 is the identity element in multiplication! Formally,

$$\frac{ab}{ac} = \frac{b}{c}.$$

This process is *cancellation*. Cancellation allows you to divide the numerator and denominator of a fraction by the *same* nonzero number. You may use cancellation to simplify fractions. Remember, you cannot divide by zero.

LEVELS OF COMPREHENSION

STEP 1   Read the problem.

STEP 2   Choose the variable(s).

STEP 3   Form the equation.

STEP 4   Solve the equation.

STEP 5   Check the equation.

MODEL PROBLEM 1

On a salad tray at a party, the ratio of pickles to olives is 5:8. If there are 16 olives, how many pickles must there be to maintain the 5:8 ratio?

READ THE PROBLEM

After reading the problem, give the answers to the following statements in the spaces provided.

Literal Level

The ratio of pickles to ___olives___ is 5:8. The ratio of ___n___ pickles to 16 olives is ___5:8___.

Interpretive Level

CHOOSE THE VARIABLE(S)

Let n = number of pickles.

FORM THE EQUATION

$$\frac{n}{16} = \frac{5}{8}$$

SOLVE THE EQUATION

$$\frac{n}{16} = \frac{5}{8}$$

$$16 \cdot \frac{n}{16} = 16 \cdot \frac{5}{8}$$

$$n = 10$$

10 pickles

CHECK THE EQUATION

$$\frac{n}{16} = \frac{5}{8}$$

$$\frac{10}{16} = \frac{5}{8}$$

$$\frac{5}{8} = \frac{5}{8}$$

$$\frac{a}{a} = 1,$$

$$a \neq 0$$

ACTIVITY EXTENSION

If the ratio of pickles to olives is to be 5:8, could the number of pickles equal the number of olives?

_No_

MODEL PROBLEM 2

A shepherd has a flock of sheep. For every two black sheep, the shepherd has 100 white sheep. How many black sheep does the shepherd have, if there are 500 white sheep?

READ THE PROBLEM

After reading the problem, give the answers to the following statements in the spaces provided.

The ratio of black sheep to white sheep is ___2:100___. This ratio is also the same as 1:50. Find the number of ___black___ sheep if there are ___500___ white sheep.

Interpretive Level

CHOOSE THE VARIABLE(S)

Let b = number of black sheep.

Application Level

FORM THE EQUATION

$$\frac{2}{100} = \frac{b}{500}$$

SOLVE THE EQUATION

$$\frac{2}{100} = \frac{b}{500}$$

$$\frac{500}{} \cdot \frac{2}{100} = 500 \cdot \frac{b}{500}$$

$$\frac{10}{} = b \text{ (number of black sheep)}$$ <u>10 sheep</u>

CHECK THE EQUATION

$$\frac{2}{100} = \frac{b}{500}$$

$$\frac{2}{100} = \frac{10}{500}$$

$$\frac{1}{50} = \frac{1}{50}$$

ACTIVITY EXTENSION

This is simply a good way to estimate or guess.

Why would a rancher find it useful to have a mixed flock of black and white sheep?

The sheep mix while grazing. If ten black sheep are counted, it is likely that they are among 500 white sheep. This is a quick way to determine how much of the entire flock is gathered in the same place.

MODEL PROBLEM 3

The ratio of the numerator of a fraction to the denominator of the fraction is 7:8. If the numerator is multiplied by 4, by what number will the denominator need to be multiplied in order for the fraction to be in the ratio of 7:8?

READ THE PROBLEM

After reading the problem, give the answers to the following statements in the spaces provided.

Literal Level

The ratio of the _____numerator_____ to the denominator of a fraction is _____7 to 8_____. After the numerator is multiplied by ___4___, the denominator is to be multiplied by some number such that the ratio of numerator to denominator is still ___7:8___.

CHOOSE THE VARIABLE(S)

Interpretive Level

Let n = number by which the denominator is multiplied.

Application Level

FORM THE EQUATION

$$\frac{7}{8} = \frac{7 \cdot 4}{8 \cdot x}$$

SOLVE THE EQUATION

$$\frac{7}{8} = \frac{7 \cdot 4}{8 \cdot x}$$

$$\frac{7}{8} = \frac{28}{8x}$$

$$8x\left(\frac{7}{8}\right) = 8x\left(\frac{28}{8x}\right)$$

$$\frac{7x}{4} = 28$$

$$x = \underline{\quad 4 \quad}$$

$$\underline{\qquad 4 \qquad}$$

CHECK THE EQUATION

$$\frac{7}{8} = \frac{7 \cdot 4}{8 \cdot x}$$

$$\frac{7}{8} = \frac{7 \cdot 4}{8 \cdot 4}$$

$$\frac{7}{8} = \frac{28}{32}$$

$$\frac{7}{8} = \frac{7}{8}$$

ACTIVITY EXTENSION

If the numerator of the fraction had been multiplied by 5, by what number would the denominator have to be multiplied to maintain a ratio of 7 to 8?

5

Name _____ Period _____

Teacher _____ Date _____ Grade _____

Ratio Problems with Help

DIRECTIONS: Each of the following problems has been given a partial solution. Solve each problem by completing the solution.

1. In simplest form, the ratio of 25 to 40 is ___5:8___ .

2. The ratio of 3 to 5 is the same ratio as 15 to ___25___ .

3. The ratio of a penny to a dollar is ___1:100___ .

4. If you have $10 and your teacher has $2, then the ratio of your money to your teacher's money is ___10:2___ or ___5:1___ . The ratio of your teacher's money to your money is ___2:10___ or ___1:5___ .

5. Bill contributes $1 to the church each time his father contributes $5. If his father contributes $25 to the church, then Bill contributes ___$5___ .

6. The ratio of compacts to station wagons in a small town is 85 to 1. If there are 16 station wagons, then there are $16 \cdot$ ___85___ compacts.

7. A recipe for strawberry-rhubarb pie calls for three cups of berries for every two cups of rhubarb. If Ann has six cups of berries, how many cups of rhubarb must she use? (*Hint:* When you write the first fraction, you must follow the same pattern in writing the second fraction.)

Let x = number of cups of rhubarb.

$$\frac{3}{2} = \frac{6}{x}$$

$$2x\left(\frac{3}{2}\right) = 2x\left(\frac{6}{x}\right)$$

$$\underline{3x} = 12$$

$$x = \underline{4}$$

Check: $\dfrac{3}{2} = \dfrac{6}{x}$

$$\frac{3}{2} = \frac{6}{4}$$

$$\frac{3}{2} = \frac{\underline{3}}{\underline{2}}$$

Cross-multiplication is introduced with proportion on page 39.

8. Two neighboring families go out for a birthday celebration. They agree to pay according to the number of persons in each family. If the ratio of Smith family members to Cooper family members is 5:2 and the bill is $350, how much should each family pay?

Let x = amount paid by the Smiths (in dollars).

$$\frac{350 - x}{} = \text{amount paid by the Coopers (in dollars)}$$

$$\frac{x}{(350 - x)} = \frac{\frac{5}{2}}{}$$

$$2(350 - x) \cdot \frac{x}{(350 - x)} = 2(350 - x) \cdot \frac{5}{2}$$

$$\frac{2x}{} = 5(350 - x)$$

$$2x = 1{,}750 - 5x$$

$$7x = 1{,}750$$

$$x = \underline{\$250} \quad \text{(amount paid by the Smiths)}$$

$$(350 - x) = \underline{\$100} \quad \text{(amount paid by the Coopers)}$$

Smith family: **$250**
Cooper family: **$100**

Check: $\dfrac{x}{(350 - x)} = \dfrac{5}{2}$

$$\frac{250}{(350 - 250)} = \frac{5}{2}$$

$$\frac{250}{100} = \frac{5}{2}$$

$$\frac{5}{2} = \frac{5}{2}$$

9. The ratio of the measures of the angles of a triangle is 2:3:5. Find the measure of each angle. (The sum of the measures of the angles of a triangle is 180°.)

Let n = number by which 2, 3, and 5 are multiplied.

$2n$ = measure of angle 1 (in degrees)

$\underline{3n}$ = measure of angle 2 (in degrees)

$5n$ = measure of angle 3 (in degrees)

$2n + 3n + 5n = \underline{180}$

$\underline{10n} = 180$

$n = \underline{18°}$ (number by which 2, 3, and 5 are multiplied)

$2n = 36°$ (measure of angle 1)

$3n = \underline{\quad 54° \quad}$ (measure of angle 2)

$5n = \underline{\quad 90° \quad}$ (measure of angle 3)

Angle 1: **36°**
Angle 2: **54°**
Angle 3: **90°**

Check: $2n + 3n + 5n = 180$

$2 \cdot \underline{\quad 18 \quad} + 3 \cdot \underline{\quad 18 \quad} + 5 \cdot \underline{\quad 18 \quad} = 180$

$36 + \underline{\quad 54 \quad} + 90 = 180$

$\underline{\quad 180 \quad} = 180$

Challenge

It is possible to do these using arithmetic only.

10. In a recipe for ambrosia, the ratio (by number) of oranges to bananas to cherries is 36:9:180. If a restaurant uses 360 oranges in its ambrosia, how many bananas and cherries should be used?

Let b = number of bananas.

$$\frac{36}{360} = \frac{9}{b}$$

$$\underline{\frac{1}{10}} = \frac{9}{b}$$

$b = \underline{\quad 90 \quad}$ (number of bananas)

Check: $\dfrac{36}{360} = \dfrac{9}{b}$

$$\frac{36}{360} = \underline{\frac{9}{90}}$$

$$\frac{1}{10} = \underline{\frac{1}{10}}$$

Let c = number of cherries.

$$\underline{\frac{36}{360}} = \frac{180}{c}$$

$$\underline{\frac{1}{10}} = \frac{180}{c}$$

$c = \underline{\quad 1{,}800 \quad}$ (number of cherries)

Bananas: **90**
Cherries: **1,800**

Check: $\dfrac{36}{360} = \dfrac{180}{c}$

$$\frac{36}{360} = \underline{\frac{180}{1{,}800}}$$

$$\frac{1}{10} = \underline{\frac{1}{10}}$$

Name _____ Period _____

Teacher _____ Date _____ Grade _____

Ratio Problems

DIRECTIONS: Use the five levels of comprehension to solve each of the following problems. Write your answers in the space provided.

1. In simplest form, the ratio of 40 to 50 is __4:5__.

2. The ratio of 5:6 is the same ratio as 50: __60__.

3. The ratio of one to a dozen is __1:12__.

4. If you have $100 and your sister has $25, then the ratio of your money to your sister's money is __100:25__ or __4:1__. The ratio of your sister's money to your money is 25:100 or __1:4__.

5. Every time a young couple saves $1,000, their parents add $5,000 to their savings. If the couple saves $10,000, then their parents add __$50,000__ to their savings.

6. The ratio of babies to senior citizens in a community is 1:1. If there are 800 senior citizens in the community, how many babies are there in the community?

   __800__

7. A recipe requires five cups of sugar for every 14 cups of tart cherries. How many cups of sugar must be used if Jane has 140 cups of cherries?

   Let c = number of cups of sugar needed.

   $$\frac{5}{14} = \frac{c}{140}$$

   $$14 \cdot 140\left(\frac{5}{14}\right) = 14 \cdot 140 \cdot \frac{c}{140}$$

   $$700 = 14c$$

   $$50 = c$$ __50 cups__

   Check: $\frac{5}{14} = \frac{c}{140}$

   $$\frac{5}{14} = \frac{50}{140}$$

   $$\frac{5}{14} = \frac{5}{14}$$

8. A wire 63 inches long is to be divided into two parts whose ratio is 5:2. Find the length of each part.

Let n = length of the longer part (in inches).

$63 - n$ = length of the shorter part (in inches)

$$\frac{n}{(63 - n)} = \frac{5}{2}$$

$$2(63 - n) \cdot \frac{n}{(63 - n)} = 2(63 - n) \cdot \frac{5}{2}$$

$2n = (63 - n)5$

$2n = 315 - 5n$

$7n = 315$

$n = 45$ inches (length of longer part)

$63 - n = 18$ inches (length of shorter part)

Longer length: **45 inches**
Shorter length: **18 inches**

Check:
$$\frac{n}{(63 - n)} = \frac{5}{2}$$

$$\frac{45}{(63 - 45)} = \frac{5}{2}$$

$$\frac{45}{18} = \frac{5}{2}$$

$$\frac{5}{2} = \frac{5}{2}$$

9. In Mary's school, the ratio of the number of math books to English books is 2:5. If there are 14,000 math and English books altogether, how many of each are there?

Let n = number by which 2 and 5 are multiplied.

$2n$ = number of math books

$5n$ = number of English books

$2n + 5n = 14,000$

$7n = 14,000$

$n = 2,000$ (number by which 2 and 5 are multiplied)

$2n = 4,000$ (number of math books)

$5n = 10,000$ (number of English books)

Math: **4,000 books**
English: **10,000 books**

Check: $2n + 5n = 14,000$

$2 \cdot 2,000 + 5 \cdot 2,000 = 14,000$

$4,000 + 10,000 = 14,000$

$14,000 = 14,000$

Challenge

10. The ratio of girls to boys in Miss Smith's class is 20:12. If two boys transfer to another school, how many girls would also need to transfer in order for the ratio of girls to boys to be 3:2?

Ratio of girls to boys originally = $\dfrac{\frac{20}{12}}{\rule{4cm}{0.4pt}}$

Ratio after two boys transfer = $\dfrac{\frac{20}{10}}{\rule{4cm}{0.4pt}}$

Let x = number of girls who would leave.

Ratio after x girls leave = $\dfrac{\frac{20 - x}{10}}{\rule{4cm}{0.4pt}}$

$\dfrac{20 - x}{10} = \dfrac{3}{2}$

$\dfrac{20 - x}{10} = \dfrac{5}{5} \cdot \dfrac{3}{2}$

$\dfrac{20 - x}{10} = \dfrac{15}{10}$

$20 - x = 15$

$-x = -5$

$x = 5$ (number of girls who would leave) $\underline{\text{5 girls}}$

Check: $\dfrac{20 - x}{10} = \dfrac{3}{2}$

$\dfrac{20 - 5}{10} = \dfrac{3}{2}$

$\dfrac{15}{10} = \dfrac{3}{2}$

$\dfrac{3}{2} = \dfrac{3}{2}$

STUDY GUIDE 3

Proportion

TERMS AND CONCEPTS

Introductory Precepts

A ratio is an indicated quotient. A *proportion* is the equality of two ratios. For instance,

$$\frac{2}{3} = \frac{20}{30}$$

Make sure students are familiar with all ratio notation.

Notice that the cross-products (2×30) and (3×20) are equal. Formally,

$$\frac{a}{b} = \frac{c}{d} \text{ if } a \cdot d = b \cdot c$$

Remind students that division by 0 is impossible.

In this equation, b and c are sometimes called *means* and a and d are sometimes called *extremes*. In a proportion, the product of the means is equal to the product of the extremes.

LEVELS OF COMPREHENSION

STEP 1 Read the problem.

STEP 2 Choose the variable(s).

STEP 3 Form the equation.

STEP 4 Solve the equation.

STEP 5 Check the equation.

MODEL PROBLEM 1

Amanda and her apprentice contracted to do a job for $2,500. They agreed to share this money in the ratio of 4:1. How much did each receive?

40

Study Guide 3

READ THE PROBLEM

After reading the problem, give the answers to the following statements in the spaces provided.

Literal Level

Amanda and her apprentice receive ____$2500____ for doing a job. Amanda will receive ____four____ times as much as her apprentice.

Interpretive Level

1. Amanda and her apprentice receive amounts that are not equal, unequal.
   ____Equal____

2. For every $4 Amanda receives, her apprentice receives $4, $2, $1, none of these.
   ____$1____

3. The ratio of $4x$ to x is one to four, x to four, 4:1.
   ____4:1____

CHOOSE THE VARIABLE(S)

Let x = amount the apprentice will receive (in dollars). Then $4x$ = amount Amanda will receive (in dollars).

Application Level

FORM THE EQUATION

$x + $ ____$4x$____ $= 2,500$

SOLVE THE EQUATION

$x + $ ____$4x$____ $= 2,500$

$5x = 2,500$

$x = $ ____$500____ (amount apprentice will receive)

$4x = $ ____$2,000____ (amount Amanda will receive)

Apprentice: **$500**
Amanda: **$2,000**

CHECK THE EQUATION

$x + 4x = 2,500$

$500 + 4(500) = 2,500$

$500 + $ ____2,000____ $= 2,500$

____2,500____ $= 2,500$

ACTIVITY EXTENSION

1. What is the ratio of $\dfrac{\$500}{\$2,000}$?
   ____1:4____

2. What is the ratio of $\dfrac{x}{4x}$?
   ____1:4____

3. If Amanda and her apprentice had shared equally, what would the ratio of the two shares be?
   ____1:1____

MODEL PROBLEM 2

A worker received $60 for working 2.5 hours. At the same rate of pay, how many hours will he have to work to earn $192?

READ THE PROBLEM

After reading the problem, give the answers to the following statements or questions in the spaces provided.

Literal Level

For working 2.5 hours, a worker receives $\underline{\$60}$. How many hours will he have to work at the same rate of pay to earn $\underline{\$192}$?

Interpretive Level

The ratio of the number of hours that were worked to the number of hours that will have to be worked equals the ratio of the number of dollars that were earned to

the number of dollars lost

the number of dollars that will be earned

$\dfrac{1}{6}$

none of these

The number of dollars that will be earned.

CHOOSE THE VARIABLE(S)

Let h = number of hours needed to make $192.

Application Level

FORM THE EQUATION

$$\frac{2.5}{h} = \frac{60}{192}$$

The equation
$$\frac{a}{b} = \frac{c}{d}$$
is solved simply by equating $a \cdot d$ and $b \cdot c$.

SOLVE THE EQUATION

$$\frac{2.5}{h} = \frac{60}{192}$$

$60 \cdot h = \underline{2.5 \cdot 192}$ (Cross-products are equal.)

$60h = 480$

$h = \underline{8}$ (number of hours needed to work to earn $192)

8 hours

CHECK THE EQUATION

$$\frac{2.5}{h} = \frac{60}{192}$$

$$\frac{\frac{2.5}{8}}{} = \frac{60}{192}$$

$$\frac{480}{} = 480$$

ACTIVITY EXTENSION

The initial equation $\frac{2.5}{h} = \frac{60}{192}$ could have been written a number of other ways and the cross-products would have been the same. (Remember that when writing the initial fraction, you are to follow the same pattern in writing the other fraction.) What two other ways could the equation for Model Problem 2 have been written?

$$\frac{2.5}{60} = \frac{h}{192}$$

$$\frac{h}{2.5} = \frac{192}{60}$$

MODEL PROBLEM 3

The denominator of a fraction is four more than the numerator. If 2 is subtracted from the numerator and 2 is added to the denominator, then the new fraction becomes $\frac{5}{13}$. Find the original fraction.

READ THE PROBLEM

After reading the problem, give the answers to the following statements in the spaces provided.

Literal Level

The denominator of a fraction is ___four___ more than the numerator. Suppose that __2__ is subtracted from the __numerator__ and __2__ is added to the denominator. The new fraction becomes $\frac{5}{13}$. Find the __original__ fraction.

CHOOSE THE VARIABLE(S)

Interpretive Level

Let n = numerator.

$n + 4$ = denominator

$\frac{n}{n + 4}$ = original fraction

Application Level

FORM THE EQUATION

$$\frac{(n - 2)}{(n + 4 + 2)} = \frac{5}{13}$$

SOLVE THE EQUATION

$$\frac{(n - 2)}{(n + 4 + 2)} = \frac{5}{13}$$

$$\frac{\frac{(n - 2)}{(n + 6)}}{} = \frac{5}{13}$$

$$13(n - 2) = 5(n + 6) \qquad \text{(Cross-products are equal.)}$$

$$\underline{13n - 26} = 5n + 30$$

$$8n = 56$$

$$n = \underline{\quad 7 \quad} \text{ (numerator)}$$

$$n + 4 = \underline{\quad 11 \quad} \text{ (denominator)}$$

$$\frac{7}{11}$$

CHECK THE EQUATION

$$\frac{(n - 2)}{(n + 6)} = \frac{5}{13}$$

$$\frac{(7 - 2)}{(7 + 6)} = \frac{5}{13}$$

$$\frac{5}{13} = \frac{5}{13}$$

MODEL PROBLEM 4

Yoko works at quality control in a company that makes lightbulbs. The standard ratio of acceptable to defective lightbulbs must be 100,000 to 7. If she finds 42 defective lightbulbs, how many bulbs must she have examined in order that the minimum standard be met?

READ THE PROBLEM

After reading the problem, give the answers to the following statements in the spaces provided.

Literal Level

The ratio of acceptable to defective lightbulbs must be __100,000__ to __7__. Yoko finds __42__ defective lightbulbs.

In a bulk order, the number of acceptable bulbs plus the number of defective bulbs are equal to

> the number of bulbs broken
> the number of bulbs shipped
> the number of bulbs examined

The number of bulbs examined

CHOOSE THE VARIABLE(S)

Let n = number of acceptable bulbs.

FORM THE EQUATION

$$\frac{n}{42} = \frac{100,000}{7}$$

SOLVE THE EQUATION

$$\frac{n}{42} = \frac{100,000}{7}$$

$$7n = 42(100,000)$$

$$\frac{7n}{} = 4,200,000$$

$$n = \underline{600,000} \text{ (number of acceptable bulbs)}$$

$$600,000 + 42 = \underline{600,042} \text{ (number of bulbs examined)}$$

600,042 bulbs

CHECK THE EQUATION

$$\frac{n}{42} = \frac{100,000}{7}$$

$$\frac{600,000}{42} = \frac{100,000}{7}$$

$$\underline{4,200,000} = \underline{4,200,000}$$

ACTIVITY EXTENSION

To the consumer, quality is the name of the game. The bulk order in which the ratio of acceptable to defective lightbulbs is 100,000:1 would have 100,000 acceptable bulbs and 1 defective bulb. Would this ratio have been better than the minimum requirement?

Yes

Name _____ Period _____

Teacher _____ Date _____ Grade _____

Proportion Problems with Help

DIRECTIONS: Each of the following problems has been given a partial solution. Solve each problem by completing the given solution.

1. A streamer 28 feet long is to be cut into two pieces whose lengths are in the ratio 2:5. Find the length of each piece.

   Let n = shorter length (in feet).

   $\underline{\ \ 28 - n\ \ }$ = longer length (in feet)

   $$\frac{n}{(28 - n)} = \frac{2}{5}$$

   $5n = 2(28 - n)$ (Cross-products are equal.)

   $\underline{5n = 56 - 2n}$

   $\underline{7n = 56}$

   $n = \underline{\ \ 8\ \ }$ feet (shorter length)

   $28 - n = \underline{\ \ 20\ \ }$ feet (longer length)

   Shorter length: **8 feet**
   Longer length: **20 feet**

   Check: $\dfrac{n}{(28 - n)} = \dfrac{2}{5}$

   $$\frac{8}{(28 - \underline{\ \ 8\ \ })} = \frac{2}{5}$$

   $$\frac{8}{20} = \frac{2}{5}$$

   $$\frac{2}{5} = \frac{2}{5}$$

2. The denominator of a fraction is two more than the numerator. By subtracting one from the numerator and adding five to the denominator, the resulting fraction is $\frac{2}{3}$. Find the original fraction.

   Let x = numerator of original fraction.

   $\underline{\ \ x + 2\ \ }$ = denominator of original fraction

   $\dfrac{x}{(x + 2)}$ = original fraction

$$\frac{(x-1)}{(x+2+5)} = \frac{2}{3}$$

$$\frac{(x-1)}{(x+7)} = \frac{2}{3}$$

$$3(x-1) = 2(x+7) \qquad \text{(Cross-products are equal.)}$$

$$3x - 3 = 2x + 14$$

$x = \underline{\quad 17 \quad}$ (numerator of original fraction)

$x + 2 = \underline{\quad 19 \quad}$ (denominator of original fraction)

$\dfrac{\underline{17}}{\underline{19}}$ = original fraction

$\dfrac{17}{19}$

Check: $\dfrac{(x-1)}{(x+2+5)} = \dfrac{2}{3}$

$$\frac{(\underline{17}-1)}{(\underline{17}+7)} = \frac{2}{3}$$

$$\frac{16}{24} = \frac{2}{3}$$

$$\frac{2}{3} = \frac{2}{3}$$

3. A housing complex has two-bedroom and three-bedroom apartments in the ratio of 2:3. If there are 1,000 apartments in all, how many of each size are there?

Let n = number of two-bedroom apartments.

$\underline{\quad 1{,}000 - n \quad}$ = number of three-bedroom apartments

$$\frac{n}{(1{,}000 - n)} = \frac{2}{3}$$

$$3n = 2(1{,}000 - n) \qquad \text{(Cross-products are equal.)}$$

$$3n = 2{,}000 - 2n$$

$$5n = 2{,}000$$

$n = \underline{\quad 400 \quad}$ (number of two-bedroom apartments)

$1{,}000 - n = \underline{\quad 600 \quad}$ (number of three-bedroom apartments)

Two-bedroom: 400
Three-bedroom: 600

Check: $\dfrac{n}{(1{,}000 - n)} = \dfrac{2}{3}$

$$\frac{400}{(1{,}000 - 400)} = \frac{2}{3}$$

$$\frac{400}{600} = \frac{2}{3}$$

$$\frac{\frac{2}{3}}{} = \frac{2}{3}$$

4. A zookeeper buys apples and bananas each day for the animals. If the ratio of apples to bananas is 4 to 76, how many pieces of each fruit are there if the sum of apples and bananas bought one day is 800?

Let n = number of apples bought.

$\underline{800 - n}$ = number of bananas bought

$$\frac{n}{(800 - n)} = \frac{4}{76}$$

$\underline{76n = 4(800 - n)}$ (Cross-products are equal.)

$76n = 3{,}200 - 4n$

$\underline{80n = 3{,}200}$

$n = \underline{40}$ (number of apples bought)   Apples: **40**

$800 - n = \underline{760}$ (number of bananas bought)   Bananas: **760**

Check: $\dfrac{n}{(800 - n)} = \dfrac{4}{76}$

$$\frac{40}{(800 - 40)} = \frac{4}{76}$$

$$\frac{40}{760} = \frac{4}{76}$$

$$\frac{1}{19} = \frac{1}{19}$$

5. A beauty salon does a ratio of ten manicures to every permanent done on any given day. How many permanents are given on a day in which 80 manicures are given?

Let n = number of permanents given.

$$\frac{10}{1} = \frac{80}{n}$$

$10n = 80$ (Cross-products are equal.)

$n = \underline{8}$ (number of permanents given)   **8 permanents**

Check: $\dfrac{10}{1} = \dfrac{80}{n}$

$$\frac{10}{1} = \frac{80}{8}$$

$$10 = \underline{10}$$

Challenge

6. To mix a certain tint, a hair stylist uses 3 ounces of peroxide and $1\frac{1}{2}$ ounces of a selected color; that is, the amount of color must be 50 percent of the number of ounces of peroxide. If 18 ounces of the tint solution are prepared for use in one day, how much peroxide should be used?

Let p = number of ounces of peroxide.

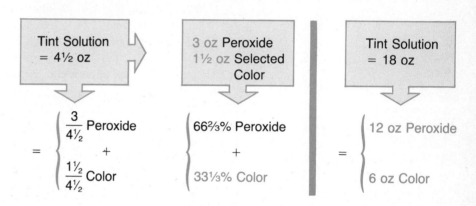

$\underline{\hspace{1cm} 18 - p \hspace{1cm}}$ = number of ounces of selected color

$$\frac{3}{4\frac{1}{2}} = \frac{p}{18}$$

$18(3) = 4\frac{1}{2}p$ (Cross-products are equal.)

$54 = \frac{9}{2}p$

$54 \cdot 2 = 9p$

$108 = 9p$

$\underline{\hspace{0.5cm} 12 = p \hspace{0.5cm}}$ (number of ounces of peroxide)

12 ounces of peroxide

Check: $\left(3 \div 4\frac{1}{2}\right) = (p \div 18)$

$3 \div \frac{9}{2} = (12 \div 18)$

$3 \times \frac{2}{9} = 12 \times \frac{1}{18}$

$\frac{2}{3} = \frac{12}{18}$

$\frac{2}{3} = \frac{2}{3}$

Name _____ Period _____

Teacher _____ Date _____ Grade _____

Proportion Problems

DIRECTIONS: Use the five levels of comprehension to solve each of the problems in the space provided. Write your answers in the blank to the right after each problem.

1. A wire 30 feet long is to be cut into two pieces whose lengths are in the ratio of 4:11. Find the length of each piece.

   Let n = length of shorter piece (in feet).

   $30 - n$ = length of longer piece (in feet)

   $$\frac{n}{(30 - n)} = \frac{4}{11}$$

   $11n = 4(30 - n)$

   $11n = 120 - 4n$

   $15n = 120$

   $n = 8$ feet (length of shorter piece)

   $30 - n = 22$ feet (length of longer piece)

   Shorter piece: **8 feet**
   Longer piece: **22 feet**

   Check: $\dfrac{n}{(30 - n)} = \dfrac{4}{11}$

   $\dfrac{8}{(30 - 8)} = \dfrac{4}{11}$

   $\dfrac{8}{22} = \dfrac{4}{11}$

   $\dfrac{4}{11} = \dfrac{4}{11}$

2. The numerator of a fraction is ten less than the denominator. By subtracting 1 from the numerator and adding 7 to the denominator, the new fraction has a value of $\dfrac{11}{17}$. Find the original fraction.

   Let d = denominator.

   $\dfrac{d - 10}{\underline{\hspace{3cm}}}$ = numerator

   $\dfrac{(d - 10)}{\underline{\hspace{2cm}}}$
   $\dfrac{\overline{d}}{\underline{\hspace{3cm}}}$ = original fraction

$$\frac{(d - 10 - 1)}{(d + 7)} = \frac{11}{17}$$

$$\frac{(d - 11)}{(d + 7)} = \frac{11}{17}$$

$$17(d - 11) = 11(d + 7)$$

$$17d - 187 = 11d + 77$$

$$6d = 264$$

$$d = 44 \text{ (denominator)}$$

$$d - 10 = 34 \text{ (numerator)}$$

$$\frac{34}{44} = \text{original fraction}$$

$$\frac{34}{44}$$

Check: $\dfrac{(d - 10 - 1)}{(d + 7)} = \dfrac{11}{17}$

$$\frac{(44 - 11)}{(44 + 7)} = \frac{11}{17}$$

$$\frac{33}{51} = \frac{11}{17}$$

$$\frac{11}{17} = \frac{11}{17}$$

3. An auto dealer has small trucks and semi-trailers in the ratio of 300 to 7. If there are 3,070 trucks in all, how many of each are there?

Let n = number of small trucks.

$3,070 - n$ = number of semi-trailers

$$\frac{n}{(3,070 - n)} = \frac{300}{7}$$

$$7n = 300(3,070 - n)$$

$$7n = 921,000 - 300n$$

$$307n = 921,000$$

$$n = 3,000 \text{ (number of small trucks)}$$

$$3,070 - n = 70 \text{ (number of semi-trailers)}$$

Small trucks: 3,000
Semi-trailers: 70

Check: $\dfrac{n}{(3{,}070 - n)} = \dfrac{300}{7}$

$$\dfrac{3{,}000}{(3{,}070 - 3{,}000)} = \dfrac{300}{7}$$

$$\dfrac{3{,}000}{70} = \dfrac{300}{7}$$

$$\dfrac{300}{7} = \dfrac{300}{7}$$

4. Mrs. Pinnacle manages a restaurant. She buys bunches of carrots and bunches of radishes each day in the ratio of 5:2. How many bunches of each does she buy if on one day the sum of bunches of carrots and the bunches of radishes is 210?

   Let c = bunches of carrots.

   210 − c = bunches of radishes

   $$\dfrac{c}{(210 - c)} = \dfrac{5}{2}$$

   2c = 5(210 − c)

   2c = 1,050 − 5c

   7c = 1,050

   c = 150 (bunches of carrots)

   210 − c = 60 (bunches of radishes)

   Carrots: **150 bunches**
   Radishes: **60 bunches**

   Check: $\dfrac{c}{(210 - c)} = \dfrac{5}{2}$

   $$\dfrac{150}{(210 - 150)} = \dfrac{5}{2}$$

   $$\dfrac{150}{60} = \dfrac{5}{2}$$

   $$\dfrac{5}{2} = \dfrac{5}{2}$$

5. A pesticide firm daily sprays a ratio of seven interiors to every two exteriors sprayed. If the total number of spray jobs in one day was 1,800, how many interiors and exteriors were sprayed?

   Let n = number of interiors done.

   1,800 − n = number of exteriors done

   $$\dfrac{n}{(1{,}800 - n)} = \dfrac{7}{2}$$

   2n = 7(1,800 − n)

$$2n = 12,600 - 7n$$

$$9n = 12,600$$

$$n = 1,400 \text{ (number of interiors)}$$

$$1,800 - n = 400 \text{ (numbers of exteriors)}$$

Interiors: **1,400**

Exteriors: **400**

Check: $\dfrac{n}{(1,800 - n)} = \dfrac{7}{2}$

$$\dfrac{1,400}{(1,800 - 1,400)} = \dfrac{7}{2}$$

$$\dfrac{1,400}{400} = \dfrac{7}{2}$$

$$\dfrac{7}{2} = \dfrac{7}{2}$$

Challenge

6. A buyer for a large chain of grocery stores places an order for 90,000 bushels of potatoes. The ratio of bushels of Irish potatoes to bushels of Idaho potatoes is 8:7. The ratio of Idaho potatoes to sweet-potatoes is 7:3. How many bushels of each are ordered?

Let $8x$ = number of bushels of Irish potatoes.

$7x$ = number of bushels of Idaho potatoes

$3x$ = number of bushels of sweet-potatoes

(The ratio of Irish to Idaho to sweet equals ____**8:7:3**____.)

(In terms of x, the ratio of Irish to Idaho to sweet also equals ____**8x:7x:3x**____.)

$8x + 7x + 3x = 90,000$

$18x = 90,000$

$x = 5,000$

$8x = 40,000$ (number of bushels of Irish potatoes)

$7x = 35,000$ (number of bushels of Idaho potatoes)

$3x = 15,000$ (number of bushels of sweet-potatoes)

Irish: **40,000 bushels**

Idaho: **35,000 bushels**

Sweet-: **15,000 bushels**

Check: $8x + 7x + 3x = 90,000$

$$8(5,000) + 7(5,000) + 3(5,000) = 90,000$$

$$40,000 + 35,000 + 15,000 = 90,000$$

$$90,000 = 90,000$$

STUDY GUIDE 4

The Lever

TERMS AND CONCEPTS

A seesaw is an example of a lever. The point at which a lever is supported is called the *fulcrum*. According to physics, when a lever is in balance, this law of the lever exists:

Introductory Precepts

$$w_1 \times d_1 = w_2 \times d_2$$

where

$\left.\begin{array}{c} w_1 \\ \\ w_2 \end{array}\right\}$ Weight

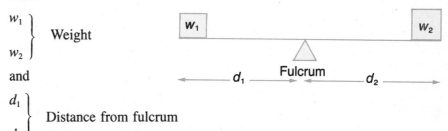

and

$\left.\begin{array}{c} d_1 \\ \\ d_2 \end{array}\right\}$ Distance from fulcrum

If $w_1d_1 > w_2d_2$, then w_1 lifts w_2. If $w_1d_1 < w_2d_2$, then w_2 lifts w_1. If $w_1d_1 = w_2d_2$, then w_1 and w_2 are balanced.

LEVELS OF COMPREHENSION

STEP 1 Read the problem.

STEP 2 Choose the variable(s).

STEP 3 Form the equation.

STEP 4 Solve the equation.

STEP 5 Check the equation.

53

MODEL PROBLEM 1

Pascuala weighs 90 pounds and sits 6 feet from the fulcrum of a seesaw. How far must Michelle, who weighs 108 pounds, sit from the fulcrum in order to balance Pascuala?

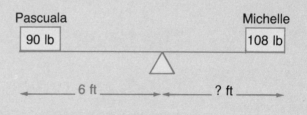

READ THE PROBLEM

After reading the problem, give the answers to the following statements in the spaces provided.

Literal Level

Pascuala weighs __90__ pounds and sits __6__ feet from the fulcrum of a seesaw. Michelle, who weighs __108__ pounds, must sit at some distance from the fulcrum in order to balance __Pascuala__.

Interpretive Level

1. The product of Pascuala's weight and her distance from the fulcrum is

   540,   450,   90-6,   none of these.   __540__

2. The product of Michelle's weight and her distance from the fulcrum is equal to

   450,   108,   450-108,   540.   __540__

3. The distance Michelle sits from the fulcrum in order to balance Pascuala is

   known,   unknown.   __Unknown__

CHOOSE THE VARIABLE(S)

Let n = distance Michelle sits from fulcrum (in feet).

FORM THE EQUATION

Application Level

$108n = $ __90__ (6)

SOLVE THE EQUATION

$108n = 90(6)$

$108n = $ __540__

$n = 5$ feet (distance Michelle sits from fulcrum)   __5 feet__

CHECK THE EQUATION

$108n = 540$

$108 \cdot \dfrac{5}{} = 540$

$\dfrac{540}{} = 540$

ACTIVITY EXTENSION

Refer students to the law
of the lever, page 53.

What happens when Michelle moves two feet farther from the fulcrum and Pascuala remains six feet from the fulcrum?

**Pascuala is lifted
into the air.**

If the seesaw is long enough, is it possible for Pascuala to move to a place some distance from the fulcrum in order to raise Michelle into the air?

**Yes, if Michelle does not
also change her position.**

MODEL PROBLEM 2

Lee weighs 200 pounds and Ramos weighs 300 pounds. If Lee sits six feet from the fulcrum of a seesaw, how far from the fulcrum must Ramos sit in order to balance Lee?

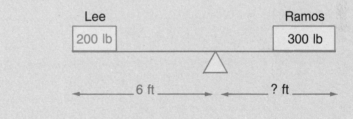

READ THE PROBLEM

After reading the problem, give the answers to the following statements in the spaces provided.

Literal Level

Lee weighs __200__ pounds and sits __six__ feet from the fulcrum of a seesaw. Ramos outweighs Lee by __100__ pounds. Ramos is to sit at a certain distance from the __fulcrum__ in order to balance __Lee__.

CHOOSE THE VARIABLE(S)

Interpretive Level

Let n = number of feet Ramos sits from fulcrum in order to balance Lee.

Application Level

FORM THE EQUATION

$300n = \underline{\ \ 200\ \ }$ (6)

SOLVE THE EQUATION

$300(n) = 200(6)$

$300n = \underline{\ \ \ \ 1200\ \ \ \ }$

$n = \underline{\ \ 4\ \ }$ feet (number of feet Ramos must sit from fulcrum in order to balance Lee)

$$\underline{\ \ \ \ \ \ 4\ feet\ \ \ \ \ \ }$$

CHECK THE EQUATION

$300n = 200(6)$

$300 (\underline{\ \ 4\ \ }) = 200(6)$

$\underline{\ \ 1{,}200\ \ } = 1{,}200$

ACTIVITY EXTENSION

Refer students to the law of the lever, page 53.

Could Lee and Ramos, with their respective weights, balance each other if the seesaw were only 8 feet long?

$$\underline{\ \ \ \ \ \ Yes\ \ \ \ \ \ }$$

MODEL PROBLEM 3

In some countries, weights are carried by placing two of them at opposite ends of a pole. When the shoulder is used as a fulcrum for the pole, it is easy to carry the weights. Chino wants to carry two wrapped parcels, one weighing 50 pounds and one weighing 40 pounds. At what point on a nine-foot pole must he place his shoulder in order to balance the two weights?

READ THE PROBLEM

After reading the problem, give the answers to the following statements in the space provided.

Literal Level

Chino has _____two_____ weights. One weighs ___50___ pounds and the ____other____ weighs __40__ pounds. The pole used to balance the weights is ____nine____ feet long. Chino must locate the point on the pole where his ___shoulder___ can be used as a fulcrum.

CHOOSE THE VARIABLE(S)

Interpretive Level

Let n = distance the 50-pound weight is from one end of the nine-foot pole to the fulcrum (in feet).

$9 - n$ = distance the 40-pound weight is from the other end of the nine-foot pole to its fulcrum (in feet)

Application Level

FORM THE EQUATION

___50n___ $= 40(9 - n)$

SOLVE THE EQUATION

$50(n) = 40(9 - n)$

$50n$ = ___360 - 40n___

___90n___ $= 360$

n = ___4___ feet (distance the 50-pound weight is from the fulcrum)

$9 - n$ = ___5___ feet (distance the 40-pound weight is from the fulcrum)

The 50-pound weight should be placed 4 feet from the fulcrum.

CHECK THE EQUATION

$50n = 40(9 - n)$

$50 \cdot 4 = 40 ($___9 - 4___$)$

___200___ $= 40 \cdot$ ___5___

$200 = $ ___200___

ACTIVITY EXTENSION

Refer students to the law of the lever, page 53.

If Chino's parcels are equal in weight, where should the fulcrum be located?

The fulcrum should be located at the midpoint of the pole.

Name _____ Period _____

Teacher _____ Date _____ Grade _____

Lever Problems with Help

DIRECTIONS: Each of the following problems has been given a partial solution. Solve each problem by completing the given solution.

1. A 50-pound weight is placed on one end of a seesaw at a distance of eight feet from the fulcrum. How far from the fulcrum should an 80-pound weight be placed in order to balance the 50-pound weight?

   Let n = number of feet from fulcrum 80-pound weight should be placed.

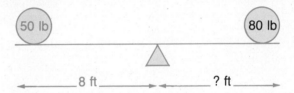

$$80n = \frac{50(8)}{}$$

$$\frac{80n}{} = 400$$

$$n = \underline{5} \text{ feet (number of feet from fulcrum 80-pound weight should be placed)}$$

5 feet

   Check: $\underline{80n = 50(8)}$

$$80(5) = 50(8)$$

$$400 = 400$$

2. Flora balances Jill as they sit on a seesaw. Flora weighs 100 pounds and sits 4 feet from the fulcrum. Jill weighs so little that she has to sit 16 feet from the fulcrum. What is Jill's weight?

   Let n = Jill's weight (in pounds).

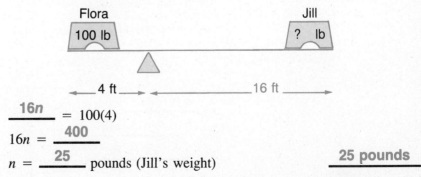

$$\frac{16n}{} = 100(4)$$

$$16n = \underline{400}$$

$$n = \underline{25} \text{ pounds (Jill's weight)}$$

25 pounds

Check: $\underline{16(n) = 100(4)}$

$16(25) = 400$

$\dfrac{400}{} = 400$

3. A hobo carries a knapsack on one end of a pole six feet long. If the hobo can exert a force of only 40 pounds with his arm at a distance of two feet from his shoulder, what is the heaviest weight he can support at a distance of four feet from the fulcrum?

Let n = heaviest weight hobo can carry.

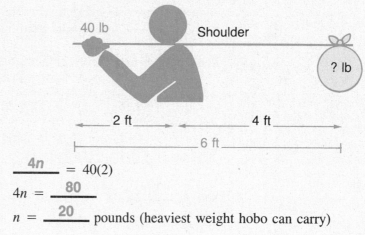

$\dfrac{4n}{} = 40(2)$

$4n = \underline{\ 80\ }$

$n = \underline{\ 20\ }$ pounds (heaviest weight hobo can carry)

$\underline{\textbf{20 pounds}}$

Check: $4n = \underline{\ 40(2)\ }$

$4(20) = 80$

$\underline{80 = 80}$

4. Vanessa sits on one end of a seesaw. Mei-ling sits on the other end. Mei-ling weighs 48 pounds more than Vanessa. What is Vanessa's weight if she sits eight feet from the fulcrum and balances Mei-ling, who sits two feet from the fulcrum?

Let n = Vanessa's weight (in pounds).

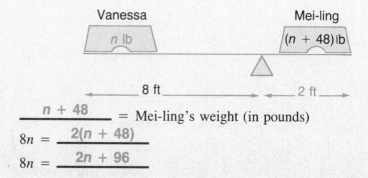

$\underline{\ n + 48\ }$ = Mei-ling's weight (in pounds)

$8n = \underline{\ 2(n + 48)\ }$

$8n = \underline{\ 2n + 96\ }$

$6n = \underline{\quad 96 \quad}$

$n = \underline{\quad 16 \quad}$ pounds (Vanessa's weight)   <u>16 pounds</u>

Check: $8n = 2(n + 48)$

$8 \cdot 16 = \underline{\quad 2(16 + 48) \quad}$

$128 = \underline{\quad 2 \cdot 64 \quad}$

$128 = \underline{\quad 128 \quad}$

Challenge

5. At a site where dynamite was being used to blast a mountain, the leg of a construction worker became pinned under a boulder. His fellow crew members attempted to free him. They were able to exert a force of 500 pounds on a lever to raise the boulder. How heavy a boulder did they move if they used a six-foot bar as a lever and placed the fulcrum so that it was two feet from the boulder?

Let n = maximum weight of boulder to be moved (in pounds).

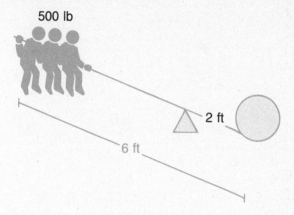

$\underline{\quad 2n \quad} = 500(4)$

$2n = 2,000$

$n = \underline{\quad 1,000 \quad}$ pounds (maximum weight of boulder moved)

<u>1,000 pounds</u>

Check: $2n = \underline{\quad 500(4) \quad}$

$\underline{\quad 2(1,000) \quad} = 2,000$

$2,000 = \underline{\quad 2,000 \quad}$

Name _____ Period _____

Teacher _____ Date _____ Grade _____

Lever Problems

DIRECTIONS: Use the five levels of comprehension to solve each of the problems in the space provided. Write your answers in the blank to the right after each problem.

1. A 70-pound weight is placed on one end of a seesaw at a distance of six feet from the fulcrum. How far from the fulcrum should a 140-pound weight be placed in order to balance the 70-pound weight?

   Let n = number of feet from fulcrum 140-pound weight should be placed.

   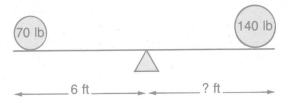

   $140n = 6(70)$

   $140n = 420$

   $n = 3$ feet (number of feet from fulcrum 140-pound weight should be placed)

   _____ 3 feet

   Check: $140n = 6(70)$

   $140(3) = 6(70)$

   $420 = 420$

2. Chris balances Dick as they sit on a seesaw. Chris weighs 90 pounds and sits ten feet from the fulcrum. Dick weighs 30 pounds less. How far should Dick sit from the fulcrum in order to balance Chris?

   Let n = distance Dick should sit from fulcrum in order to balance Chris (in feet).

   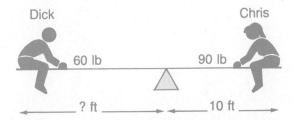

$60n = 90(10)$

$60n = 900$

$n = 15$ feet (distance Dick should sit from fulcrum in order to balance Chris)

15 feet

Check: $60n = 90(10)$

$60(15) = 90(10)$

$900 = 900$

3. A backpacker carries all her hiking equipment in a sack on one end of an eight-foot pole. On the other end, she carries a jug of water weighing ten pounds. If she uses her shoulder as a fulcrum at a point four feet from the ends of the pole, are the weights balanced if her hiking equipment weighs 10 pounds?

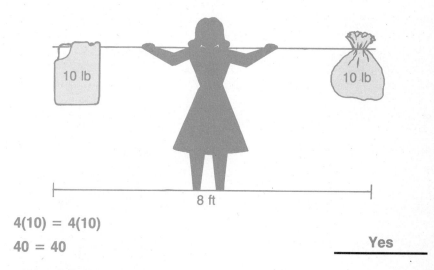

$4(10) = 4(10)$

$40 = 40$

Yes

Check: $4(10) = 4(10)$

$40 = 40$

4. Clint sits on one end of a seesaw. Heidi sits on the other end. Clint weighs 50 pounds more than Heidi. What is Heidi's weight if she sits 15 feet from the fulcrum and balances Clint, who sits 10 feet from the fulcrum?

Let n = weight of Heidi (in pounds).

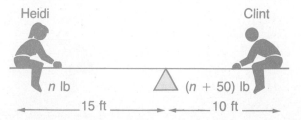

$n + 50 =$ weight of Clint

$15n = 10(n + 50)$

$15n = 10n + 500$

$5n = 500$

$n = 100$ pounds (weight of Heidi)

100 pounds

Check: $15n = 10(n + 50)$

$15(100) = 10(100 + 50)$

$1,500 = 10(150)$

$1,500 = 1,500$

Challenge

5. A large piece of furniture falls on the arm of a man in a warehouse accident. To free him, his fellow workers use a ten-foot bar as a lever and place the fulcrum two feet from the end of the bar (the end nearest the furniture). How much weight must be exerted by the men in order to move the piece of furniture, which weighs 500 pounds?

Let $n =$ weight to be exerted by workers (in pounds).

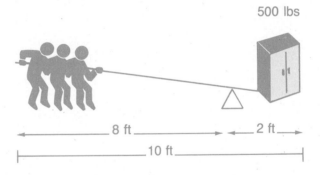

$8n = 2(500)$

$8n = 1,000$

$n = 125$ pounds (weight to be exerted by workers)

125 pounds

Check: $8n = 2(500)$

$8(125) = 1,000$

$1,000 = 1,000$

STUDY GUIDE 5

Averages

Introductory Precepts

Inform students that average and arithmetic mean are the same.

TERMS AND CONCEPTS

Average height, average rainfall, average grades, and average speed are all numerical in nature. In general, to find the average of a set of numbers, first find the sum of the numbers in the set. Then divide that sum by the number of elements in the set. For example, to find the average of five algebra test grades, find the sum of the five grades and then divide by 5 (the number of grades). Use 0 as the lower limit and 100 as the upper limit of all school grades.

LEVELS OF COMPREHENSION

STEP 1 Read the problem.

STEP 2 Choose the variable(s).

STEP 3 Form the equation.

STEP 4 Solve the equation.

STEP 5 Check the equation.

MODEL PROBLEM 1

Find the average height of three children if the height of the tallest is five feet, the height of the next tallest is four feet, and the height of the shortest is three feet.

READ THE PROBLEM

After reading the problem, give the answers to the following statements in the space provided.

The heights of the three children are ___five___ feet, ___four___ feet, and ___three___ feet. Find the ___average___ height. The ___sum___ of the heights of the children and the ___number___ of children are two facts that will be used to find the average height.

CHOOSE THE VARIABLE(S)

Let a = average height (in feet).

FORM THE EQUATION

$$a = \frac{5 + 4 + 3}{3}$$

SOLVE THE EQUATION

$$a = \frac{12}{3} \quad \text{(a fraction)}$$

$$a = \underline{4} \text{ feet}$$

___4 feet___

CHECK THE EQUATION

$$a = \frac{5 + 4 + 3}{3}$$

$$\frac{4}{} = \frac{5 + 4 + 3}{3}$$

$$4 = \frac{12}{3}$$

$$4 = \underline{4}$$

ACTIVITY EXTENSION

Is it possible for the average of twelve numbers to be less than the smallest number? (All are positive).

___No___

MODEL PROBLEM 2

Allan received these grades on five algebra tests: 80, 90, 70, 60, and 50. Find the least grade he must receive on a sixth test in order to have an average of at least 70.

READ THE PROBLEM

After reading the problem, give the answers to the following statements in the space provided.

Literal Level

So far, Allan has received five grades: __80__, __90__, __70__, __60__, and __50__. He is to take a sixth test. Find the least grade he can receive on the __sixth__ test in order for his average for the six tests to be 70.

Interpretive Level

1. To find the average of six grades, it is necessary to know their
   sum,   product,   reciprocals,   none of these.

   _____sum_____

2. Then it would be necessary to divide this number by
   4,   5,   6,   none of these.

   _____6_____

CHOOSE THE VARIABLE(S)

Let x = least grade in order for Allan's average to be 70.

Application Level

FORM THE EQUATION

$$\frac{80 + 90 + 70 + 60 + 50 + x}{6} = 70$$

SOLVE THE EQUATION

$$\frac{80 + 90 + 70 + 60 + 50 + x}{6} = 70$$

$$\frac{350 + x}{6} = 70$$

$$350 + x = \underline{420}$$

$$x = \underline{70}$$

_____70_____

CHECK THE EQUATION

$$\frac{80 + 90 + 70 + 60 + 50 + x}{6} = 70$$

$$\frac{80 + 90 + 70 + 60 + 50 + \underline{70}}{6} = 70$$

$$\frac{420}{6} = 70$$

$$\underline{70} = 70$$

Inform students that to be realistic about grades requires an understanding of average.

ACTIVITY EXTENSION

With Allan's five grades, could he make a grade on the sixth test sufficient to raise his average to 85?

$$\underline{\text{No}}$$

EXPLANATION

$$\frac{80 + 90 + 70 + 60 + 50 + x}{6} = 85$$

$$\frac{350 + x}{6} = 85$$

$$350 + x = 510$$

$$x = 160$$

It is impossible to make a single percentage score of 160!

ACTIVITY EXTENSION

Using Allan's first five scores, could he score low enough on the sixth test to have an average of 50? (Zero is the lowest grade his teacher assigns.)

$$\underline{\text{No}}$$

EXPLANATION

If 0 is his sixth grade, Allan's average would be

$$\frac{80 + 90 + 70 + 60 + 50 + 0}{6} = \frac{350}{6} = 58\frac{1}{3}$$

Name _____ Period _____

Teacher _____ Date _____ Grade _____

Averages Problems with Help

DIRECTIONS: Each of the following problems has been given a partial solution. Solve each problem by completing the given solution.

1. Julie had grades of 90, 80, 80, 70, and 20 on five tests. What is her average?

   Let a = Julie's average.

   $a = \dfrac{90 + 80 + 80 + 70 + 20}{5}$ (Supply numerator and denominator.)

   $a = \dfrac{340}{5}$

   $a = \underline{68}$

   $\underline{68}$

   Check: $a = \dfrac{90 + 80 + 80 + 70 + 20}{5}$

   $68 = \dfrac{340}{5}$

   $68 = \underline{68}$

2. Bernardo scored 70, 80, 50, 60, and 30 on five tests. What score is needed on the sixth test (worth 100 points) in order for Bernardo to have an average score of 70?

   Let x = score needed for average to be 70.

   $\dfrac{70 + 80 + 50 + 60 + 30 + x}{6} = \underline{70}$

   $\dfrac{290 + x}{6} = 70$

   $290 + x = \underline{420}$

   $x = 420 - 290$

   $x = \underline{130}$

   $\underline{130}$

   Explanation: It is impossible to score 130 as a test grade. Bernardo's luck just ran out!

3. Andrew had bowling scores of 180, 200, and 151. Find Andrew's average score.

Let a = Andrew's average score.

$$a = \frac{180 + 200 + 151}{3}$$

$$a = \frac{531}{3}$$

$$\underline{\quad a \quad} = 177 \text{ (Andrew's average score)}$$

$$\underline{\quad 177 \quad}$$

Check: $a = \dfrac{180 + 200 + 151}{3}$

$$177 = \frac{531}{3}$$

$$\underline{177} = \underline{177}$$

4. Alice bowled games of 250, 300, and 200. Find her average score.

Let a = Alice's average score.

$$a = \frac{250 + 300 + 200}{3}$$

$$a = \frac{750}{3}$$

$$a = \underline{\quad 250 \quad} \text{ (Alice's average score)}$$

$$\underline{\quad 250 \quad}$$

Check: $a = \dfrac{250 + 300 + 200}{3}$

$$\underline{250} = \frac{750}{3}$$

$$250 = \underline{\quad 250 \quad}$$

5. Hank liked to brag about his bowling scores. He told his friends that he had scores of 200 and 300 on two games. On the third game, he said he had a score sufficient to give him an average of 300 on the three games. Could Hank have done this?

Let n = Hank's third score.

$$\frac{200 + 300 + n}{3} = \underline{\quad 300 \quad}$$

$$\frac{500 + n}{3} = 300$$

$$500 + n = \underline{900}$$
$$n = \underline{400} \text{ (Hank's third score)}$$

$\underline{\text{No}}$

Explanation: No. Evidently, Hank did not know that 300 is a perfect score, or he thought his friends did not know that 300 is a perfect score.

6. Dianne's bowling average was 180 before she started using a knee brace. While wearing the knee brace, she had scores of 200, 220, and 180. How many points did her bowling average increase?

Let a = average.

$$a = \frac{200 + 220 + 180}{3}$$

$$a = \underline{200} \text{ (average)}$$

Dianne's average increased 20 points.

Check: $a = \dfrac{200 + 220 + 180}{3}$

$$200 = \frac{600}{3}$$

$$200 = \underline{200}$$

7. At the tire company where he works, Sam changed 30 tires on Monday, 40 tires on Tuesday, and 50 tires on Wednesday. How many tires must he change on Thursday in order for the average number of tire changes for the four days to be 50?

Let n = number of tire changes to be made on Thursday.

$$\frac{30 + 40 + 50 + n}{4} = 50$$

$$\frac{120 + n}{4} = 50$$

$$120 + n = 200$$

$$n = 200 - 120$$

$$n = \underline{80} \text{ (number of tire changes to be made on Thursday)}$$

$\underline{80}$

Check: $\dfrac{30 + 40 + 50 + n}{4} = 50$

$$\frac{30 + 40 + 50 + 80}{4} = \underline{50}$$

$$\frac{200}{4} = 50$$

$$50 = 50$$

Challenge

8. A major league baseball player gets three hits out of every eight times at bat. What is his batting average?

Let a = batting average.

$$a = \frac{3}{8}$$

$$a = \underline{\quad 0.375 \quad} \qquad\qquad\qquad \underline{\quad 0.375 \quad}$$

A batting average of 0.375 is said to be 375; this means that if the player is consistent, he gets 375 hits out of every 1,000 times at bat. If a player increases a batting average of 375 by 75 percent, what will his new batting average be?

Suggest that students use the distributive property whenever possible.

Let n = new batting average.

$$n = \frac{3}{8} + \frac{3}{4}\left(\frac{3}{8}\right)$$

$$n = \underline{\quad \frac{3}{8}\left(1 + \frac{3}{4}\right) \quad}$$

$$n = \underline{\quad \frac{3}{8}\left(1\frac{3}{4}\right) \quad}$$

$$n = \frac{3}{8} \cdot \frac{7}{4}$$

$$n = \underline{\quad \frac{21}{32} \quad}$$

$$n = \underline{\quad 0.65625 \quad} \text{ (or } 656\frac{1}{4} \text{ or } 656) \qquad \underline{\quad .62625 \text{ or } 656\frac{1}{4} \text{ or } 656 \quad}$$

Check: $n = \frac{3}{8} + \frac{3}{4}\left(\frac{3}{8}\right)$

$$\underline{\quad .65625 \quad} = \frac{3}{8} + \frac{3}{4}\left(\frac{3}{8}\right)$$

$$.65625 = \frac{3}{8} + \underline{\quad \frac{9}{32} \quad}$$

$$.65625 = \frac{12 + 9}{32}$$

$$.65625 = \underline{\quad \frac{21}{32} \quad}$$

$$.65625 = .65625$$

Name _____ Period _____

Teacher _____ Date _____ Grade _____

Averages Problems

DIRECTIONS: Use the five levels of comprehension to solve each of the problems in the space provided. Write your answers in the blank to the right after each problem.

1. Mr. Vigaro sells used cars. If he sells 25 on Monday, 45 on Tuesday, and 80 on Wednesday, what is the average number of sales for the three days?

   Let a = average sales for the three-day period.

   $$a = \frac{25 + 45 + 80}{3}$$

   $$a = \frac{150}{3}$$

   $a = 50$ (average sales for three-day period)

   _____50_____

   Check: $a = \frac{25 + 45 + 80}{3}$

   $$50 = \frac{25 + 45 + 80}{3}$$

   $$150 = 150$$

2. Jack has grades of 50, 60, 90, 100, and 70. If his next grade is 0, what is his average?

   Let a = average of Jack's grades.

   $$a = \frac{50 + 60 + 90 + 100 + 70 + 0}{6}$$

   $$a = \frac{370}{6}$$

   $$a = 61\frac{2}{3} \cong 61.67$$

   _____$61\frac{2}{3}$ or 61.67_____

Check: $a = \dfrac{50 + 60 + 90 + 100 + 70 + 0}{6}$

$61.67 = \dfrac{50 + 60 + 90 + 100 + 70 + 0}{6}$

$61.67 = \dfrac{370}{6}$

$61.67 = 61.67$

3. Rhonda's total of four test grades is 245. What grade must she earn on a fifth test to have an average of 60?

Let n = Rhonda's grade on her fifth test.

$\dfrac{245 + n}{5} = 60$

$245 + n = 300$

$n = 55$ (Rhonda's grade on the fifth test) $\underline{\quad\quad 55 \quad\quad}$

Check: $\dfrac{245 + n}{5} = 60$

$\dfrac{245 + 55}{5} = 60$

$\dfrac{300}{5} = 60$

$60 = 60$

4. Dave gets three hits in ten times at bat. How many hits must he have in the next 15 times at bat to earn a batting average of 720? (An average of 720 means $\dfrac{720}{1,000}$, or 0.720.)

Let x = number of hits in 15 times at bat, for a batting average of 720.

$\dfrac{3 + x}{25} = 0.720$

$3 + x = 18$

$x = 15$ (Number of hits in 15 times at bat, for a batting average of 720)

     $\underline{\quad\quad 15 \quad\quad}$

Check: $\dfrac{3 + x}{25} = 0.720$

$\dfrac{3 + 15}{25} = 0.720$

$$\frac{18}{25} = 0.720$$

$$0.720 = 0.720$$

5. If Rob gets 3 hits in his first 10 times at bat, is it possible to bring his batting average up to 800 in 25 more times at bat?

Let x = number of hits in 35 times at bat, for a batting average of 800.

$$\frac{3 + x}{35} = 0.800$$

$$3 + x = 28$$

$$x = 25$$

Yes, he needs 25 hits

Check: $\dfrac{3 + x}{35} = 0.800$

$$\frac{3 + 25}{35} = 0.800$$

$$\frac{28}{35} = 0.800$$

$$0.800 = 0.800$$

6. Mr. Carson earned $10,000 per month for 11 months. What is his salary for the 12th month if his average salary for the 12 months is $12,000?

Let n = salary for the 12th month (in dollars).

$$\frac{110{,}000 + n}{12} = 12{,}000$$

$$110{,}000 + n = 144{,}000$$

$$n = 34{,}000 \text{ (salary for 12th month in dollars)}$$

$34,000

Check: $\dfrac{110{,}000 + n}{12} = 12{,}000$

$$\frac{110{,}000 + 34{,}000}{12} = 12{,}000$$

$$12{,}000 = 12{,}000$$

Challenge

7. In competition, a racecar driver drove 500 miles during the first 5 hours. What was her rate of speed for the final 6 hours if her average rate of speed was 200 miles/hour for the entire race? Would this speed be realistic for a junkyard derby?

Let r = rate of speed for the final 6 hours (in miles per hour).

6r = distance covered in 6 hours

$$\frac{500 + 6r}{11} = 200$$

500 + 6r = 2,200

6r = 1,700

A rate of $283\frac{1}{3}$ miles per hour is realistic on salt flats.

$r = 283\frac{1}{3}$ miles/hour (rate of speed for the final 6 hours)

$283\frac{1}{3}$ miles/hour; No

Check: $\dfrac{500 + 6r}{11} = 200$

500 + 6r = 2,200

$500 + 6\left(\dfrac{1,700}{6}\right) = 2,200$

500 + 1,700 = 2,200

2,200 = 2,200

STUDY GUIDE 6

Digits

TERMS AND CONCEPTS

In the decimal (base 10) system, numbers are represented by ten symbols called *numerals* or *digits*. They are 0, 1, 2, 3, 4, 5, 6, 7, 8, and 9.

In representing a number by symbols, *place value* is important. Each place is given a value that is ten times the place to its right. As an example, 238 means 2 hundreds + 3 tens + 8 ones or $2(100) + 3(10) + 8(1)$. In 238, 2 is the hundreds digit, 3 is the tens digit, and 8 is the units digit.

A two-digit number whose tens digit is t and whose units digit is u is expressed as $t(10) + u(1)$. This is usually written as $10t + u$. If the digits are reversed, the expression becomes $10u + t$.

Example:

Two-digit number	Represented with numerals	Represented with original variables, t and u
72	$= 10(7) + 1(2)$	$= t(10) + u(1)$ $= 10t + u$ (t = tens digit and u = units digit)

With digits reversed		
27	$= 10(2) + 1(7)$	$= u(10) + t(1)$ $= 10u + t$ (u = tens digit and t = units digit)

LEVELS OF COMPREHENSION

STEP 1 Read the problem.

STEP 2 Choose the variable(s).

STEP 3 Form the equation.

STEP 4 Solve the equation.

STEP 5 Check the equation.

MODEL PROBLEM 1

The age of a senior citizen is less than 100. The sum of the digits is 16 and the difference of the digits is 2. Find the age of the senior citizen if the tens digit is greater than the units digit.

READ THE PROBLEM

After reading the problem, give the answers to the following statements or questions in the space provided.

Literal Level

The number referred to in this problem has __two__ digits. The sum of the digits is __16__ and the difference of the digits is __2__. The __tens__ digit is larger than the __units__ digit.

Interpretive Level

1. If t represents the tens digit and u represents the units digit, then the number is represented by

   $10t + u$, $10u + t$, $10ut$,   none of these.

   __$10t + u$__

2. If the sum of the digits is 16 and t represents the tens digit and u represents the units digit, then which of the following represents this sum?

   $t + u = 16$, $t - u = 16$, $tu = 16$,   none of these.

   __$t + u = 16$__

3. If the difference of the digits is 2 and t represents the tens digit and u represents the units digit, then which of the following represents the difference? (Remember the tens digit is larger than the units digit.)

   $t - u = 2$, $t - 2u = t$, $u - t = 2$,   none of these.

   __$t - u = 2$__

CHOOSE THE VARIABLE(S)

Let t = tens unit.
Let u = units digit.

FORM THE EQUATIONS

Application Level

1. $t + u = 16$
2. $t - u = 2$

SOLVE THE EQUATIONS

Graphing is an excellent method to verify the solution. Spiral effects enhance retention.

Some options for solving this problem are the addition-subtraction method, the substitution method, and the comparison method. As illustrated below, the two equations can be solved easily by any one of the methods.

Addition Method: Find the sum of the lefthand members of the two equations and equate them to the sum of the righthand members of the two equations. Then solve for the unknown.

Three methods of solving are shown. Some problems are more easily solved by one method than the other. Therefore, the student has discriminating perspective.

$$
\begin{aligned}
\textbf{1.} \quad t + u &= 16 \\
\textbf{2.} \quad + \; t - u &= 2 \\
\hline
2t &= 18 \\
t &= 9
\end{aligned}
$$

Substitute the value of t in one equation to determine the value for u.

1. $t + u = 16$

$9 + u = 16$

$u = 7$

Number: $9(10) + 7 = 97$

$$\underline{\hspace{2cm} 97 \hspace{2cm}}$$

Check: $t + u = 16$

$9 + 7 = 16$

$16 = 16$

Substitution Method: Solve the first equation for t in terms of u.

1. $t + u = 16$

$t = 16 - u$

Then substitute this value for t in the second equation and solve for u.

2. $t - u = 2$

$16 - u - u = 2$

$16 - 2u = 2$

$-2u = -14$

$u = 7$

Now substitute the value of u in either equation to determine the value for t.

1. $t + u = 16$ **2.** $t - u = 2$

$t + 7 = 16$ $t - 7 = 2$

$t = 9$ $t = 9$

Number: $9(10) + 7 = 97$

$$\underline{\qquad\qquad 97}$$

Check: $t - u = 2$

$9 - 7 = 2$

$2 = 2$

Comparison Method: Solve the first and second equations for t in terms of u.

1. $t + u = 16$

$t = 16 - u$

2. $t - u = 2$

$t = 2 + u$

Then equate the two values of t in one equation and solve for u.

$16 - u = 2 + u$

$14 = 2u$

$2u = 14$

$u = 7$

Now substitute the value of u in either equation to determine the value for t.

1. $t + u = 16$ **2.** $t - u = 2$

$t + 7 = 16$ $t - 7 = 2$

$t = 9$ $t = 9$

Number: $9(10) + 7 = 97$

$$\underline{\qquad\qquad 97}$$

Check: $t + u = 16$

$9 + 7 = 16$

$16 = 16$

A large number minus a smaller number is >0.

A small number minus a larger number is <0.

ACTIVITY EXTENSION

Was it necessary in the statement of Model Problem 1 to specify that the tens digit is larger than the units digit?

$$\underline{\qquad\text{Yes}\qquad}$$

> ### MODEL PROBLEM 2
>
> Solving by use of one variable. The sum of the digits of a two-digit number is 16. If the digits are reversed, the original number exceeds the new number by 18. Find the original number.

READ THE PROBLEM

After reading the problem, give the answers to the following statements in the space provided.

Literal Level

The problem refs to a ____two____-digit number, the sum of whose digits is __16__ . If the digits are __reversed__ , the original number __exceeds__ the new number by __18__ .

Interpretive Level

CHOOSE THE VARIABLE(S)

Original Number: Let n = units digit; then $16 - n$ = tens digit. The expression for the original number is $10(16 - n) + n$.

New Number: Let n = tens digit; then $16 - n$ = units digit. The new number (represented with digits reversed) is $10n + (16 - n)$.

Application Level

FORM THE EQUATION

$$[10(16 - n) + n] - [10n + (16 - n] = \underline{\quad 18 \quad}$$

SOLVE THE EQUATION

$$[10(16 - n) + n] - [10n + (16 - n)] = 18$$
$$(160 - 10n + n) - (10n + 16 - n) = 18$$
$$160 - 9n - (9n + 16) = 18$$
$$160 - 9n \underline{\;-9n - 16\;} = 18$$
$$-18n + \underline{\;144\;} = 18$$
$$-18n = -126$$
$$n = \underline{\;7\;} \text{ (units digit)}$$
$$16 - n = \underline{\;9\;} \text{ (tens digit)}$$

Original number = __97__   __97__

Check: $[10(16 - n) + n] - [10n + (16 - n)] = 18$

$[10(16 - 7) + 7] - [(10 \cdot 7) + (16 - 7)] = 18$

$(10 \cdot 9 + 7) - (70 + 16 - 7) = \underline{18}$

$97 - \underline{79} = 18$

$18 = 18$

Reiterate that a large number minus a smaller number is >0; a small number minus a larger number is <0.

ACTIVITY EXTENSION

You are given the sum of the digits of a two-digit number. If the digits are reversed, will the difference always be positive?

$\underline{\text{No}}$

MODEL PROBLEM 3

The sum of the digits of a two-digit number is 16. If the digits are reversed, the original number exceeds the new number by 18. Using two variables, find the original number. Solve by using the addition method.

READ THE PROBLEM

After reading the problem, give the answers to the following statements or questions in the space provided.

Literal and Interpretive Levels

1. If t represents the tens digit and u represents the units digit, then the original number is represented by

   $10u + t,$ $10t + u,$ neither of these

   $\underline{10t + u}$

2. If the digits are reversed, then the new number is represented by

   $10u + 10t,$ $10u + t,$ $10t + u,$ none of these

   $\underline{10u + t}$

3. Which equation represents that the sum of the two digits is 16?

   $t + u = 16,$ $u - t = 16,$ $10t + u = 16,$ none of these

   $\underline{t + u = 16}$

4. Which equations represent that the digits are reversed and that the original number exceeds the new number by 18?

$$10t + u = 10u + t + 18$$

$$10t + u = 10t + u + 18$$

$$10t + u - 18 = 10u + t$$

none of these

$$\underline{\begin{aligned} 10t + u - 18 &= 10u + t \\ 10t + u &= 10u + t + 18 \end{aligned}}$$

CHOOSE THE VARIABLE(S)

Let t = tens digit; let u = units digit. Then $10t + u$ = original number, and $10u + t$ = new number with digits reversed.

Application Level

FORM THE EQUATIONS

1. $t + u = 16$

2. $10t + u = 10u + t + 18$

SOLVE THE EQUATIONS

1. $t + u = 16$

2. $\underline{10t + u = 10u + t + 18}$

Multiply both sides of the first equation by 9 so one variable will disappear:

1. $9(t + u) = 9(16)$

2. $\underline{10t - t + u - 10u = 18}$

Then

$$\begin{array}{r} 9t + 9u = 144 \\ +\underline{(9t - 9u) = 18} \\ 18t = 162 \end{array}$$

and $t = \underline{9}$.

Substitute 9 for t in one equation to determine the value for u:

$$t + u = 16$$

$$\underline{9} + u = 16$$

$$\underline{u} = 7$$

CHECK THE ORIGINAL EQUATIONS

1. $t + u = 16$

$$9 + 7 = 16$$

$$\underline{16} = 16$$

2. $10t + u = 10u + t + 18$

$$10 \underline{(9)} + 7 = 10 \underline{(7)} + 9 + 18$$

$$90 + 7 = 70 + 9 + 18$$

$$97 = 97$$

Number: $9(10) + 7 =$ ___ 97 ___

97

ACTIVITY EXTENSION

Why was it not necessary in the statement of Model Problem 3 to specify which is larger—the tens digit or the units digit?

$t + u = 16$. (This means that neither t nor u could be negative.) The only possibilities for t and u are (9, 7), (7, 9), or (8, 8). Since the difference between the original number and the new (reversed-digit) number is positive, the order of the digits must be larger–smaller. Therefore, (9, 7) is the only possible solution.

Name _____ Period _____

Teacher _____ Date _____ Grade _____

Digits Problems with Help

DIRECTIONS: Each of the following problems has been given a partial solution. Solve each problem by completing the solution.

Each solution uses the addition-subtraction method. Encourage your students to verify the solution by substitution or comparison. The spiral effect enhances retention.

1. Samantha and Mary live on the same street opposite each other. The sum of Mary's house number and Samantha's house number is 59 and the difference is 1. (Samantha's number is greater than Mary's number.) What is the number of each house?

    Let m = Mary's number.

    Let s = Samantha's number.

    1. $m + s = 59$

    2. $\underline{s - m = 1}$

    $$s + m = 59$$
    $$\underline{+\ s - m = 1}$$
    $$2s \qquad = \underline{\ 60\ }$$

    $s = \underline{\ 30\ }$ (Samantha's number)

    Mary: **29**
    Samantha: **30**

    $m + s = 59$

    $m + 30 = \underline{\ 59\ }$

    $m = 59 - 30$

    $m = \underline{\ 29\ }$ (Mary's number)

    Check: $m + s = 59$

    $\underline{\ 30\ } + 29 = 59$

    $59 = \underline{\ 59\ }$

2. Orestes has a vintage car manufactured in the early 1900s. His sister has a compact car. If the last two digits of the year in which Orestes's car was built are interchanged, they tell the year in which his sister's compact was manufactured. If the sum of the last two digits for the date of each car is 110 and the difference between the last two digits for the dates of the cars is 54, in what year was each car made? (The years will be two-digit "abbreviations.")

    Let $10t + u$ = year Orestes's car was manufactured.

    Let $10u + t$ = year sister's car was manufactured.

1. $(10t + u) + (10u + t) = 110$

2. $(10u + t) - (10t + u = 54)$

$\overline{10t + t + 10u + u = 110}$

$\underline{-10t + t + 10u - u = 54}$

$11t + 11u = 110$

$\underline{\underline{-9t + 9u = 54}}$

$9(11t + 11u) = 9(110)$

$11(-9t + 9u) = 11(54)$

$\underline{99t + 99u = 990}$

$\underline{+(-99t + 99u) = 594}$

$198u = 1{,}584$

$u = \underline{8}$

$(10t + u) + (10u + t) = 110$

$11t + 11u = 110$

$11t + 11 \cdot \underline{8} = 110$

$11t + 88 = 110$

$11t = \underline{22}$

$t = \underline{2}$

$10t + u = \underline{28}$ (the year Orestes's car was manufactured)

$10u + t = \underline{82}$ (the year his sister's car was manufactured)

Orestes's car: '28
His sister's car: '82

Check: $(10t + u) + (10u + t) = \underline{110}$

$(10 \cdot 2 + 8) + (10 \cdot 8 + 2) = 110$

$(20 + 8) + (80 + 2) = 110$

$28 + \underline{82} = 110$

$\underline{110} = 110$

3. A two-digit number represents the number of days it rained over a six-month period in 1985 in Miami. Interchanging the digits, the number of days it rained in Yuma, Arizona, over the same period is determined. The sum of the two digits for Miami's days of rainfall over this period of time is 5. (The sum of the two digits for Yuma's days of rainfall over this period of time is also 5.) How many days did it rain in each city for the same time span?

Let t = tens digit of rainfall in Miami; u = tens digit of rainfall in Yuma.

Let u = units digit of rainfall in Miami; t = units digit of rainfall in Yuma.

1. $t + u = 5$

2. $u + t = 5$

$\overline{0 = 0}$

The solution set can't be determined with this information. Numbers such as 23 and 32, 50 and 5, 41 and 14 all are possibilities. At this point, the answer is not unique.

If you are given the following additional information, can you find the rainfall for both places? The sum of the rainfall in Miami and Yuma is 55 inches and the difference in rainfall between the two cities is 45 inches. (Yuma's rainfall is less than that of Miami.)

Let $10t + u$ = rainfall in Miami (in inches).

$\underline{10u + t}$ = rainfall in Yuma (in inches).

1. $10t + u + 10u + t = \underline{55}$

2. $(10t + u) - (10u + t) = \underline{45}$

$11t + 11u = 55$

$\underline{9t - 9u = 45}$

$9(11t + 11u) = 9(55)$

$\underline{11(9t - 9u) = 11(45)}$

$\underline{99t + 99u = 495}$

$+ (99t - 99u) = 495$

$\underline{198t = 990}$

$t = \underline{5}$

$10t + u + 10u + t = 55$

$10 \cdot \underline{5} + u + 10u + \underline{5} = 55$

$11u + \underline{55} = 55$

$11u = \underline{0}$

$u = \underline{0}$

$10t + u = \underline{50}$ (rainfall in Miami)

$10u + t = \underline{5}$ (rainfall in Yuma)

Miami: **50 inches**

Yuma: **5 inches**

Check: $10t + u + 10u + t = 55$

$10 \cdot 5 + 0 + 10 \cdot 0 + 5 = \underline{\quad 55 \quad}$

$50 + \underline{\quad 5 \quad} = 55$

$55 = \underline{\quad 55 \quad}$

4. Two beautiful urns—one red and the other white—were presented to two diners celebrating an anniversary. Each urn is inscribed with the last two digits of the year of its manufacture. The sum of the years on both urns is 110, but the difference between the two sets of digits is 56. The digits on the red urn form a larger number than the digits on the white urn form. What digits are inscribed on each urn?

Let w = digits inscribed on the white urn.

Let r = digits inscribed on the red urn.

$w + r = \underline{\quad 110 \quad}$

$r - w = 56$

1. $w + r = 110$

2. $\underline{+(-w + r) = \quad 56 \quad}$

$\underline{\quad 2r \quad} = \underline{\quad 166 \quad}$

$r = \underline{\quad 83 \quad}$ (digits inscribed on the red urn)

$w + r = 110$

$w + \underline{\quad 83 \quad} = 110$

$w = \underline{\quad 27 \quad}$ (digits inscribed on the white urn)

Red urn: **83**

White urn: **27**

Check: $w + r = 110$

$27 + \underline{\quad 83 \quad} = 110$

$\underline{\quad 110 \quad} = 110$

5. If the tens digit and the units digit in the cost of a pencil are interchanged, the cost of a pen is determined. Each costs less than one dollar, and the pencil costs less than the pen. Find the cost of each if the sum of the cost of a pen and a pencil is 121¢, and the difference in the cost of the two is 63¢. (Solve using two variables.)

Let t = tens digit in cost of a pencil.

Let u = units digit in cost of a pencil.

$10t + u$ = cost of a pencil (in cents)

$10u + t$ = cost of a pen (in cents)

1. $(10u + t) + (10t + u) = 121$

2. $(10u + t) - (10t + u) = 63$

$11u + 11t = 121$

$9u - 9t = 63$

$9(11u + 11t) = 9(121)$
$11(9u - 9t) = 11(63)$

$99u + 99t = 1{,}089$
$+99u - 99t =\ \ \ \ 693$

$198u\ \ \ \ \ \ \ \ \ = 1{,}782$

$u = \underline{\quad 9 \quad}$ (units digit in cost of a pencil)

$(10u + t) + (10t + u) = 121$

$10 \cdot \underline{\quad 9 \quad} + t + 10t + \underline{\quad 9 \quad} = 121$

$90 + \underline{\quad 11t \quad} + 9 = 121$

$11t + \underline{\quad 99 \quad} = 121$

$11t = \underline{\quad 22 \quad}$

$t = \underline{\quad 2 \quad}$ (tens digit in cost of a pencil)

$10t + u = 10(2) + 9 = \underline{\quad 29¢ \quad}$ (cost of a pencil)

$10u + t = 10(9) + 2 = \underline{\quad 92¢ \quad}$ (cost of a pen)

Cost of a pencil: **29¢**
Cost of a pen: **92¢**

Check: $(10u + t) + (10t + u) = 121$

$10 \cdot \underline{\quad 9 \quad} + \underline{\quad 2 \quad} + 10 \cdot \underline{\quad 2 \quad} + \underline{\quad 9 \quad} = 121$

$90 + 2 + 20 + 9 = 121$

$\underline{\quad 121 \quad} = 121$

Challenge

6. If the tens digit and the units digit in Liza's age are interchanged, the age of her grandmother is revealed. The sum of their ages is 88. Four years from now, the difference in their ages will be 54. How old is each now? (Solve using two variables.)

Let $10t + u$ = Liza's present age (in years).

Let $10u + t$ = Liza's grandmother's present age (in years).

$\underline{(10t + u) + 4}$ = Liza's age four years from now

$\underline{(10u + t) + 4}$ = Liza's grandmother's age four years from now

1. $\underline{(10t + u) + (10u + t) = 88}$

2. $(10u + t + 4) - (10t + u + 4) = 54$

$$11t + 11u = 88$$
$$\underline{-9t + 9u = 54}$$

$$9(11t + 11u) = 9(88)$$
$$\underline{11(-9t + 9u) = 11(54)}$$

$$99t + 99u = 792$$
$$\underline{+ (-99t + 99u) = 594}$$

$$198u = 1{,}386$$

$u = \underline{7}$ (units digit in Liza's age)

$11t + 11u = 88$

$11t + 11 \cdot 7 = 88$

$11t + \underline{77} = 88$

$11t = \underline{11}$

$t = \underline{1}$ (tens digit in Liza's age)

Liza's age: $10t + u = 10(1) + 7 = \underline{17}$

Grandmother's age: $10u + t = 10(7) + 1 = \underline{71}$

Liza's age: **17**
Grandmother's age: **71**

Check: $(10u + t + 4) - (10t + u + 4) = 54$

$(10 \cdot \underline{7} + \underline{1} + 4) - (10 \cdot \underline{1} + \underline{7}$
$+ 4) = 54$

$(70 + 5) - (10 + 11) =$

$75 - \underline{21} = 54$

$\underline{54} = 54$

Digits Problems

DIRECTIONS: Use the five levels of comprehension to solve each of the problems in the space provided. Write your answers in the blank to the right after each problem.

1. Joan's house number is a two-digit number. The tens digit exceeds the units digit by five. If the digits are reversed, the sum of the original number and the new number is 143. Find Joan's house number. (Use one variable.)

   Let t = tens digit.

   Let $t - 5$ = units digit.

   $10t + (t - 5)$ = Joan's house number

   $10(t - 5) + t$ = reverse of Joan's house number

   $10t + (t - 5) + 10(t - 5) + t = 143$

   $10t + t - 5 + 10t - 50 + t = 143$

   $22t - 55 = 143$

   $22t = 198$

   $t = 9$ (tens digit)

   $t - 5 = 4$ (units digit)

   Joan's house number = 94 $\underline{\quad 94 \quad}$

   Check: $10t + (t - 5) + 10(t - 5) + t = 143$

   $\qquad\qquad 10 \cdot 9 + (9 - 5) + 10(9 - 5) + 9 = 143$

   $\qquad\qquad 90 + 4 + 10(4) + 9 = 143$

   $\qquad\qquad 103 + 40 = 143$

   $\qquad\qquad 143 = 143$

2. Solve Problem 1 again, this time by using two variables.

   Let t = tens digit.

   Let u = units digit.

   $10t + u$ = Joan's house number

   $10u + t$ = new number with digits reversed

1. $t = u + 5$

2. $\underline{10t + u + 10u + t = 143}$

$t - u = 5$

$\underline{11t + 11u = 143}$

$\underline{11(t - u) = 11(5)}$

$\underline{11t + 11u = 143}$

$11t - 11u = 55$

$\underline{+\,11t + 11u = 143}$

$22t = 198$

$t = 9$

$t = u + 5$

$9 = u + 5$

$u = 4$

Joan's house number = 94.

$$\underline{94}$$

Check: $t = u + 5$

$9 = 4 + 5$

$9 = 9$

$10t + u + 10u + t = 143$

$10 \cdot 9 + 4 + 10 \cdot 4 + 9 = 143$

$90 + 4 + 40 + 9 = 143$

$94 + 49 = 143$

$143 = 143$

3. Rose and Beatrice have consecutive student numbers of two digits each. The sum of their numbers is 75. Rose has the smaller number. If the digits in her number are reversed, the new number is 35 greater than Beatrice's number. What is Rose's student number? (Use two variables.)

Let t = tens digit of Rose's number.

Let u = units digit of Rose's number.

$10t + u$ = Rose's number

$10t + u + 1$ = Beatrice's number

$10u + t$ = Rose's new number (reversed digits)

1. $10u + t - 35 = 10t + u + 1$

2. $10t + u + 10t + u + 1 = 75$

$10u - u + t - 10t = 1 + 35$

$u + u + 10t + 10t = 75 - 1$

$9u - 9t = 36$

$2u + 20t = 74$

$-2(9u - 9t) = -2(36)$

$9(2u + 20t) = 9(74)$

$-18u + 18t = -72$

$+18u + 180t = 666$

$198t = 594$

$t = 3$

$10u + t - 35 = 10t + u + 1$

$10u + 3 - 35 = 10 \cdot 3 + u + 1$

$10u - 32 = 30 + u + 1$

$10u - 32 = 31 + u$

$9u = 63$

$u = 7$

Rose's student number is 37.

Check: $10u + t - 35 = 10t + u + 1$

$10 \cdot 7 + 3 - 35 = 10 \cdot 3 + 7 + 1$

$70 + 3 - 35 = 30 + 7 + 1$

$73 - 35 = 38$

$38 = 38$

$10t + u + 10t + u + 1 = 75$

$10 \cdot 3 + 7 + 10 \cdot 3 + 7 + 1 = 75$

$30 + 7 + 30 + 7 + 1 = 75$

$75 = 75$

37

4. Solve Problem 3 by using one variable.

Let n = Rose's student number.

$n + 1$ = Beatrice's student number

$n + (n + 1) = 75$

$2n + 1 = 75$

$2n = 74$

$n = 37$ (Rose's student number)

$n + 1 = 38$ (Beatrice's student number)

$\underline{\hspace{3cm}37}$

Check: $n + (n + 1) = 75$

$\qquad 37 + (37 + 1) = 75$

$\qquad 37 + 38 = 75$

$\qquad 75 = 75$

5. The sum of the digits of a two-digit number is 11. If 27 is subtracted from the number, the order of the digits is reversed. Find the original number. (Use one variable.)

Let u = units digit.

$11 - u$ = tens digit

$10(11 - u) + u$ = original number

$10u + (11 - u)$ = new number with digits reversed

$10(11 - u) + u - 27 = 10u + (11 - u)$

$110 - 10u + u - 27 = 9u + 11$

$-9u + 83 = 9u + 11$

$-18u = -72$

$u = 4$ (units digit)

$11 - u = 7$ (tens digit)

Original number = $10(11 - 4) + 4 = 110 - 40 + 4 = 74$

$\underline{\hspace{3cm}74}$

Check: $10(11 - u) + u - 27 = 10u + (11 - u)$

$\qquad 10(11 - 4) + 4 - 27 = 10 \cdot 4 + 11 - 4$

$\qquad 10(7) + 4 - 27 = 40 + 11 - 4$

$\qquad 70 - 23 = 51 - 4$

$\qquad 47 = 47$

6. Ann's school bus number has two digits. The tens digit is greater than the units digit. The sum of the digits is 9 and the difference in the digits is 7. What is Ann's school bus number? (Use one or two variables.)

Method 1 (one variable): Let t = tens digit.

$\qquad 9 - t$ = units digit

$\qquad t - (9 - t) = 7$

$\qquad t - 9 + t = 7$

$$2t = 16$$

$$t = 8 \text{ (tens digit)}$$

$$9 - t = 1 \text{ (units digit)}$$

School bus number = 81

81

Check: $t - (9 - t) = 7$

$$8 - (9 - 8) = 7$$

$$8 - 1 = 7$$

$$7 = 7$$

Method 2 (two variables): Let t = tens digit.

Let u = units digit.

1. $t + u = 9$

2. $\underline{+t - u = 7}$

$$2t \qquad = 16$$

$$t \qquad = 8 \text{ (tens digit)}$$

$$t + u = 9$$

$$8 + u = 9$$

$$u = 1 \text{ (units digit)}$$

School bus number = 81

81

Check: $t + u = 9$

$$8 + 1 = 9$$

$$9 = 9$$

$$t - u = 7$$

$$8 - 1 = 7$$

$$7 = 7$$

Challenge

7. Stan and Mimi have social security cards on which the fourth and fifth digits are reversed. The digits on Stan's card form a number that is smaller than the number formed by the digits on Mimi's card. The sum of the fourth and fifth digits for both Stan and Mimi is 77. The difference of the two-digit numbers is 27. Find the fourth and fifth digits on the social security cards of Stan and Mimi.

Let t = tens digit on Stan's card.

Let u = units digit on Stan's card.

$10t + u$ = two digits on Stan's card

$10u + t$ = two digits on Mimi's card

1. $10t + u + 10u + t = 77$

2. $10u + t - (10t + u) = 27$

$$11t + 11u = 77$$

$$\underline{-9t + 9u = 27}$$

$$9(11t + 11u) = 9(77)$$

$$\underline{11(-9t + 9u) = 11(27)}$$

$$99t + 99u = 693$$

$$\underline{+(-99t + 99u) = 297}$$

$$198u = 990$$

$$u = 5 \text{ (units digit on Stan's card)}$$

$10t + u + 10u + t = 77$

$10t + 5 + 10 \cdot 5 + t = 77$

$11t + 55 = 77$

$11t = 22$

$t = 2$ (tens digit on Stan's card)

$10t + u = 25$ (digits on Stan's card)

$10u + t = 52$ (digits on Mimi's card)

Mimi: 52
Stan: 25

Check: $10t + u + 10u + t = 77$

$10 \cdot 2 + 5 + 10 \cdot 5 + 2 = 77$

$20 + 5 + 50 + 2 = 77$

$77 = 77$

$10u + t - (10t + u) = 27$

$10 \cdot 5 + 2 - (10 \cdot 2 + 5) = 27$

$50 + 2 - 25 = 27$

$27 = 27$

STUDY GUIDE 7

Integers

TERMS AND CONCEPTS

An *integer* is any whole number that is positive, negative, or zero.

Examples: 3   0   −8   21

An *even integer* ends in 0, 2, 4, 6, or 8 and is always two times some integer.

Examples: 12: $12 = 2 \times 6$
               28:    $28 = 2 \times 14$
               30:    $30 = 2 \times 15$

An *odd integer* ends in 1, 3, 5, 7, or 9 and is always two times some integer plus 1.

Examples: 21: $21 = (2 \times 10) + 1$
               43:    $43 = (2 \times 21) + 1$
               51:    $51 = (2 \times 25) + 1$

Consecutive integers follow one after the other in order, forming a designated sequence:

Examples: 12, 13, 14, 15   (consecutive integers)
               12, 14, 16, 18   (consecutive even integers)
               13, 15, 17, 19   (consecutive odd integers)

The difference between any two consecutive integers is always 1.

Example: $29 - 28 = 1$

The difference between any two consecutive even or consecutive odd integers is always 2.

Examples: 48, 50: $50 - 48 = 2$
               71, 73: $73 - 71 = 2$

The sum of *n* consecutive integers is either even or odd, depending on the kind and number of integers in the sequence.

99

Have the student prove that an even number plus an even number is even: $2a + 2b = 2(a + b)$; two times any quantity is even.

Examples: 20, 21: $20 + 21 = 41$
              20, 21, 22: $20 + 21 + 22 = 63$
              20, 21, 22, 23: $20 + 21 + 22 + 23 = 86$

The sum of even integers is always even.

Example: 20, 28: $20 + 28 = 48$

The sum of odd integers is either even or odd.

Examples: 1, 3: $1 + 3 = 4$
              1, 3, 5: $1 + 3 + 5 = 9$

Have students prove that an odd number plus an odd number is even $(2a + 1) + (2b + 1) = 2a + 2b + 2 = 2(a + b + 1) =$ always an even number.

Have students show that the sum of three odd numbers is odd: $(2a + 1) + (2b + 1) + (2c + 1) = 2a + 2b + 2c + 2 + 1 = 2(a + b + c + 1) + 1 =$ always an odd number.

LEVELS OF COMPREHENSION

STEP 1   Read the problem.

STEP 2   Choose the variable(s).

STEP 3   Form the equation.

STEP 4   Solve the equation.

STEP 5   Check the equation.

MODEL PROBLEM 1

Find three consecutive integers such that twice the largest exceeds the smallest by 91.

READ THE PROBLEM

After reading the problem, give the answers to the following statements in the spaces provided.

Literal Level

The number of consecutive integers is _____three_____ . If the largest is to be multiplied by ____two____ , then the product will be __91__ more than the smallest.

1. The sum of the three integers will be

    even,   odd,   even or odd   **Even or odd**

2. If n represents the smallest integer, then the next consecutive integer will be

    $n + 2,$ $n - 2,$ $n + 1,$ n **$n + 1$**

3. The largest integer would then be represented by

    $n,$ $n + 2,$ $n - 2,$ $n + 4$ **$n + 2$**

CHOOSE THE VARIABLE(S)

Let $n =$ the smallest integer.

$n + 1 =$ the next consecutive integer

$n + 2$ $=$ the largest integer

FORM THE EQUATION

$2(n + 2) = n +$ **91**

SOLVE THE EQUATION

$2(n + 2) = n + 91$

$2n + 4 = n + 91$

$n + 4 = 91$

$n =$ **87** (smallest integer)

$n + 1 =$ **88** (next consecutive integer)

$n + 2 =$ **89** (largest integer)

Smallest integer: **87**
Next consecutive integer: **88**
Largest integer: **89**

CHECK THE EQUATION

$2(n + 2) = n + 91$

$2(87 + 2) = 87 + 91$

$2 \cdot 89 = 87 + 91$

$178 =$ **178**

ACTIVITY EXTENSION

If you had decided to let $n =$ the largest integer, what would represent the smallest integer?

$n - 2$

MODEL PROBLEM 2

The sum of the first and third of four consecutive odd integers exceeds the fourth by 129. Find the integers.

READ THE PROBLEM

After reading the problem, give the answers to the following statements in the spaces provided.

Literal Level

The number of integers is _____four_____. They are consecutive and ____odd____. If the fourth integer is subtracted from the sum of the first and third, then the difference is __129__.

Interpretive Level

1. The sum of four consecutive odd integers will be

   even,   odd,   even or odd   _____Even_____

2. If a sum of the first and third consecutive odd integers exceeds a fourth consecutive odd integer by 129, then the difference between this sum and the fourth one is

   129, -129, $129 - 2$, $129 + 2$ _____129_____

CHOOSE THE VARIABLE(S)

Let n = the first odd integer.

$n + 2$ = the second consecutive odd integer

____$n + 4$____ = the third consecutive odd integer

____$n + 6$____ = the fourth consecutive odd integer

Application Level

FORM THE EQUATION

$[n + (n + 4)] - (n + 6) = 129$

SOLVE THE EQUATION

$[n + (n + 4)] - (n + 6) = 129$

$n + n + 4 - n - 6 = 129$

$n = $ __131__ (first integer)

$n + 2 = 133$ (second integer)

$n + 4 = $ __135__ (third integer)

$n + 6 = $ __137__ (fourth integer)

First integer: **131**
Second integer: **133**
Third integer: **135**
Fourth integer: **137**

CHECK THE EQUATION

$[n + (n + 4)] - (n + 6) = 129$

$\underline{131} + (131 + 4) - (\underline{131 + 6}) = 129$

$131 + 135 - 137 = 129$

$\underline{129} = 129$

ACTIVITY EXTENSION

Consider a problem posed in which four consecutive even numbers are involved. Would the initial expressions be the same to represent each of the four as in this problem?

<u>Yes</u>

MODEL PROBLEM 3

The sum of the numbers of the top five floors of an office building is 40. What are the numbers of the top five floors?

READ THE PROBLEM

After reading the problem, give the answers to the following statements in the spaces provided.

Literal Level

The sum of the numbers of the top five floors is ___40___. Find the ___numbers___ at the top five floors.

Interpretive Level

CHOOSE THE VARIABLE(S)

Let n = the number of highest floor in sequence.

$n - 1$ = the number of fourth floor

$n - 2$ = the number of third floor

$n - 3$ = the number of second floor

$n - 4$ = the number of lowest floor in sequence

Application Level

FORM THE EQUATION

$n + (n - 1) + (n - 2) + (n - 3) + (n - 4) = 40$

SOLVE THE EQUATION

$n + (n - 1) + (n - 2) + (n - 3) + (n - 4) = 40$

$n + n - 1 + n - 2 + n - 3 + n - 4 = 40$

$$\frac{5n}{} = 50$$

$n = \underline{\quad 10 \quad}$ (number of highest floor in sequence)

$n - 1 = \underline{\quad 9 \quad}$ (number of fourth floor)

$n - 2 = \underline{\quad 8 \quad}$ (number of third floor)

$n - 3 = \underline{\quad 7 \quad}$ (number of second floor)

$n - 4 = \underline{\quad 6 \quad}$ (number of lowest floor in sequence)

6, 7, 8, 9, 10

CHECK THE EQUATION

$n + (n - 1) + (n - 2) + (n - 3) + (n - 4) = 40$

$\underline{\quad 10 \quad} + (10 - 1) + (10 - 2) + (10 - 3) + (10 - 4) = 40$

$10 + \underline{\quad 9 \quad} + \underline{\quad 8 \quad} + \underline{\quad 7 \quad} + \underline{\quad 6 \quad} = 40$

$\underline{\quad 40 \quad} = 40$

ACTIVITY EXTENSION

In cultures where the number 13 is considered to be unlucky, sometimes there is no numeral for the first consecutive integer after *12* on the elevator panel. Write an expression for the sum of the numbers of floors beginning with 10 and ending with 15.

$n + (n + 1) + (n + 2) + (n + 4) + (n + 5)$

Name _____ Period _____

Teacher _____ Date _____ Grade _____

Integer Problems with Help

DIRECTIONS: Each of the following problems has been given a partial solution. Solve each problem by completing the given solution.

1. There are four rooms in a hallway. Their numbers are in consecutive even order. If the sum of the four room numbers is 860, find the room number of each room.

   Let n = the number of first room.

   __$n + 2$__ = the number of second room

   $n + 4$ = the number of third room

   __$n + 6$__ = the number of fourth room

   $n + (n + 2) + (n + 4) + ($__$n + 6$__$) = $__860__

   $4n + 12 = 860$

   __$4n$__ = __848__

   $n = 212$ (number of first room)

   $n + 2 = $__214__ (number of second room)

   $n + 4 = $__216__ (number of third room)

   $n + 6 = $__218__ (number of fourth room)

   First room: 212
   Second room: 214
   Third room: 216
   Fourth room: 218

   Check: $n + (n + 2) + ($__$n + 4$__$) + (n + 6) = 860$

   $212 + ($__$212 + 2$__$) + (212 + 4) + (212 + 6) = 860$

   $212 + 214 + 216 + 218 = 860$

   __860__ $= 860$

2. The shoe sizes in a family of five, from youngest to oldest, are consecutive odd integers. If the sum of the first four sizes, beginning with the smallest, is decreased by the size of the largest, the difference is 19. What are the shoe sizes of the family members?

   Let n = the shoe size of the first (youngest) member.

   $n + 2$ = the shoe size of the second member

   __$n + 4$__ = the shoe size of the third member

   $n + 6$ = the shoe size of the fourth member

   __$n + 8$__ = the shoe size of the fifth (oldest) member

$[n + (n + 2) + (n + 4) + (n + 6)] - (\underline{\quad n + 8 \quad}) = 19$

$n + n + 2 + n + 4 + n + 6 - n - 8 = 19$

$\underline{\quad 3n + 4 \quad} = 19$

$3n = 15$

$n = 5$ (the shoe size of the first or youngest member)

$n + 2 = \underline{\quad 7 \quad}$ (second size)

$n + 4 = \underline{\quad 9 \quad}$ (third size)

$n + 6 = \underline{\quad 11 \quad}$ (fourth size)

$n + 8 = \underline{\quad 13 \quad}$ (shoe size of fifth or oldest member)

First size: **5**
Second size: **7**
Third size: **9**
Fourth size: **11**
Fifth size: **13**

Check: $[n + (n + 2) + (n + 4) + (n + 6)] - (\underline{\quad n + 8 \quad})$
$= 19$

$[5 + (5 + 2) + (5 + 4) + (5 + 6)] - (\underline{\quad 5 + 8 \quad})$
$= 19$

$(5 + 7 + 9 + 11) - 13 = \underline{\quad 19 \quad}$

$\underline{\quad 32 - 13 \quad} = 19$

$\underline{\quad 19 \quad} = \underline{\quad 19 \quad}$

3. Find three consecutive even integers such that four times the first decreased by two times the second exceeds one-half of the first by 116.

Let $n =$ the first integer.

$n + 2 = \underline{\quad \text{second integer} \quad}$

$\underline{\quad n + 4 \quad} =$ third integer

$[4n - 2(n + 2)] - \underline{\quad \frac{1}{2}n \quad} = 116$

$\underline{\quad (4n - 2n - 4) - \frac{1}{2}n \quad} = 116$

$2n - \frac{1}{2}n - 4 = 116$

$\underline{\quad \frac{3}{2}n \quad} = 120$

$n = \underline{\quad 80 \quad}$ (first integer)

$n + 2 = \underline{\quad 82 \quad}$ (second integer)

$n + 4 = \underline{\quad 84 \quad}$ (third integer)

First integer: **80**
Second integer: **82**
Third integer: **84**

Check: $[4n - (2n + 4)] - \frac{1}{2}n = 116$

$$[4 \cdot 80 - (2 \cdot 80 + 4)] - \frac{1}{2} \cdot 80 = 116$$

$$320 - (\underline{\quad 160 + 4 \quad}) - 40 = 116$$

$$320 - (164) - 40 = 116$$

$$116 = \underline{\quad 116 \quad}$$

4. Concepcion and Al are thinking of two consecutive integers. Four times Concepcion's integer (the smaller) exceeds Al's integer by 248. What are the integers?

   Let n = the integer Concepcion is thinking of.

   $\underline{\quad n + 1 \quad}$ = the integer Al is thinking of

   $4n - (\underline{\quad n + 1 \quad}) = 248$

   $4n - n - 1 = 248$

   $\underline{\quad 3n - 1 \quad} = 248$

   $\underline{\quad 3n \quad} = 249$

   $n = \underline{\quad 83 \quad}$ (integer Concepcion is thinking of)

   $n + 1 = \underline{\quad 84 \quad}$ (integer Al is thinking of)

   Concepcion's integer: **83**
   Al's integer: **84**

   Check: $4n - (n + 1) = \underline{\quad 248 \quad}$

   $4 \cdot 83 - (\underline{\quad 83 + 1 \quad}) = 248$

   $332 - \underline{\quad 84 \quad} = 248$

   $248 = 248$

5. Joanne, Julia, and Jacqueline are newborn triplets who have been put in separate rooms during their stay at the hospital. They are in rooms of consecutive order: Joanne is in the room having the smallest number; Jacqueline is in the room having the largest number. The sum of the room numbers of Joanne and Julia decreased by Jacqueline's room number is 450. Find the room numbers of the triplets.

   Let n = Joanne's room number.

   $n + 1 = \underline{\textbf{Julia's room number}}$

   $\underline{\quad n + 2 \quad}$ = Jacqueline's room number

   $n + (n + 1) - (\underline{\quad n + 2 \quad}) = 450$

   $n + n + 1 - n - 2 = \underline{\quad 450 \quad}$

   $\underline{\quad n - 1 \quad} = 450$

   $n = \underline{\quad 451 \quad}$ (Joanne's room number)

$n + 1 =$ ___452___ (Julia's room number)

$n + 2 =$ ___453___ (Jacqueline's room number)

Joanne's room: **451**
Julia's room: **452**
Jacqueline's room: **453**

Check: $n + (n + 1) - ($ ___$n + 2$___ $) = 450$

$451 + (451 + 1) - ($ ___$451 + 2$___ $) = 450$

$451 + 452 - 453 = 450$

___450___ $= 450$

6. There are four consecutive odd integers such that the sum of the third and fourth exceeds the sum of the first and second by 8. Find each integer. Explain.

Let $n =$ the first integer.

___$n + 2$___ $=$ the second integer

___$n + 4$___ $=$ the third integer

___$n + 6$___ $=$ the fourth integer

___$(n + 4) + (n + 6) - (n + n + 2)$___ $= 8$

$(2n + 10) - (2n + 2) = 8$

$2n + 10 - 2n - 2 = 8$

$8 =$ ___8___

Every set of four
consecutive odd integers

For every set of four consecutive odd integers, the sum of the third and fourth minus the sum of the first and second is always 8. Observe these sets:

$\left.\begin{array}{r}81\\83\end{array}\right\}$ 164 $\qquad$ $\left.\begin{array}{r}13\\15\end{array}\right\}$ 28

$\left.\begin{array}{r}85\\87\end{array}\right\}$ 172 $\qquad$ $\left.\begin{array}{r}17\\19\end{array}\right\}$ 36

$172 - 164 = 8$ $\qquad$ $36 - 28 = 8$

$\left.\begin{array}{r}3\\5\end{array}\right\}$ 8 $\qquad$ $\left.\begin{array}{r}91\\93\end{array}\right\}$ 184

$\left.\begin{array}{r}7\\9\end{array}\right\}$ 16 $\qquad$ $\left.\begin{array}{r}95\\97\end{array}\right\}$ 192

$16 - 8 = 8$ $\qquad$ $192 - 184 = 8$

Challenge

7. A corporation assigned its chain of convenience stores in one district numbers that are consecutive integers. If the sum of the numbers of the seven stores is 378, find the numbers of the stores.

Let n = the number of the first store.

$\underline{\quad n + 1 \quad}$ = the number of the second store

$\underline{\quad n + 2 \quad}$ = the number of the third store

$\underline{\quad n + 3 \quad}$ = the number of the fourth store

$\underline{\quad n + 4 \quad}$ = the number of the fifth store

$\underline{\quad n + 5 \quad}$ = the number of the sixth store

$\underline{\quad n + 6 \quad}$ = the number of the seventh store

$n + (n + 1) + (n + 2) + (n + 3) + (n + 4) + (n + 5)$
$+ (n + 6) = 378$

$\underline{n + n + 1 + n + 2 + n + 3 + n + 4 + n + 5 + n + 6}$ = 378

$7n + 21 = 378$

$\underline{\quad 7n \quad} = 357$

$n = \underline{\quad 51 \quad}$ (number of first store)

$n + 1 = \underline{\quad 52 \quad}$ (number of second store)

$n + 2 = \underline{\quad 53 \quad}$ (number of third store)

$n + 3 = \underline{\quad 54 \quad}$ (number of fourth store)

$n + 4 = \underline{\quad 55 \quad}$ (number of fifth store)

$n + 5 = \underline{\quad 56 \quad}$ (number of sixth store)

$n + 6 = \underline{\quad 57 \quad}$ (number of seventh store)

First store: **51**
Second store: **52**
Third store: **53**
Fourth store: **54**
Fifth store: **55**
Sixth store: **56**
Seventh store: **57**

Check: $n + (n + 1) + (n + 2) + (n + 3) + (n + 4) + (n + 5)$
$+ (n + 6) = 378$

$\underline{\quad 51 \quad} + (\underline{\quad 51 \quad} + 1) + (\underline{\quad 51 \quad} + 2) + (\underline{\quad 51 \quad} +$
$3) + (\underline{\quad 51 \quad} + 4) + (\underline{\quad 51 \quad} + 5) + (\underline{\quad 51 \quad} + 6)$
$= 378$

$51 + 52 + 53 + 54 + 55 + 56 + 57 = 378$

$\underline{\quad 378 \quad} = 378$

Name _____ Period _____

Teacher _____ Date _____ Grade _____

Integer Problems

DIRECTIONS: Use the five levels of comprehension to solve each of the problems in the space provided. Write your answers in the blank to the right after each problem.

1. Contrary to the laws of probability, Mrs. Smith had six children, each born on the same date but two years apart. On their birthdate this year, the sum of their ages is 510. If they are all still living, what are the ages of the children?

   Let a = the age of the youngest (in years).

   $a + 2$ = the age of the second

   $a + 4$ = the age of the third

   $a + 6$ = the age of the fourth

   $a + 8$ = the age of the fifth

   $a + 10$ = the age of the sixth

   $a + (a + 2) + (a + 4) + (a + 6) + (a + 8) + (a + 10) = 510$

   $6a + 30 = 510$

   $6a = 480$

   $a = 80$ (age of youngest)

   $a + 2 = 82$ (age of second)

   $a + 4 = 84$ (age of third)

   $a + 6 = 86$ (age of fourth)

   $a + 8 = 88$ (age of fifth)

   $a + 10 = 90$ (age of sixth)

   Age of youngest: 80
   Age of second: 82
   Age of third: 84
   Age of fourth: 86
   Age of fifth: 88
   Age of sixth: 90

   Check: $a + (a + 2) + (a + 4) + (a + 6) + (a + 8) + (a + 10) = 510$

   $80 + (80 + 2) + (80 + 4) + (80 + 6) + (80 + 8) + (80 + 10) = 510$

   $80 + 82 + 84 + 86 + 88 + 90 = 510$

   $510 = 510$

2. Mr. and Mrs. Smith and Mr. and Mrs. Jacobs were issued window seats on a plane whose numbers were consecutive even integers. If the sum of the first and third seat numbers is increased by the sum of the second and fourth seat numbers, their sum is 204. What are the four seat assignments?

Let n = the number of the first seat.

$n + 2$ = the number of the second seat

$n + 4$ = the number of the third seat (all consecutive even integers)

$n + 6$ = the number of the fourth seat

$[n + (n + 4)] + [(n + 2) + (n + 6)] = 204$

$n + n + 4 + n + 2 + n + 6 = 204$

$4n + 12 = 204$

$4n = 192$

$n = 48$ (number of first seat)

$n + 2 = 50$ (number of second seat)

$n + 4 = 52$ (number of third seat)

$n + 6 = 54$ (number of fourth seat)

First seat: **48**
Second seat: **50**
Third seat: **52**
Fourth seat: **54**

Check: $[n + (n + 4)] + [(n + 2) + (n + 6)] = 204$

$48 + (48 + 4) + (48 + 2) + (48 + 6) = 204$

$48 + 52 + 50 + 54 = 204$

$204 = 204$

3. There are five consecutive integers. The sum of the third, fourth, and fifth exceeds the sum of the first and second by 19. The sum of the first, second, fourth, and fifth is 52. What are the five numbers? Is there more information than is needed in this problem?

Let n = first integer.

$n + 1$ = the second integer

$n + 2$ = the third integer

$n + 3$ = the fourth integer

$n + 4$ = the fifth integer

$(n + 2) + (n + 3) + (n + 4) - (n + n + 1) = 19$

$n + 2 + n + 3 + n + 4 - n - n - 1 = 19$

$$n + 8 = 19$$
$$n = 11$$

First integer: **11**
Second integer: **12**
Third integer: **13**
Fourth integer: **14**
Fifth integer: **15**
Excess information?: **Yes**

Check: $(n + 2) + (n + 3) + (n + 4) - (n + n + 1) = 19$

$(11 + 2) + (11 + 3) + (11 + 4) - (11 + 11 + 1)$
$\quad = 19$

$13 + 14 + 15 - 23 = 19$

$19 = 19$

4. In a certain city, police cars are given consecutive integers as numbers. If the sum of the consecutive numbers of six police cars is 21, what is the number of each squad car?

Let $n = $ the number of the first car.

$n + 1 = $ **the number of the second car**

$n + 2 = $ **the number of the third car**

$n + 3 = $ **the number of the fourth car**

$n + 4 = $ **the number of the fifth car**

$n + 5 = $ **the number of the sixth car**

$n + (n + 1) + (n + 2) + (n + 3) + (n + 4) + (n + 5) = 21$

$n + n + 1 + n + 2 + n + 3 + n + 4 + n + 5 = 21$

$6n + 15 = 21$

$6n = 6$

$n = 1$ **(number of first car)**

$n + 1 = 2$ **(number of second car)**

$n + 2 = 3$ **(number of third car)**

$n + 3 = 4$ **(number of fourth car)**

$n + 4 = 5$ **(number of fifth car)**

$n + 5 = 6$ **(number of sixth car)**

First car: **1**
Second car: **2**
Third car: **3**
Fourth car: **4**
Fifth car: **5**
Sixth car: **6**

Check: $n + (n + 1) + (n + 2) + (n + 3) + (n + 4) + (n + 5) = 21$

$1 + (1 + 1) + (1 + 2) + (1 + 3) + (1 + 4) + (1 + 5) = 21$

$1 + 2 + 3 + 4 + 5 + 6 = 21$

$21 = 21$

5. The last two digits of three car tags are consecutive odd integers. The sum of the first and third exceeds the second by 93. Find the last two digits of each car tag.

Let x = the last two digits of the tag on the first car.

$x + 2$ = the last two digits of the second tag

$x + 4$ = the last two digits of the third tag

$x + (x + 4) - (x + 2) = 93$

$x + x + 4 - x - 2 = 93$

$x + 2 = 93$

$x = 91$ (last two digits of tag on first car)

$x + 2 = 93$ (last two digits of second tag)

$x + 4 = 95$ (last two digits of third tag)

First tag: 91
Second tag: 93
Third tag: 95

Check: $x + (x + 4) - (x + 2) = 93$

$91 + (91 + 4) - (91 + 2) = 93$

$91 + 95 - 93 = 93$

$93 = 93$

6. Three consecutive even integers indicate the seating capacity of three areas of a restaurant. If maximum capacity is reached for all three areas, how many diners are in each area if there are 120 diners altogether?

Let m = the seating capacity of the first area.

$m + 2$ = the seating capacity of the second area

$m + 4$ = the seating capacity of the third area

$m + (m + 2) + (m + 4) = 120$

$m + m + 2 + m + 4 = 120$

$3m + 6 = 120$

$3m = 114$

$m = 38$ (seating capacity of first area)

$m + 2 = 40$ (seating capacity of second area)

$m + 4 = 42$ (seating capacity of third area)

First area: 38
Second area: 40
Third area: 42

Check: $m + (m + 2) + (m + 4) = 120$

$38 + (38 + 2) + (38 + 4) = 120$

$38 + 40 + 42 = 120$

$120 = 120$

Challenge

7. Four baseball fans have consecutive seat numbers. The product of the second and fourth (largest) decreased by the product of the first and second is 99. What are the seat numbers?

Let $n =$ the number of the first seat (smallest).

$n + 1 =$ the number of the second seat

$n + 2 =$ the number of the third seat

$n + 3 =$ the number of the fourth seat (largest)

Even if students have not covered product of binomials, the distributive property is applicable.

$(n + 1) (n + 3) - (n)(n + 1) = 99$

$(n + 1)(n) + (n + 1)(3) - [n(n) + n(1)] = 99$

$n^2 + n + (3n + 3) - (n^2 + n) = 99$

$n^2 + n + 3n + 3 - n^2 - n = 99$

$3n + 3 = 99$

$3n = 96$

$n = 32$ (number of first seat)

$n + 1 = 33$ (number of second seat)

$n + 2 = 34$ (number of third seat)

$n + 3 = 35$ (number of fourth seat)

First seat: **32**
Second seat: **33**
Third seat: **34**
Fourth seat: **35**

It is revealing to see how many students use the distributive property in checking.

Check: $(n + 1)(n + 3) - n(n + 1) = 99$

$(32 + 1)(32 + 3) - (32)(32 + 1) = 99$

$(33)(35) - (32)(33) = 99$

$33(35 - 32) = 99 \quad$ *or* $\quad 1{,}155 - 1{,}056 = 99$

$33(3) = 99 \qquad\qquad\qquad 99 = 99$

$99 = 99$

STUDY GUIDE 8

Age

TERMS AND CONCEPTS

If you are now 14 years old, then five years ago you were nine years old and five years in the future you will be 19 years old. Translated, if you are x years of age now, then five years ago your age was $(x - 5)$ years, and five years from now your age will be $(x + 5)$ years.

LEVELS OF COMPREHENSION

STEP 1 Read the problem.

STEP 2 Choose the variable(s).

STEP 3 Form the equation.

STEP 4 Solve the equation.

STEP 5 Check the equation.

MODEL PROBLEM 1

Bill is now 30 years old. In six years Bill's father will be twice as old as Bill will then be. How old is Bill's father now?

READ THE PROBLEM

After reading the problem, give the answers to the following statements in the spaces provided.

Bill is ___30___ years old now. I do not know the age of Bill's father
___now___. Six years from now, Bill's father will be
___twice___ as old as Bill will be.

1. Bill is 30 years old now. Six years from now, Bill's age will be

24,　　36,　　60,　　none of these

___36___

2. If Bill's father is x years old now, six years from now, he will be

$(x + 6)$ years
$(x - 6)$ years
$(x + 30)$ years
none of these

___(x + 6) years___

CHOOSE THE VARIABLE(S)

Sometimes a tabular arrangement helps in understanding a problem.

Let x = present age of Bill's father (in years). Then the other information in the problem can be arranged as follows:

Person	Present age	Age 6 years from now
Bill	30	36
Bill's father	x	$x + 6$

FORM THE EQUATION

$x + 6 = 2(36)$

SOLVE THE EQUATION

$x + 6 = 2(36)$
$x + 6 = $ ___72___
$x = $ ___66___ (present age of Bill's father)
$x + 6 = $ ___72___ (age of Bill's father six years from now)

___66 years old___

CHECK THE EQUATION

$x + 6 = 2(36)$
___66___ $+ 6 = 72$
___72___ $= 72$

ACTIVITY EXTENSION

1. If Bill is 30 now and his father is 66 at present, will Bill's father always be $2\frac{1}{5}$ times the age of Bill?

<u>No</u>

2. How many years older than Bill will Bill's father always be?

<u>36 years</u>

MODEL PROBLEM 2

Mary is 80 years old and Susann is 40 years old. How many years ago was Mary six times as old as Susann was then?

READ THE PROBLEM

After reading the problem, give the answers to the following statements or questions in the space provided.

Literal Level

Mary is <u>80</u> years old now. Susann is <u>40</u> years old now. How many years ago was Mary's age <u>six</u> times as old as Susann was then?

Interpretive Level

1. If Mary is 80 years old now, then x years ago her age was

$80 + x,$ $80 - x,$ $x - 80,$ none of these

<u>$80 - x$</u>

2. If Susann is 40 years old now, then x years ago her age was

$40 + x,$ $x - 40,$ $40 - x,$ none of these

<u>$40 - x$</u>

CHOOSE THE VARIABLE(S)

Let $x =$ the required number of years ago (in years). Complete this tabular arrangement.

Person	Present age	Age x years ago
Mary	80	$80 - x$
Susann	40	$40 - x$

FORM THE EQUATION

$80 - x = 6(40 - x)$

SOLVE THE EQUATION

$80 - x = 6(40 - x)$

$80 - x = \underline{240 - 6x}$

$80 + 5x = 240$

$\underline{5x} = 160$

$x = \underline{32}$ **32 years ago**

CHECK THE EQUATION

$80 - x = 6(40 - x)$

$80 - 32 = 6(40 - 32)$

$48 = 6(8)$

$48 = \underline{48}$

ACTIVITY EXTENSION

Is Mary always twice the age of Susann?   **No**

How many years younger than Mary will Susann
always be?   **40 years**

MODEL PROBLEM 3

Howard is five years older than Jason. Ten years ago, the sum of their
ages was 25 years. How old is each now?

READ THE PROBLEM

After reading the problem, give the answers to the following statements in
the spaces provided.

Howard is __five__ years older than __Jason__. __Ten__ years
earlier, the __sum__ of their ages was __25 years__. Find the
__present__ age of each. Howard will always be __five__ years older
than Jason. Jason will always be five years __younger__ than
Howard.

If n = Jason's present age, then $n + 5$ = Howard's __present__ age. If n = Jason's present age, then $n - 10$ = Jason's age __ten__ years ago.

Interpretive Level

CHOOSE THE VARIABLE(S)

Let n = Jason's age now (in years). Complete this tabular arrangement.

Person	Present age	Age 10 years ago
Jason	n	$n - 10$
Howard	$n + 5$	$(n + 5) - 10$

Application Level

FORM THE EQUATION

$n - 10 + (n + 5) - 10 =$ __25__

SOLVE THE EQUATION

$n - 10 + (n + 5) - 10 = 25$

$n - 10 + n + 5 - 10 = 25$

$2n - 15 = 25$

$2n = 40$

$n =$ __20__ (Jason's present age)

$n + 5 =$ __25__ (Howard's present age)

Jason: **20 years old**
Howard: **25 years old**

CHECK THE EQUATION

$n - 10 + (n + 5) - 10 = 25$

__20__ $- 10 + ($ __20__ $+ 5) - 10 = 25$

$10 + 25 - 10 = 25$

__25__ $= 25$

ACTIVITY EXTENSION

Will Jason always be five years younger than Howard? (Howard must be older than five years.)

__Yes__

MODEL PROBLEM 4

Ruby is five years older than Nan. In 20 years, Ruby will be $1\frac{1}{6}$ times Nan's age then. How old is each now? (Solve by use of one variable.)

READ THE PROBLEM

After reading the problem, give the answers to the following statements in the spaces provided.

Literal Level

Ruby is __five__ years older than __Nan__. In 20 years, __Ruby__ will be $1\frac{1}{6}$ times Nan's age then. Find the __present__ ages of Ruby and Nan.

CHOOSE THE VARIABLE(S)

Interpretive Level

Let n = Nan's present age (in years). Complete this tabular arrangement.

Person	Present age	Age 20 years from now
Ruby	$n + 5$	$(n + 5) + 20$
Nan	n	$n + 20$

Application Level

FORM THE EQUATION

$$(n + 5) + 20 = \left(1\frac{1}{6}\right)(n + 20)$$

SOLVE THE EQUATION

$$n + 5 + 20 = \left(1\frac{1}{6}\right)(n + 20)$$

$$n + 5 + 20 = \underline{\frac{7}{6}}\ (n + 20)$$

$$n + \underline{25} = \left(\frac{7}{6}\right)(n + 20)$$

$$6n + 150 = 7(n + 20)$$

$$6n + 150 = 7n + \underline{140}$$

$$-n = \underline{-10}$$

$$n = \underline{10}\ \text{(Nan's present age)}$$

$$n + 5 = \underline{15}\ \text{(Ruby's present age)}$$

Nan: **10 years old**
Ruby: **15 years old**

CHECK THE EQUATION

$$(n + 5) + 20 = \left(1\frac{1}{6}\right)(n + 20)$$

$$(\underline{10} + 5) + 20 = \left(\frac{7}{6}\right)(\underline{10} + 20)$$

$$15 + 20 = \left(\frac{7}{6}\right)(30)$$

$$35 = \left(\frac{7}{6}\right)(30)$$

$$\underline{35} = \underline{35}$$

MODEL PROBLEM 5

Ruby is five years older than Nan. In 20 years, Ruby will be $1\frac{1}{6}$ times Nan's age then. How old is each now? (Solve by using two variables.)

READ THE PROBLEM

After reading the problem, give the answers to the following statements in the spaces provided.

Literal Level

Ruby is __five__ years older than __Nan__. In 20 years, __Ruby__ will be __$1\frac{1}{6}$__ times Nan's age then. Find the __present__ ages of Ruby and Nan.

CHOOSE THE VARIABLE(S)

Interpretive Level

Let n = Nan's present age (in years); let r = Ruby's present age (in years).

Inform students that if two variables are chosen, two equations must be used.

Person	Present age	Age 20 years from now
Ruby	r	$r + 20$
Nan	n	$n + 20$

FORM THE EQUATIONS

Application Level

1. $r = n + 5$

2. $r + 20 = \left(\frac{7}{6}\right)(n + 20)$

SOLVE THE EQUATIONS

1. $r = n + 5$

2. $\underline{\quad r + 20 = \left(\frac{7n}{6}\right) + \frac{140}{6} \quad}$

SOLVING BY SUBSTITUTION

1. $r + 20 = \left(\dfrac{7n}{6}\right) + \dfrac{140}{6}$

$\underline{\quad (n + 5) \quad} + 20 = \left(\dfrac{7n}{6}\right) + \dfrac{140}{6}$

$n + 25 = \left(\dfrac{7n}{6}\right) + \dfrac{140}{6}$

$6n + 150 = \underline{\quad 7n + 140 \quad}$

$-n = -10$

$n = \underline{\quad 10 \quad}$ (Nan's present age)

2. $r = n + 5$

$r = \underline{\quad 15 \quad}$ (Ruby's present age)

Nan: **10 years old**
Ruby: **15 years old**

CHECK EQUATION 1

$r = n + 5$

$15 = \underline{\quad 10 \quad} + 5$

$\underline{\quad 15 \quad} = 15$

CHECK EQUATION 2

$r + 20 = \left(\dfrac{7}{6}\right)(n + 20)$

$\underline{\quad 15 \quad} + 20 = \left(\dfrac{7}{6}\right)(\underline{\quad 10 \quad} + 20)$

$35 = \left(\dfrac{7}{6}\right)(30)$

$\underline{\quad 35 \quad} = \underline{\quad 35 \quad}$

ACTIVITY EXTENSION

What is the difference between Ruby's age and Nan's age at any given time? (Ruby must be older than five years.)

$\underline{\quad \textbf{5 years} \quad}$

Name _____ Period _____

Teacher _____ Date _____ Grade _____

Age Problems with Help

DIRECTIONS: Each of the following problems has been given a partial solution. Solve each problem by completing the given solution.

Depending on text presentation, students first solving age problems usually find it easiest to use one variable. Only later do they develop facility in the use of two variables for this sort of problem.

1. Brenda is six times as old as Julianna. In nine years, Brenda will be three times as old as Julianna is then. How old is each now?

   Let j = Julianna's present age (in years).

Person	Present age	Age 9 years from now
Brenda	$6j$	$6j + 9$
Julianna	j	$j + 9$

   $6j + 9 = \underline{3(j + 9)}$

   $6j + 9 = 3j + 27$

   $\underline{3j} = 18$

   $j = \underline{6}$ (Julianna's present age)

   $6j = \underline{36}$ (Brenda's present age)

   Julianna: 6 years old
   Brenda: 36 years old

   Check: $6j + 9 = 3(j + 9)$

   $6j + 9 = \underline{3j + 27}$

   $6\underline{(6)} + 9 = 3\underline{(6)} + 27$

   $36 + 9 = \underline{18 + 27}$

   $\underline{45} = 45$

2. Miss Jones is 25 years older than Miss Smith. In 25 years Miss Smith's age will be two-thirds the age of Miss Jones then. How old is each now?

   Let n = Miss Smith's present age (in years).

Person	Present age	Age 25 years from now
Miss Jones	$n + 25$	$(n + 25) + 25$
Miss Smith	n	$n + 25$

$$n + 25 = \frac{\frac{2}{3}(n + 50)}{\underline{\hspace{2cm}}}$$

$$3n + 75 = 2(n + 50)$$

$$\underline{3n + 75} = 2n + 100$$

$$n = \underline{25} \text{ (Miss Smith's present age)}$$

$$n + 25 = \underline{50} \text{ (Miss Jones' present age)}$$

Miss Smith: **25 years old**
Miss Jones: **50 years old**

Check: $\dfrac{n + 25}{\underline{\hspace{2cm}}} = \left(\dfrac{2}{3}\right)(n + 50)$

$$25 + 25 = \left(\dfrac{2}{3}\right)(25 + 50)$$

$$\underline{50} = \left(\dfrac{2}{3}\right)(75)$$

$$\underline{50} = \underline{50}$$

3. Rita is 21 years older than Sam. Four years ago, Rita was four times as old as Sam was then. What is the age of each at present?

Let n = Sam's present age (in years).

Person	Present age	Age 4 years ago
Rita	$n + 21$	$(n + 21) - 4$
Sam	n	$n - 4$

$$n + 17 = 4(n - 4)$$
$$\underline{n + 17 = 4n - 16}$$
$$\underline{-3n = -33}$$
$$\underline{n = 11} \text{ (Sam's present age)}$$
$$\underline{n + 21} = 32 \text{ (Rita's present age)}$$

Sam: **11 years old**
Rita: **32 years old**

Check: $n + 17 = 4(n - 4)$
$$11 + 17 = \underline{4(11 - 4)}$$
$$28 = \underline{4(7)}$$
$$28 = \underline{28}$$

4. Mrs. Akita was 45 years old when her daughter was born. Now the mother's age exceeds three times the daughter's age by 25. How old are they now?

Let n = daughter's present age (in years).

Person	Present age
Mrs. Akita	$n + 45$
Daughter	n

$$\dfrac{(n + 45) - 3n}{} = 25$$

$$n + 45 - 3n = 25$$

$$-2n = -20$$

$n = \underline{10}$ (daughter's present age)

$n + 45 = \underline{55}$ (Mrs. Akita's present age)

Mrs. Akita: **55 years old**
Daughter: **10 years old**

Check: $(n + 45) - 3n = 25$

$(10 + 45) - 3(10) = 25$

$\dfrac{55 - 30}{} = 25$

$25 = 25$

5. The sum of Sid and Agatha's ages is 45. Two years ago, Agatha's age exceeded Sid's age by 25 years. How old is each now?

Let s = Sid's present age (in years).

Person	Present age	Age 2 years ago
Sid	s	$s - 2$
Agatha	$45 - s$	$(45 - s) - 2$

$$(45 - s) - 2 - (s - 2) = 25$$

$$\underline{45 - s - 2 - s + 2} = 25$$

$$45 - 2s = 25$$

$$-2s = -20$$

$s = \underline{10}$ (Sid's present age)

$45 - s = \underline{35}$ (Agatha's present age)

Sid: **10 years old**
Agatha: **35 years old**

Check: $(45 - s) - 2 - (s - 2) = 25$

$\underline{45 - 10 - 2 - 10 + 2 = 25}$

$\underline{25 = 25}$

6. A man is 40 years old now and his son is four years old. In how many years will the father be four times as old as his son is then?

Let x = the required number of years.

Person	Present age	Age x years from now
Man	40	40 + x
Son	4	4 + x

$40 + x = 4(4 + x)$
$40 + x = 16 + 4x$

$-3x = -24$

$x = \underline{\quad 8 \quad}$ (number of years before father will be four times as old as his son)

$\underline{\text{8 years}}$

Check: $40 + x = 4(4 + x)$
$40 + 8 = 4(4 + 8)$
$40 + 8 = 4(12)$
$48 = 48$

7. Lily and Natasha had blind dates. When their dates asked them how old they were, Lily answered, "My present age plus one-fourth of it is 25. The sum of Natasha's present age and 25 percent of it is 20." How old is each girl? (Use two variables.)

Let L = Lily's present age (in years).

Let N = Natasha's present age (in years).

$L + \left(\dfrac{1}{4}\right)L = \underline{\quad 25 \quad}$

$\left(\dfrac{5}{4}\right)L = 25$

$5L = 100$

$L = \underline{\quad 20 \quad}$

$N + \left(\dfrac{1}{4}\right)N = 20$

$\left(\dfrac{5}{4}\right)N = 20$

$5N = \underline{\quad 80 \quad}$

$N = \underline{\quad 16 \quad}$

Lily: **20 years old**
Natasha: **16 years old**

Check 1: $L + \left(\dfrac{1}{4}\right)L = 25$

$20 + \left(\dfrac{1}{4}\right)(20) = 25$

$$20 + \frac{5}{\underline{\hspace{1cm}25\hspace{1cm}}} = 25$$

$$\underline{\hspace{1cm}} = 25$$

Check 2: $N + \left(\frac{1}{4}\right)N = 20$

$$16 + \left(\frac{1}{4}\right)\frac{16}{\underline{\hspace{1cm}}} = 20$$

$$16 + \frac{4}{\underline{\hspace{1cm}20\hspace{1cm}}} = 20$$

$$20 = \underline{\hspace{0.5cm}20\hspace{0.5cm}}$$

$\frac{9}{8} = 1.125 = 112\frac{1}{2}$

percent.

8. Lily and Natasha sensed that their two dates knew each other's ages, and asked the guys if that was so. One, a college graduate, said, "I am five years older than Young. In 20 years, I will be $112\frac{1}{2}$ percent of Young's age then." How old are the guys? (Use one variable.)

Let y = Young's present age.

Person	Present age	Age 20 years from now
Young	y	$y + 20$
College graduate	$y + 5$	$(y + 5) + 20$

$$y + 5 + 20 = \left(\frac{112\frac{1}{2}}{100}\right)(y + 20)$$

$$y + 25 = \frac{\frac{9}{8}}{\underline{\hspace{1cm}}}(y + 20)$$

$$y + 25 = \frac{\left(\frac{9}{8}\right)(y) + \left(\frac{9}{8}\right) \cdot 20}{\underline{\hspace{2cm}}}$$

$$8y + 200 = \underline{\hspace{0.3cm}9y + 180\hspace{0.3cm}}$$

$$\underline{\hspace{0.3cm}20\hspace{0.3cm}} = y \text{ (Young's present age)}$$

$$\underline{\hspace{0.3cm}25\hspace{0.3cm}} = y + 5 \text{ (college graduate's present age)}$$

Young: **20 years old**
College graduate: **25 years old**

Check: $y + 5 + 20 = \frac{112\frac{1}{2}}{100}(y + 20)$

$$20 + 5 + 20 = \left(\frac{9}{8}\right)(20 + 20)$$

$$45 = \frac{\left(\frac{9}{8}\right)(40)}{\underline{\hspace{1cm}}}$$

$$45 = \underline{\hspace{0.3cm}45\hspace{0.3cm}}$$

Challenge

9. Gina said to Joyce, "I am your age increased by 20." In 20 years, the ratio of Gina's age to Joyce's age will be 4:3. How old is each now? (Use one variable.)

Let n = Joyce's present age (in years).

$n + 20$ = Gina's present age (in years)

Person	Present age	Age 20 years from now
Joyce	n	$n + 20$
Gina	$n + 20$	$(n + 20) + 20$

$$\frac{(n + 20) + 20}{n + 20} = \frac{4}{3}$$

$$\frac{n + 20 + 20}{n + 20} = \frac{4}{3}$$

$$\frac{n + 40}{n + 20} = \frac{4}{3}$$

$$4n + 80 = 3n + 120$$

$$n = 40 \quad \text{(Joyce's present age)}$$

$$n + 20 = 60 \quad \text{(Gina's present age)}$$

Joyce: **40 years old**
Gina: **60 years old**

Check: $\dfrac{(n + 20) + 20}{n + 20} = \dfrac{4}{3}$

$$\frac{(40 + 20) + 20}{40 + 20} = \frac{4}{3}$$

$$\frac{80}{60} = \frac{4}{3}$$

$$\frac{4}{3} = \frac{4}{3}$$

Name _____ Period _____

Teacher _____ Date _____ Grade _____

Age Problems

DIRECTIONS: Use the five levels of comprehension to solve each of the problems in the space provided. Write your answers in the blank to the right after each problem.

1. Four years ago, Patricia was $1\frac{1}{2}$ times as old as Donna. Four years from now, Patricia will be $1\frac{1}{3}$ times as old as Donna. How old is each? (Use two variables.)

Depending on text presentation, students first solving age problems usually find it easiest to use one variable. Only later do they develop facility in the use of two variables for this sort of problem.

Let p = Patricia's present age (in years).

Let d = Donna's present age (in years).

Person	Age now	Age 4 years ago	Age 4 years from now
Patricia	p	$p - 4$	$p + 4$
Donna	d	$d - 4$	$d + 4$

1. $p - 4 = \left(1\frac{1}{2}\right)(d - 4)$

2. $p + 4 = \left(1\frac{1}{3}\right)(d + 4)$

$p - 4 = \left(\frac{3}{2}\right)(d - 4)$

$p + 4 = \left(\frac{4}{3}\right)(d + 4)$

$2p - 8 = 3(d - 4)$

$3p + 12 = 4(d + 4)$

$2p - 8 = 3d - 12$

$3p + 12 = 4d + 16$

$2p - 3d = -4$

$3p - 4d = 4$

$\quad -6p + 9d = 12$

$+ \quad 6p - 8d = \underline{8}$

$d = 20$ (Donna's present age)

$$p - 4 = \left(1\frac{1}{2}\right)(d - 4)$$

$$p - 4 = \left(\frac{3}{2}\right)(20 - 4)$$

$$p - 4 = \left(\frac{3}{2}\right)(16)$$

$$p - 4 = 24$$

$$p = 28 \text{ (Patricia's present age)}$$

Donna: **20 years old**
Patricia: **28 years old**

Check 1: $p - 4 = \left(1\frac{1}{2}\right)(d - 4)$

$$28 - 4 = \left(\frac{3}{2}\right)(20 - 4)$$

$$24 = \left(\frac{3}{2}\right)(16)$$

$$24 = 24$$

Check 2: $p + 4 = \left(1\frac{1}{3}\right)(d + 4)$

$$28 + 4 = \left(\frac{4}{3}\right)(20 + 4)$$

$$32 = \left(\frac{4}{3}\right)(24)$$

$$32 = 32$$

2. Mr. Smith's three sons, Tom, Dick, and Harry, are grown and have moved to houses of their own. Tom's house is three years older than Dick's house. Harry's house is four times as old as the combined ages of the houses belonging to Tom and Dick. Mr. Smith's house is as old as the sum of the ages of Dick's house and Harry's house. Mr. Smith's mother lives in a house that is as old as all of the houses together—103! How old is Dick's house?

Let a = the age of Dick's house (in years).

$a + 3$ = the age of Tom's house (in years)

$4[a + (a + 3)]$ = age of Harry's house (in years)

$4[a + (a + 3)] + a$ = age of Mr. Smith's house (in years)

$a + (a + 3) + 4[a + (a + 3)] + 4[a + (a + 3)] + a = 103$

$a + a + 3 + 4(2a + 3) + 4(2a + 3) + a = 103$

$a + a + 3 + 8a + 12 + 8a + 12 + a = 103$

$19a + 27 = 103$

$19a = 76$

$a = 4$ (age of Dick's house)

4 years old

Check: $a + (a + 3) + 4 [a + (a + 3)] + 4 [a + (a + 3)] + a$
$= 103$

$\quad 4 + (4 + 3) + 4 [4 + (4 + 3)] + 4 [4 + (4 + 3)] + 4$
$\quad = 103$

$\quad\quad 4 + 7 + 4(11) + 4(11) + 4 = 103$

$\quad\quad 103 = 103$

3. Jane is two years older than Joe. Six years ago, Joe's age was $\frac{2}{3}$ of Jane's age then. Six years from now, Joe will be $\frac{8}{9}$ of Jane's age then. How old is each? (Use two variables.)

Let n = Joe's present age (in years).

Let j = Jane's present age (in years).

Person	Present age	Age 6 years ago	Age 6 years from now
Jane	j	$j - 6$	$j + 6$
Joe	n	$n - 6$	$n + 6$

$j = n + 2$

$n = j - 2$

1. $n - 6 = \left(\dfrac{2}{3}\right)(j - 6)$

2. $n + 6 = \left(\dfrac{8}{9}\right)(j + 6)$

$3n - 18 = 2(j - 6)$

$9n + 54 = 8(j + 6)$

$3n - 18 = 2j - 12$

$9n + 54 = 8j + 48$

$3n - 2j = 6$

$9n - 8j = -6$

$\quad 9n + 6j = -18$

$+9n - 8j = -6$

$\quad\quad -2j = -24$

$j = 12$ (Jane's present age)

$n = j - 2 = 12 - 2 = 10$ (Joe's present age)

Jane: **12 years old**
Joe: **10 years old**

Check 1: $n - 6 = \left(\dfrac{2}{3}\right)(j - 6)$

$10 - 6 = \left(\dfrac{2}{3}\right)(12 - 6)$

$4 = \left(\dfrac{2}{3}\right)(6)$

$4 = 4$

Check 2: $n + 6 = \left(\dfrac{8}{9}\right)(j + 6)$

$10 + 6 = \left(\dfrac{8}{9}\right)(12 + 6)$

$16 = \left(\dfrac{8}{9}\right)(18)$

$16 = 16$

4. Minna is presently twice as old as Molly. Ten years ago, Molly's age was one-third of Minna's age then. Ten years from now, Molly's age will be three-fifths of Minna's age then. How old is each? (Use two variables.)

Let n = Molly's age (in years).

Let y = Minna's age (in years).

Person	Present age	Age 10 years ago	Age 10 years from now
Molly	n	$n - 10$	$n + 10$
Minna	y	$y - 10$	$y + 10$

$y = 2n$

1. $n - 10 = \left(\dfrac{1}{3}\right)(y - 10)$

2. $n + 10 = \left(\dfrac{3}{5}\right)(y + 10)$

$3n - 30 = y - 10$

$5n + 50 = 3(y + 10)$

$$3n - y = 20$$

$$5n - 3y = -20$$

$$-9n + 3y = -60$$

$$+5n - 3y = -20$$

$$-4n \quad\quad = -80$$

$$n = 20 \text{ (Molly's present age)}$$

$$y = 2n$$

$$y = 40 \text{ (Minna's present age)}$$

Molly: **20 years old**
Minna: **40 years old**

Check 1: $(n - 10) = \left(\dfrac{1}{3}\right)(y - 10)$

$$20 - 10 = \left(\dfrac{1}{3}\right)(40 - 10)$$

$$10 = \left(\dfrac{1}{3}\right)(30)$$

$$10 = 10$$

Check 2: $(n + 10) = \left(\dfrac{3}{5}\right)(y + 10)$

$$(20 + 10) = \left(\dfrac{3}{5}\right)(40 + 10)$$

$$30 = \left(\dfrac{3}{5}\right)(50)$$

$$30 = 30$$

5. John said to Mr. Smith, ''I am your age decreased by 50; but in 5 years, the ratio of my age then to your age then will be 1:3. How old is Mr. Smith? (Use one variable).

Let n = Mr. Smith's present age (in years).

Person	Present age	Age 5 years from now
Mr. Smith	n	$n + 5$
John	$n - 50$	$n - 50 + 5$

$$\frac{n - 50 + 5}{n + 5} = \frac{1}{3}$$

$$\frac{n - 45}{n + 5} = \frac{1}{3}$$

$$3n - 135 = n + 5$$

$2n = 140$

$n = 70$ (Mr. Smith's present age)   Mr. Smith: **70 years old**

Check: $\dfrac{n - 50 + 5}{n + 5} = \dfrac{1}{3}$

$\dfrac{70 - 50 + 5}{70 + 5} = \dfrac{1}{3}$

$\dfrac{25}{75} = \dfrac{1}{3}$

$\dfrac{1}{3} = \dfrac{1}{3}$

Challenge

6. Mr. Reed did not want his algebra class to know his age. When asked, he replied, "My present age, when increased by $23\frac{1}{13}$ percent, is four times my age 45 years ago." How old is Mr. Reed? (Use one variable.)

$\dfrac{23\frac{1}{13}}{100} = \left(23\frac{1}{13}\right) \div 100 = \dfrac{300}{13} \div 100$

$= \left(\dfrac{300}{13}\right) \cdot \left(\dfrac{1}{100}\right) = \dfrac{3}{13}$

Let $r =$ Mr. Reed's present age (in years).

$r - 45 =$ Mr. Reed's age 45 years ago (in years)

$r + \left(\dfrac{3}{13}\right)r = 4(r - 45)$

$\left(\dfrac{16}{13}\right)r = 4r - 180$

$16r = 52r - 2{,}340$

$-36r = -2{,}340$

$r = 65$ (Mr. Reed's present age)   **65 years old**

Check: $r + \left(\dfrac{3}{13}\right)r = 4(r - 45)$

$65 + \left(\dfrac{3}{13}\right) \cdot 65 = 4(65 - 45)$

$65 + 15 = 4(20)$

$80 = 80$

STUDY GUIDE 9

Distance, Rate, Time

TERMS AND CONCEPTS

Introductory Precepts

Multiplication and division are related operations. For instance, if $72 = 8 \times 9$, then $72 \div 8 = 9$, and $72 \div 9 = 8$. When multiplication and division operations are used with the distance formulae, the following equations are true:

Distance = rate $\times$ time $\qquad d = rt$

Distance $\div$ rate = time $\qquad d \div r = t \quad$ or $\quad t = d \div r$

Distance $\div$ time = rate $\qquad d \div t = r \quad$ or $\quad r = d \div t$

In this study guide, time is expressed in terms of hours, distance in miles, and rate in miles per hour.

If your father's uniform (constant) rate of speed by car is 50 miles per hour, then in three hours the distance traveled is 150 miles.

$d = rt$

$r = 50$ miles/hour; $t = 3$ hours

$d = (50$ miles/hour$) (3$ hours$)$

$d = 150$ miles

On the other hand, if you can make a trip of 600 miles between two cities in ten hours, then the average rate of speed is $600 \div 10$ or 60 miles per hour.

$r = d \div t$

$d = 600$ miles; $t = 10$ hours

$r = 600 \div 10$

$r = 60$ miles/hour

If a trip of 1,200 miles can be made at an average rate of 40 miles per hour, then it will take 30 hours to complete the trip.

$t = d \div r$

$d = 1,200$ miles; $r = 40$ miles/hour

$t = 1,200 \div 40$

$t = 30$ hours

LEVELS OF COMPREHENSION

STEP 1 Read the problem.

STEP 2 Choose the variable(s).

STEP 3 Form the equation.

STEP 4 Solve the equation.

STEP 5 Check the equation.

MODEL PROBLEM 1

At 8 A.M. Geraldo left his home by car, traveling at the rate of 30 miles per hour. His sister, Ramona, discovered that Geraldo had forgotten his wallet and driver's license. Two hours later, Ramona left home and started after her brother, using the same route but traveling at the rate of 60 miles per hour. In how many hours will Ramona overtake Geraldo?

READ THE PROBLEM

After reading the problem, give the answers to the following statements or questions in the spaces provided.

Literal Level

Geraldo traveled at a rate of _____ **30 miles per hour** _____. Ramona traveled at a rate of _____ **60 miles per hour** _____. Geraldo left _____ **two** _____ hours earlier than Ramona. Ramona left two hours _____ **later** _____ than Geraldo. Brother and sister both started from (where?) _____ **their home, or, the same place** _____.

Interpretive Level

1. If Geraldo travels for t hours before being overtaken by Ramona, then Ramona travels for

$(t + 2)$ hours, $(t - 2)$ hours, t hours

_____ **$(t - 2)$ hours** _____

2. If Ramona travels for t hours before overtaking Geraldo, then Geraldo travels for

$(t + 2)$ hours, $(t - 2)$ hours,   two hours

<u> $(t + 2)$ hours   </u>

3. If Ramona overtakes Geraldo, then the distance traveled by each should be

equal,   unequal

<u>   **equal**   </u>

Sometimes it is helpful to draw a diagram of the problem such as this:

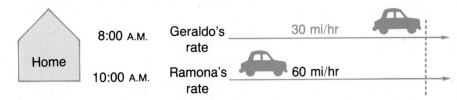

CHOOSE THE VARIABLE(S)

Frequently a chart helps in solving the problem. This distance-rate-time *(drt)* problem follows this form.

Let $t =$ the time Geraldo travels before being overtaken (in hours).

Person	Distance $d = rt$ (miles)	Rate (miles/hour)	Time (hours)
Geraldo	$30 \cdot t$	$\underline{30}$	t
Ramona	$60 \cdot (t - 2)$	60	$\underline{(t - 2)}$

FORM THE EQUATION

Application Level

$60(t - 2) = 30t$

SOLVE THE EQUATION

$60(t - 2) = 30t$

$60t - 120 = 30t$

$30t = 120$

$t = \underline{4}$ hours

$t - 2 = 2$ hours

<u>   **2 hours**   </u>

CHECK THE EQUATION

$60(t - 2) = 30t$

$60(4 - 2) = \underline{30(4)}$

$60(2) = 120$

$120 = 120$

ACTIVITY EXTENSION

1. If you had chosen to let t = the time it takes Ramona to overtake her brother, what would the resulting equation have been?

$$30(t + 2) = 60t$$

2. If Ramona had traveled at an average rate of 30 miles per hour or less, could she have overtaken Geraldo?

No

MODEL PROBLEM 2

Centerville and Mudville are 400 miles apart. Two trains started at the same time from these stations and traveled toward each other. The rate of the faster train exceeded that of the slower train by 20 miles per hour. At the end of two hours, the trains were 100 miles apart. What was the speed of each train?

READ THE PROBLEM

After reading the problem, give the answers to the following statements in the spaces provided.

Literal Level

The trains leave from ____two different____ stations that are ____400____ miles apart, traveling ____toward____ each other. The rate of the faster train is ____20 miles per hour____ greater than the rate of the slower train. At the end of two hours, the trains are still ____100____ miles apart.

Interpretive Level

1. Each train travels the same

    time,   distance,   rate

time

2. The sum of the distances traveled by the faster and slower train is

    400 miles,   300 miles,   not enough information to tell

300 miles

3. At the end of two hours, the trains are separated by

    100 miles,   400 miles,   300 miles

100 miles

Sometimes it is helpful to draw a diagram of the problem such as this:

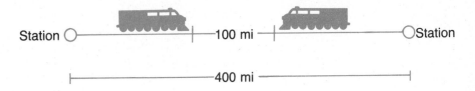

Station O————————|—100 mi—|————————O Station

|————————400 mi————————|

CHOOSE THE VARIABLE(S)

Frequently a chart helps in solving the problem. This *drt* problem follows this form.

Let r = the rate of the slower train (in miles/hour).

Train	Distance $d = rt$	Rate (miles/hour)	Time (hours)
Faster	$2(r + 20)$	$r + 20$	$\dfrac{2}{}$
Slower	$2r$	r	$\dfrac{2}{}$

FORM THE EQUATION

Application Level

$2(r + 20) + 2r + 100 = 400$

or $2(r + 20) + 2r = 300$

SOLVE THE EQUATION

$2(r + 20) + 2r = 300$

$2r + 40 + 2r = 300$

$\underline{\overset{4r}{}} = 260$

$r = \underline{\overset{65}{}}$ miles/hour (rate of slower train)

$r + 20 = \underline{\overset{85}{}}$ miles/hour (rate of faster train)

65 miles/hour and 85 miles/hour

CHECK THE EQUATION

$2(r + 20) + 2r = 300$

$2(\underline{\overset{65}{}} + 20) + 2\underline{\overset{(65)}{}} = 300$

$2(85) + 2(65) = 300$

$170 + 130 = 300$

$\underline{\overset{300}{}} = \underline{\overset{300}{}}$

ACTIVITY EXTENSION

1. If you had represented the rate of the faster train by r, what would the resulting equation have been?

$2(r - 20) + 2r = 300$

2. If the faster train traveled toward the slower train at 150 miles per hour for two hours and the slower train planned to travel toward the faster train at a rate of 75 miles per hour for two hours, would the two trains be on a collision course?

Yes
_____

MODEL PROBLEM 3

A boy can row a boat at a rate of five miles per hour in still water. The rate of the current in a river is two miles per hour. He is in a remote outpost and must make the trip to get needed medication for a camp member. If the hospital is 15 miles from camp, is there any way that he can leave at noon and return by 6 P.M.?

READ THE PROBLEM

After reading the problem, give the answers to the following statements in the spaces provided.

Literal Level

The boy can row the boat at a rate of __five miles per hour__ in still water.
The rate of the current is __two miles per hour__. The round trip can take only __six__ hours.

Interpretive Level

1. The overall speed going upstream is

   two miles per hour,   seven miles per hour,
   three miles per hour,   none of these

   3 miles per hour
   _____

2. The overall speed going downstream is

   three miles per hour,   five miles per hour,
   seven miles per hour

   7 miles per hour
   _____

3. The distances to and from the hospital are

   equal,   unequal

   equal
   _____

Draw diagrams depicting the information.

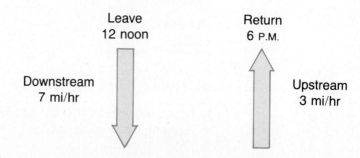

| Leave 12 noon | Return 6 P.M. |
| Downstream 7 mi/hr | Upstream 3 mi/hr |

The speed going downstream is the rowing rate in still water + the speed of the current:

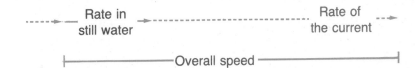

The speed going upstream is the rowing rate in still water − the speed of the current:

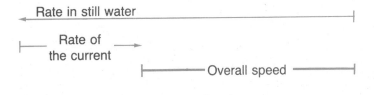

CHOOSE THE VARIABLE(S)

Set up a chart for this problem. Let d = the distance traveled downstream (in miles).

Application Level

Direction	Distance (miles)	Rate (miles/hour)	Time $t = \dfrac{d}{r}$ (hours)
Downstream	d	<u>7</u>	$\dfrac{d}{7}$
Upstream	d	<u>3</u>	$\dfrac{d}{3}$

FORM THE EQUATION

$$\left(\frac{d}{7}\right) + \left(\frac{d}{3}\right) = \underline{\ 6\ }$$

SOLVE THE EQUATION

$$\frac{d}{7} + \frac{d}{3} = \underline{\ 6\ }$$

$$21 \cdot \left(\frac{d}{7}\right) + 21 \cdot \left(\frac{d}{3}\right) = 21 \cdot 6$$

$$3d + 7d = \underline{\ 126\ }$$

$$10d = 126$$

$$d = \underline{\ 12.6\ } \text{ miles (distance traveled downstream)}$$

$$d = 12\frac{3}{5} \text{ miles (as a fraction)} \qquad\qquad \underline{\ \text{No}\ }$$

CHECK THE EQUATION

$$\left(\frac{d}{7}\right) + \left(\frac{d}{3}\right) = 6$$

$$\left[\left(\frac{63}{5}\right) \div 7\right] + \left[\left(\frac{\underline{63}}{5}\right) \div 3\right] = 6$$

$$\left[\left(\frac{63}{5}\right) \cdot \left(\frac{1}{7}\right)\right] + \left[\left(\frac{63}{5}\right) \cdot \left(\frac{1}{3}\right)\right] = 6$$

$$\frac{9}{5} + \frac{21}{5} = 6$$

$$\frac{\dfrac{30}{5}}{\underline{}} = 6$$

$$6 = 6$$

ACTIVITY EXTENSION

The boy could get to the hospital and back if and only if the distance from the camp to the hospital is how many miles? (This, of course, allows for 0 minutes time at the hospital.)

12.6 miles

Distance, Rate, Time Problems with Help

DIRECTIONS: Each of the following problems has been given a partial solution. Solve each problem by completing the given solution.

1. Carl and Fred started driving from the same point, Carl traveling due east and Fred traveling due west. The rate at which Carl drove was twice that of Fred. After four hours, they were 600 miles apart. Find the rate of each.

Let r = Fred's rate (miles/hour).

$2r$ = Carl's rate (miles/hour)

Person	Distance $d = rt$ (miles)	Rate (miles/hour)	Time (hours)
Fred	$4r$	r	4
Carl	$4(2r)$	$2r$	4

$$\underline{4r} + 4(2r) = 600$$

$$4r + 8r = 600$$

$$12r = \underline{600}$$

r = 50 miles/hour (Fred's rate)

$2r = \underline{100}$ miles/hour (Carl's rate)

Carl: 100 miles/hour
Fred: 50 miles/hour

Check: $4r + 4(2r) = 600$

$$4r + 8r = 600$$

$$4\underline{(50)} + 8\underline{(50)} = 600$$

$$\underline{200} + \underline{400} = 600$$

$$\underline{600} = 600$$

2. A motor boat, traveling eight miles per hour, left a marina. After three hours, a speed boat going 30 miles per hour began to follow the motor

boat. How long was required for the speed boat to overtake the motor boat?

Let t = the time traveled by the motor boat (in hours).

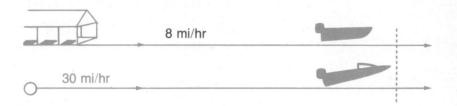

Boat	Distance $d = rt$ (miles)	Rate (miles/hour)	Time (hours)
Motor boat	$8 \cdot t$	8	t
Speed boat	$30 \cdot (t - 3)$	30	$(t - 3)$

$8t = \underline{\quad 30(t - 3) \quad}$

$8t = 30t - 90$

$-22t = \underline{\quad -90 \quad}$

$t = \dfrac{\left(\dfrac{90}{22}\right)}{\quad}$ hours (time the motor boat traveled)

$t - 3 = \dfrac{\dfrac{24}{22} \text{ hours}}{\quad}$ (time the speed boat traveled) $\dfrac{24}{22}$ hours

Check: $8t = 30(t - 3)$

$\qquad 8t = 30t - 90$

$\qquad 8\left(\dfrac{90}{22}\right) = 30\left(\dfrac{90}{22}\right) - 90$

$\qquad \dfrac{720}{22} = \dfrac{2{,}700}{22} - \dfrac{1{,}980}{22}$

$\qquad \dfrac{720}{22} = \dfrac{720}{22}$

3. Jerry, walking 3 miles per hour, started toward his aunt's house 12 miles away. One-half hour later, his cousin Darryl started from the aunt's house on a bicycle to meet him, riding 10 miles per hour. How long will Darryl ride before he meets Jerry?

Let t = Jerry's time (in hours).

Jerry: 3 mi/hr   Darryl: 10 mi/hr

|⟵————————— 12 mi —————————⟶|

Person	Distance $d = rt$ (miles)	Rate miles/hour	Time (hours)
Jerry	$3 \cdot t$	__3__	t
Darryl	$10 \cdot (t - \frac{1}{2})$	10	$\underline{t - \dfrac{1}{2}}$

$$3t + 10(t - \frac{1}{2}) = 12$$

$$\underline{3t + 10t - 5 = 12}$$

$$13t - 5 = 12$$

$$13t = 17$$

$$t = \underline{\frac{17}{13}} \text{ hours (Jerry's time)}$$

$$t - \frac{1}{2} = \frac{17}{13} - \frac{1}{2} = \frac{34 - 13}{26} = \frac{21}{26} \text{ hours (Darryl's time)}$$

$$\frac{34}{26} - \frac{13}{26} = \underline{\frac{21}{26}} \text{ hours (time of Darryl)} \qquad \underline{\frac{21}{26} \text{ hours}}$$

Check: $3t + 10\left(t - \frac{1}{2}\right) = 12$

$$3 \cdot \frac{17}{13} + 10(\underline{\frac{17}{13} - \frac{1}{2}}) = 12$$

$$\frac{51}{13} + 10\left(\frac{34}{26} - \frac{13}{26}\right) = 12$$

$$\frac{51}{13} + 10\left(\frac{21}{26}\right) = 12$$

$$\frac{51}{13} + \frac{210}{26} = 12$$

$$102 + \underline{210} = 312$$

$$\underline{312} = 312$$

4. A car traveling 50 miles per hour is followed by a second car starting from the same place two hours later. The second car overtakes the first car in two and one-half hours. What is the rate of the second car?

Let r = the rate of the second car (in miles/hour).

50 mi/hr

r (mi/hr)

Car	Distance $d = rt$ (miles)	Rate (miles/hour)	Time (hours)
First	$50 \cdot 4\frac{1}{2}$	$\underline{50}$	$4\frac{1}{2}$
Second	$r \cdot 2\frac{1}{2}$	r	$2\frac{1}{2}$

$$2\frac{1}{2} \cdot r = 50 \cdot 4\frac{1}{2}$$

$$\frac{5}{2}r = 50\left(\frac{9}{2}\right)$$

$$5r = 50(9)$$

$$5r = \underline{450}$$

$$r = \underline{90} \text{ miles/hour (rate of second car)} \qquad \underline{90 \text{ miles/hour}}$$

Check: $2\frac{1}{2}r = 50\left(4\frac{1}{2}\right)$

$$\frac{5}{2}r = \underline{\frac{50\left(\frac{9}{2}\right)}{}}$$

$$\frac{5}{2} \cdot 90 = 50\left(\frac{9}{2}\right)$$

$$225 = \underline{225}$$

5. A train travels between two cities at an average rate of 40 miles per hour. An express train traveling at a rate of 60 miles per hour makes the trip in two hours less time. What is the distance between the cities?

Let t = the time of the slower train (in hours).

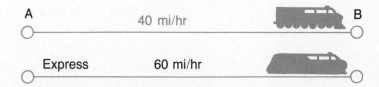

A   40 mi/hr   B

Express   60 mi/hr

Train	Distance $d = rt$ (miles)	Rate (miles/hour)	Time (hours)
Slower	$40 \cdot t$	$\underline{40}$	t
Faster	$60(t - 2)$	$\underline{60}$	$t - 2$

$40t = 60(t - 2)$

$\underline{40t = 60t - 120}$

$-20t = -120$

$t = \underline{\quad 6 \quad}$ hours (time of slower train)

$d = (40)(6)$

$d = \underline{\quad 240 \quad}$ miles (distance between cities)   **240 miles**

Check: $40t = 60(t - 2)$

$40(6) = 60(\underline{\quad 6 - 2 \quad})$

$240 = 240$

6. Abigail and Lila travel from the same point in opposite directions. Abigail travels 20 miles per hour faster than Lila. How fast did each travel if they were 250 miles apart at the end of four hours?

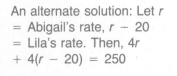
An alternate solution: Let r = Abigail's rate, $r - 20$ = Lila's rate. Then, $4r + 4(r - 20) = 250$

Let $r =$ Lila's rate (miles/hour).

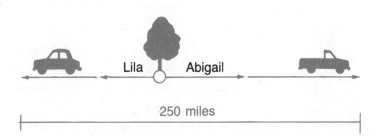

Lila   Abigail

250 miles

Person	Distance $d = rt$ (miles)	Rate (miles/hour)	Time (hours)
Abigail	$4 \cdot (r + 20)$	$r + 20$	4
Lila	$\underline{4 \cdot r}$	r	$\underline{4}$

$r + 20 =$ Abigail's rate (miles/hour)

$4(r + 20) + 4r = 250$

$\underline{4r + 80 + 4r = 250}$

$8r + 80 = 250$

$\underline{8r} = 170$

$r =$ _____21.25_____ miles/hour (Lila's rate)

$r + 20 =$ _____41.25_____ miles/hour (Abigail's rate)

Lila's rate = **21.25 miles/hour**

Abigail's rate = **41.25 miles/hour**

Check: $4(r + 20) + 4r =$ _____250_____

$4(21.25 + 20) + 4(21.25) =$ _____250_____

$4(41.25) + 4(21.25) =$ _____250_____

$\dfrac{165 + 85}{} = 250$

$250 = 250$

Challenge

7. A country doctor in the second decade of this century used a horse and buggy to make house calls. The horse and buggy would take him 5 miles in approximately one hour. To reach one of his patients he had to cross a river over which there was no bridge. He tied the horse and buggy to a tree and used a rowboat to cross the river. This maneuver took about 20 minutes. On the other side of the river, a farmer kept another horse for the doctor to ride to complete the journey. The rate of this mode of travel was 10 miles per hour. If the house call lasted one hour and the distance from the patient's home to the river was five miles, how far was it from the doctor's home to the river if the time required for the entire trip was six hours?

Let d = the distance from the doctor's house to the river (in miles).

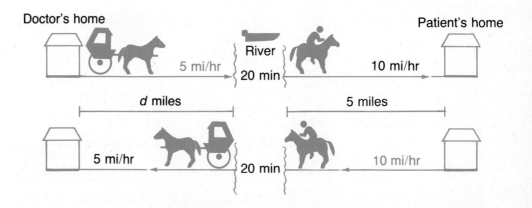

Journey	Doctor's home to river (miles)	Rate (miles/hour)	Time $t = \dfrac{d}{r}$
Going	d	5	$\dfrac{d}{5}$
Returning	d	5	$\dfrac{d}{5}$

And

Journey	River crossing (hours)	Patient's house to river (miles)	Rate (miles/hour)	Time $t = \dfrac{d}{r}$
Going		5	_10_	$\dfrac{5}{10}$
Returning	$\dfrac{1}{3}$	5	10	$\dfrac{5}{10}$

1 hour = the length of the house call

6 hours = the total time, including the house call

$$\frac{d}{5} + \frac{1}{3} + \frac{5}{10} + \underline{1} + \frac{5}{10} + \frac{1}{3} + \frac{d}{5} = \underline{6}$$

$$\frac{2d}{5} + \frac{2}{3} + 1 + 1 = 6$$

$$\frac{2d}{5} + \frac{8}{3} = 6$$

$$6d + 40 = 90$$

$$\underline{6d} = 50$$

$$d = \frac{50}{6} = 8\frac{1}{3} \text{ miles (distance from doctor's house to the river)}$$

$$\underline{8\frac{1}{3} \text{ miles}}$$

Check:

$$\frac{d}{5} + \frac{1}{3} + \frac{5}{10} + 1 + \frac{5}{10} + \frac{1}{3} + \frac{d}{5} = 6$$

$$\left(\frac{50}{6} \div 5\right) + \frac{1}{3} + \frac{5}{10} + 1 + \frac{5}{10} + \frac{1}{3} + \left(\frac{50}{6} \div 5\right) = 6$$

$$\frac{50}{30} + \frac{2}{3} + 1 + \underline{1} + \frac{50}{30} = 6$$

$$50 + 20 + 30 + 30 + 50 = 180$$

$$\underline{180} = 180$$

Name _____ Period _____

Teacher _____ Date _____ Grade _____

Distance, Rate, Time Problems

DIRECTIONS: Use the five levels of comprehension to solve each of the problems in the space provided. Write your answers in the blank to the right after each problem.

1. A compact car starts from a certain point and travels at the rate of 50 miles per hour. Three hours later, a sports car begins to pursue the compact car. How fast must the sports car travel in order to overtake the compact in three hours?

   Let r = the rate of the sports car (in miles/hour).

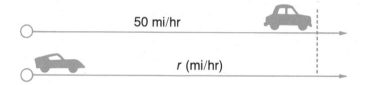

Car	Distance $d = rt$ (miles)	Rate (miles/hour)	Time (hours)
Compact car	6 · 50	50	6
Sports car	3 · r	r	3

   $3r = 50(6)$

   $3r = 300$

   $r = 100$ miles/hour (rate of sports car)   100 miles/hour

   Check: $3r = 50(6)$

   $\qquad$ $3(100) = 50(60)$

   $\qquad$ $300 = 300$

2. Two boys on bicycles start from the same place at the same time. One rides at a rate of eight miles per hour and the other at six miles per hour. They travel in the same direction. In how many hours will they be 20 miles apart?

   Let t = the time of each boy (in hours).

Boy	Distance $d = rt$	Rate (miles/hour)	Time (hours)
Boy 1	$8 \cdot t$	8	t
Boy 2	$6 \cdot t$	6	t

$8t - 6t = 20$

$2t = 20$

$t = 10$ hours (time of each)   **10 hours**

Check: $8t - 6t = 20$

$8(10) - 6(10) = 20$

$80 - 60 = 20$

$20 = 20$

3. Becky starts from a certain point, traveling four miles per hour. Five hours later, Ella starts from the same point and travels in the same direction at eight miles per hour. In how many hours will Ella overtake Becky?

Let t = Becky's time (in hours).

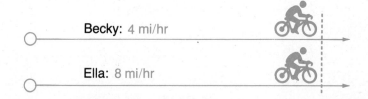

Person	Distance $d = rt$ (time)	Rate (miles/hour)	Time (hours)
Becky	$4 \cdot t$	4	t
Ella	$8 \cdot (t - 5)$	8	$t - 5$

$8(t - 5) = 4t$

$8t - 40 = 4t$

$4t = 40$

$t = 10$ hours (Becky's time)

$t - 5 = 5$ hours (Ella's time)

$\underline{\text{5 hours}}$

Check: $8(t - 5) = 4t$

$8t - 40 = 4t$

$8(10) - 40 = 4(10)$

$80 - 40 = 40$

$40 = 40$

4. A girl can row a boat in still water at a rate of five miles per hour. If the rate of the current is two miles per hour, how far downstream can she row if she starts at 3 P.M. and must return by 6 P.M.?

Let $d =$ the distance she can row downstream in order to return at 6 P.M. (in miles).

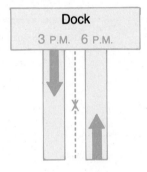

Direction	Distance (miles)	Rate (miles/hour)	Time $t = \dfrac{d}{r}$ (hours)
Downstream	d	$5 + 2 = 7$	$\dfrac{d}{7}$
Upstream	d	$5 - 2 = 3$	$\dfrac{d}{3}$

$2 =$ rate of current (miles/hour)

$5 =$ rate girl can row in still water (miles/hour)

$\dfrac{d}{7} + \dfrac{d}{3} = 3$

$3d + 7d = 63$

$10d = 63$

$d = \dfrac{63}{10} = 6.3$ miles

$\underline{\text{6.3 miles}}$

156

Check: $\dfrac{d}{7} + \dfrac{d}{3} = 3$

$$\left(\frac{63}{10} \div 7\right) + \left(\frac{63}{10} \div 3\right) = 3$$

$$\left(\frac{63}{10} \cdot \frac{1}{7}\right) + \left(\frac{63}{10} \cdot \frac{1}{3}\right) = 3$$

$$\frac{9}{10} + \frac{21}{10} = 3$$

$$\frac{30}{10} = 3$$

$$3 = 3$$

5. At 3 P.M., a train traveling at 60 miles per hour started from Newberry to Columbia. At 4 P.M., a train traveling 40 miles per hour started from Columbia traveling toward Newberry. Newberry is 500 miles from Columbia. When will the engines of the two trains pass each other? (Assume the trains are on parallel tracks.)

Let t = the time of the Newberry-to-Columbia train (in hours).

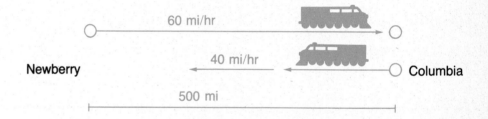

Direction	Distance $d = rt$ (miles)	Rate (miles/ hour)	Time (hours)
Newberry to Columbia	$60 \cdot t$	60	t
Columbia to Newberry	$40 \cdot (t - 1)$	40	$t - 1$

$60t + 40(t - 1) = 500$

$60t + 40t - 40 = 500$

$100t - 40 = 500$

$100t = 540$

$t = 5.4$ hours (time of Newberry-to-Columbia train)

$t - 1 = 4.4$ hours (time of Columbia-to-Newberry train)

3:00 P.M.		4:00 P.M.
$+5:24$	or	$+4:24$
8:24 P.M.		8:24 P.M.

8:24 P.M.

Check: $60t + 40(t - 1) = 500$

$\qquad 60(5.4) + 40(5.4 - 1) = 500$

$\qquad 324 + 40(4.4) = 500$

$\qquad 324 + 176 = 500$

$\qquad 500 = 500$

6. A motorist was clocked at a certain point traveling at 90 miles per hour. A patrol officer was alerted to chase the motorist. The patrol officer was three miles behind the speeding car when he received the message. How fast must the patrol officer have traveled in order to overtake the speeding car in 20 minutes if the car continued to travel 90 miles per hour?

Let r = the rate of the patrol officer (in miles/hour).

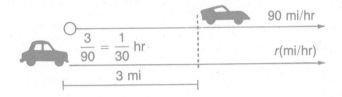

Vehicle	Distance $d = rt$ (miles)	Rate (miles/hour)	Time (hours)
Car	$90 \cdot \left(\dfrac{1}{3} + \dfrac{1}{30}\right)$	90	$\left(\dfrac{1}{3} + \dfrac{1}{30}\right)$
Patrol	$r \cdot \dfrac{1}{3}$	r	$\dfrac{1}{3}$

Solution 1: $90\left(\dfrac{1}{3} + \dfrac{1}{30}\right) = \left(\dfrac{1}{3}\right)r$

$\qquad 30 + 3 = \left(\dfrac{1}{3}\right)r$

$\qquad 33 = \left(\dfrac{1}{3}\right)r$

$\qquad 99 \text{ miles/hour} = r \text{ (rate of patrol officer)}$

Alternative Solution: $\left(\dfrac{1}{3}\right)r - 3 = 90 \cdot \left(\dfrac{1}{3}\right)$

$\qquad r - 9 = 90$

$\qquad r = 99 \text{ miles per hour (rate of patrol officer)}$

$\qquad\qquad\qquad \underline{99 \text{ miles/hour}}$

Check: $90\left(\dfrac{1}{3} + \dfrac{1}{30}\right) = \dfrac{1}{3}r$

$30 + 3 = \dfrac{1}{3}(99)$

$33 = 33$

Check: $\dfrac{1}{3}r - 3 = 90 \cdot \dfrac{1}{3}$

$\dfrac{1}{3} \cdot 99 - 3 = 30$

$33 - 3 = 30$

$30 = 30$

Challenge

7. A well-known race horse, Zippy, can travel $1\dfrac{1}{2}$ miles on a race course in two minutes (equivalent to $\dfrac{3}{2}$ miles in $\dfrac{1}{30}$ hour, or $30 \cdot \dfrac{3}{2} = \dfrac{90}{2} = 45$ miles per hour). After running for one mile at this rate, the horse received an injury, and his speed slowed to ten miles per hour. Another horse, Glue Factory Bound, traveled the $1\dfrac{1}{2}$-mile distance in five minutes. Did Zippy finish ahead of Glue Factory Bound? What was Glue Factory Bound's rate of speed?

Zippy (without injury): $\vdash\!\!-\!\!-\!\!-\!\!-\!\!-\!\!-\!\!-\!\!-\!\!-\!\!-\!\!-\!\!-\!\!-\!\!\dashv$
$1\dfrac{1}{2}$ mi
$\dfrac{1}{30}$ hr

Zippy (with injury): $\vdash\!\!-\!\!-\!\!-\!\!-\!\!-\!\!-\!\!\dashv\!\!-\!\!-\!\!-\!\!\dashv$
1 mi $\quad\quad$ $\dfrac{1}{2}$ mi
45 mi/hr $\quad$ 10 mi/hr

Glue Factory Bound: $\vdash\!\!-\!\!-\!\!-\!\!-\!\!-\!\!-\!\!-\!\!-\!\!-\!\!-\!\!-\!\!-\!\!-\!\!-\!\!\dashv$
$1\dfrac{1}{2}$ mi
$\dfrac{1}{12}$ hr

Horse	Distance d (miles)	Time $t = \dfrac{d}{r}$ (hours)	Rate $r = \dfrac{d}{t}$ (miles/hour)
Zippy	1	$\dfrac{1}{45}\left(=\dfrac{4}{180}\right)$	45
	$\dfrac{1}{2}$	$\dfrac{1}{20}\left(=\dfrac{9}{180}\right)$	10
	$1\dfrac{1}{2}$	$\dfrac{1}{45}+\dfrac{1}{20}=$	$20\dfrac{10}{13}$
		$\dfrac{4}{180}+\dfrac{9}{180}=\dfrac{13}{180}$	
		$=\quad 4\dfrac{1}{3}$ min	
Glue Factory Bound	$1\dfrac{1}{2}$	$\dfrac{1}{12}=5$ min	18
			Yes; 18 miles/hour

STUDY GUIDE 10

Air Travel

TERMS AND CONCEPTS

Introductory Precepts

The overall rate of travel by water is determined by the rate of a boat in still water with adjustments to allow for the rate of the current and the direction of travel. The same principle, distance = rate × time, applies to travel by airplane. The overall rate is determined by the rate of the plane in calm air with adjustments to make up for the wind speed and the direction of travel.

Students should use two equations and two un- knowns.

Mode of travel	Speed in still air	Wind speed	Speed relative to the ground	
			With wind	Against wind
Airplane	500 miles/ hour	50 miles/ hour	(500 + 50) miles/hour	(500 − 50) miles/hour
In general	x miles/ hour	y miles/ hour	$(x + y)$ miles/ hour	$(x - y)$ miles/hour

These definitions are helpful in solving air travel problems:

1. *Air speed:* The velocity of an airplane in still air.

2. *Wind speed:* The velocity of the wind.

3. *Tail wind:* A wind that blows in the same direction as that in which the aircraft is traveling. The tail wind increases the air speed. (If you are flying with the wind, the air speed is increased by the wind speed.) A tail wind can be diagrammed as follows:

Ground speed = air speed + wind speed

4. *Head wind:* A wind that blows in the opposite direction of that taken by the aircraft. A head wind decreases the air speed. (If you are flying against the wind, the air speed is decreased by the wind speed.) A head wind can be diagrammed as shown on the following page:

161

Ground speed | Head wind

Air speed

Ground speed = air speed − wind speed

5. *Ground speed:* The velocity of the airplane relative to a designated place on the ground.

LEVELS OF COMPREHENSION

STEP 1   Read the problem.

STEP 2   Choose the variable(s).

STEP 3   Form the equation.

STEP 4   Solve the equation.

STEP 5   Check the equation.

MODEL PROBLEM

With a tail wind, a small plane can fly 800 miles in four hours. Going against the wind, the plane can fly the same distance in five hours. Find the wind speed and the air speed of the plane.

READ THE PROBLEM

After reading the problem, give the answers to the following statements in the spaces provided.

Literal Level

With a tail wind, the plane can travel 800 miles in __four__ hours. With a head wind, the plane can travel __800__ miles in __five__ hours. The two distances are __equal__ but the two times are __different__.

Interpretive Level

1. If x = air speed in miles per hour and y = wind speed in miles per hour, then the ground speed with a tail wind is:

$(x + y)$ miles/hour, $(x - y)$ miles/hour, (xy) miles/hour

$(x + y)$ **miles/hour**

2. If $x =$ air speed in miles per hour and $y =$ wind speed in miles per hour, then the ground speed with a head wind is:

$(x + y)$ miles/hour, $(x - y)$ miles/hour, (xy) miles/hour

$(x - y)$ **miles/hour**

3. With a tail wind, the distance traveled in four hours is:

$4(x + y)$ miles, $4(x - 7)$ miles, $4xy$ miles

$4(x + y)$ **miles**

4. With a head wind, the distance traveled in five hours is:

$5(x + y)$ miles, $5(x - y)$ miles, $5xy$ miles

$5(x - y)$ **miles**

5. The distance traveled with a tail wind and the distance traveled with a head wind are:

equal,   unequal,   impossible to compute

equal

CHOOSE THE VARIABLE(S)

Let $x =$ air speed of plane (in miles/hour).

Let $y =$ wind speed of plane (in miles/hour).

Sometimes it is helpful to draw a diagram of the problem such as this:

Wind speed:
 y mi/hr

Air speed: x mi/hr   Wind speed: y mi/hr

Ground speed $(x + y)$ mi/hr

800 miles

Air speed: x mi/hr

Wind speed: y mi/hr

Ground speed
$(x - y)$ mi/hr

Frequently a chart helps in solving a distance-rate-time problem. Let $x =$ air speed of plane (in miles/hour) and $y =$ wind speed (in miles/hour). Then

Wind direction	Ground speed (miles/hour)	Time (hours)	Distance $d = rt$ (miles)
Tail wind	$x + y$	4	$4(x + y)$
Head wind	$x - y$	5	$5(x - y)$

FORM THE EQUATIONS

1. $4(x + y) = 800$

2. $5(x - y) = 800$

SOLVE THE EQUATIONS

1. $4(x + y) = 800$

2. $5(x - y) = 800$

$$x + y = 200$$
$$+ \ x - y = 160$$
$$2x \qquad = 360$$
$$x = \underline{\ 180\ } \text{ miles/hour (air speed)}$$
$$4(x + y) = 800$$
$$\underline{4(180 + y)} = 800$$
$$720 + 4y = 800$$
$$4y = 80$$
$$y = \underline{\ 20\ } \text{ miles/hour (wind speed)}$$

Air speed: **180 miles/hour**
Wind speed: **20 miles/hour**

CHECK THE EQUATIONS

$4(x + y) = 800$

$4(180 + 20) = 800$

$4(200) = 800$

$800 = 800$

$5(x - y) = 800$

$5 \ \underline{(180 - 20)} = 800$

$5(160) = 800$

$\underline{800} = 800$

Application Level

ACTIVITY EXTENSION

1. If the air speed of the plane and the wind speed are equal, could the plane make forward progress traveling with a tail wind?

_____ Yes _____

2. If the air speed of the plane and the wind speed are equal, could the plane make progress traveling with a head wind?

_____ No _____

Name _____ Period _____

Teacher _____ Date _____ Grade _____

Air Travel Problems with Help

DIRECTIONS: Each of the following problems has been given a partial solution. Solve each problem by completing the given solution.

1. The air speed of a small plane was 200 miles per hour. The plane could travel from Denver to Carlsbad in four hours with the wind. It flew from Carlsbad to Denver in six hours against the wind. Find the wind speed.

   Let x = wind speed (in miles per hour) and 200 = air speed (in miles per hour). Then

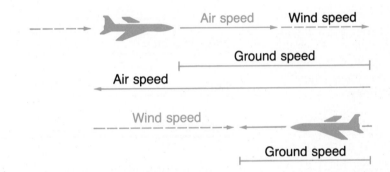

Wind direction	Ground speed (miles/hour)	Time (hours)	Distance $d = rt$ (miles)
Tail wind	200 + x	4	4(200 + x)
Head wind	200 − x	6	6(200 − x)

   $4(200 + x) = \underline{6(200 - x)}$

   $800 + 4x = 1{,}200 - 6x$

   $10x = \underline{400}$

   $x = \underline{40}$ miles/hour (wind speed)   **40 miles/hour**

   Check: $4(200 + x) = 6(200 - x)$

   $\underline{4(200 + 40)} = 6(200 - 40)$

   $4(240) = 6(160)$

   $960 = \underline{960}$

2. Not including time on the roof or ground, an evacuation helicopter carrying flood victims from the roof of a hotel to a safe place ten miles

away can make the round trip in 30 minutes. The helicopter flies four miles with the wind in the time it flies two miles against the wind. What is the wind speed?

Let x = wind speed (in miles/hour) and y = air speed (in miles/hour).

Then to form an equation for y, compile a table of data:

Wind direction	Ground speed (miles/hour)	Time (hours)	Distance (miles)
Tail wind	$y + x$	$\dfrac{4}{(y + x)}$	$\underline{4}$
Head wind	$\underline{y - x}$	$\dfrac{2}{(y - x)}$	2

And to form an equation for x, compile a table of data:

Wind direction	Ground speed (miles/hour)	Time (hours)	Distance (miles)
Tail wind	$y + x$	$\dfrac{10}{(y + x)}$	$\underline{10}$
Head wind	$\underline{y - x}$	$\dfrac{10}{(y - x)}$	10

Whenever there are two unknowns, there must be two equations. From the first equation, the air speed is three times the wind speed.

Form and solve an equation for y (air speed) by equating the two times in the first table of data.

$$\frac{4}{(y + x)} = \frac{2}{(y - x)}$$

$4y - 4x = \underline{2x + 2y}$

$2y - 6x = 0$

$\underline{y - 3x = 0}$

$y = 3x$

Form and solve an equation for x (wind speed) by equating the sum of the two times to $\dfrac{1}{2}$ in the second table of data.

From the second equation, and substituting $3x$ for y in the equation at *, the wind speed is 15 miles/hour. Therefore, the air speed is $3 \cdot 15$ or 45 miles/hour.

$$\frac{10}{(y + x)} + \frac{10}{(y - x)} = \frac{1}{2}$$

$$10(y - x) + 10(y + x) = \frac{1}{2}(y^2 - x^2)$$

$$10y - 10x + 10y + 10x = \frac{1}{2}(y^2 - x^2)$$

$$20y = \frac{1}{2}(y^2 - x^2)$$

$$\underline{40y = y^2 - x^2}$$

Substitute $3x$ for y:

$$*x^2 + 40y - y^2 = 0$$

$$x^2 + 40(3x) - (3x)^2 = 0$$

$$x^2 + 120x - 9x^2 = 0$$

$$-8x^2 + 120x = 0$$

$$\underline{8x^2 - 120x = 0}$$

$$8x(x - 15) = 0$$

$$\underline{8x = 0} \qquad x - 15 = 0$$

$$x = 0 \qquad x = 15$$

Wind speed only at $x = 15$ miles/hour

$$y = 3x$$

$$y = 3 \cdot 15$$

$$y = 45 \text{ miles/hour (air speed)}$$

Wind speed: **15 miles/hour**
Air speed: **45 miles/hour**

Check 1: $\dfrac{4}{y + x} = \dfrac{2}{y - x}$

$$\frac{4}{45 + 15} = \frac{2}{45 - 15}$$

$$\frac{4}{60} = \frac{2}{30}$$

$$\frac{2}{30} = \frac{2}{30}$$

Check 2: $\dfrac{10}{y + x} + \dfrac{10}{y - x} = \dfrac{1}{2}$

$$\frac{10}{45 + 15} + \frac{10}{45 - 15} = \frac{1}{2}$$

$$\frac{10}{60} + \frac{10}{\underline{\quad 30 \quad}} = \frac{1}{2}$$

$$\frac{1}{\underline{6}} + \frac{1}{3} = \frac{1}{2}$$

$$\frac{1}{2} = \frac{1}{\underline{2}}$$

3. A private plane, flying with a tail wind, can fly from Dallas to an oilwell site 400 miles away in three hours. The return flight with a head wind takes two hours longer. Find the air speed of the plane and the wind speed.

Let a = air speed (in miles/hour) and w = wind speed (in miles/hour).

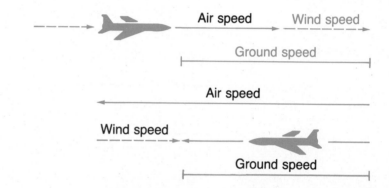

Wind direction	Ground speed (miles/hour)	Time (hours)	Distance $d = rt$ (miles)
Tail wind	$a + w$	3	$3(a + w)$
Head wind	$a - w$	$\underline{5}$	$5(a - w)$

Stress that answers left in
fractional form, such as
$\frac{320}{3}$ or $\frac{80}{3}$ are easy to
check.

1. $3(a + w) = 400$

2. $\underline{5(a - w) = 400}$

$3a + 3w = 400$

$\underline{5a - 5w = 400}$

$\underline{15a + 15w = 2{,}000}$

$\underline{+15a - 15w = 1{,}200}$

$30a \qquad = \underline{\quad 3{,}200 \quad}$

$a = \underline{\quad 106\frac{2}{3} \quad}$ miles/hour (air speed)

$3(a + w) = 400$

$3a + 3w = 400$

$$3\left(\frac{3,200}{30}\right) + 3w = 400$$

$$320 + 3w = 400$$

$$3w = 80$$

$$w = \underline{\quad 26\frac{2}{3} \quad} \text{ miles/hour (wind speed)}$$

Air speed: $106\frac{2}{3}$ miles/hour

Wind speed: $26\frac{2}{3}$ miles/hour

Check 1: $\dfrac{3(a + w)}{\underline{\quad\quad}} = 400$

$$3\left(\frac{320}{3} + \underline{\quad \frac{80}{3} \quad}\right) = 400$$

$$3\left(\frac{400}{3}\right) = \underline{\quad 400 \quad}$$

$$400 = 400$$

Check 2: $5(a - w) = 400$

$$5\left[\left(\frac{320}{3}\right) - \left(\frac{80}{3}\right)\right] = 400$$

$$\left(\underline{\quad \frac{1,600}{3} \quad}\right) - \left(\frac{400}{3}\right) = 400$$

$$\frac{1,200}{3} = 400$$

$$\underline{\quad \frac{400}{\quad} \quad} = 400$$

4. A helicopter, flying with a tail wind, can pick up receipts from a bank 150 miles away in two hours. The return flight with a head wind takes three hours. Find the air speed of the helicopter and the wind speed.

   Let a = air speed (in miles/hour) and w = wind speed (in miles/hour). Then

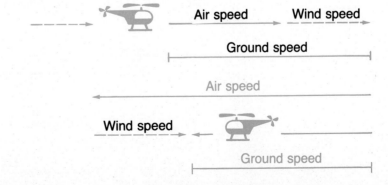

Wind direction	Ground speed (miles/hour)	Time (hours)	Distance $d = rt$ (miles)
Tail wind	$a + w$	2	$2(a + w)$
Head wind	$a - w$	3	$3(a - w)$

1. $2(a + w) = 150$

2. $3(a - w) = 150$

$2a + 2w = 150$

$3a - 3w = 150$

$6a + 6w = 450$

$+ 6a - 6w = 300$

$12a \qquad = 750$

$a = 62.5$ miles/hour (air speed)

$2(a + w) = 150$

$2(62.5 + w) = 150$

$125.0 + 2w = 150$

$2w = 25$

$w = 12.5$ miles/hour (wind speed)

Air speed: 62.5 miles/hour
Wind speed: 12.5 miles/hour

Check: $2(a + w) = 150$

$2(62.5 + 12.5) = 150$

$2(75) = 150$

$150 = 150$

Challenge

5. A highway patrol helicopter flying against the wind reaches a stakeout 80 miles away in two hours. On the return flight with a tail wind, the trip only takes one hour. Find the air speed of the patrol helicopter.

Let a = air speed (in miles/hour) and w = wind speed (in miles/hour). Then

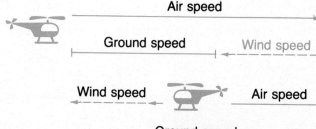

Wind direction	Ground speed (miles/hour)	Time (hours)	Distance $d = rt$ (miles)
Tail wind	$a + w$	1	$(a + w) \cdot 1$
Head wind	$a - w$	2	$(a - w) \cdot 2$

1. $(a + w) \cdot 1 = 80$

2. $2(a - w) = 80$

$a + w = 80$

$2a - 2w = 80$

$2a + 2w = 160$
$+ 2a - 2w = 80$

$4a = 240$

$a = 60$ miles/hour (air speed)

$\dfrac{(a + w) \cdot 1}{} = 80$

$(60 + w) \cdot 1 = 80$

$60 + w = 80$

$w = \underline{\quad 20 \quad}$ miles/hour (wind speed)

Air speed: **80 miles/hour**
Wind speed: **20 miles/hour**

Check 1: $(a + w) \cdot 1 = 80$

$(60 + 20) \cdot 1 = 80$

$80 \cdot 1 = 80$

$80 = 80$

Check 2: $2(a - w) = 80$

$2(60 - 20) = 80$

$2(40) = 80$

$80 = 80$

Name _____ Period _____

Teacher _____ Date _____ Grade _____

Air Travel Problems

DIRECTIONS: Use the five levels of comprehension to solve each of the problems in the space provided. Write your answers in the blank to the right after each problem.

1. The air speed of an evacuation plane was 300 miles per hour. If the plane could travel the same distance in five hours with the wind as it flew in eight hours against the wind, what was the wind speed?

   Let x = wind speed (in miles/hour) and ___300___ = air speed (in miles/hour). Then

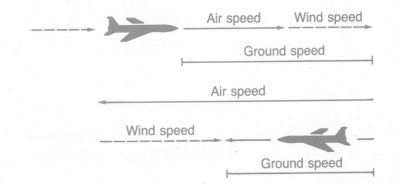

Wind direction	Ground speed (miles/hour)	Time (hours)	Distance $d = rt$ (miles)
Tail wind	300 + x	5	5(300 + x)
Head wind	300 − x	8	8(300 − x)

$$5(300 + x) = 8(300 - x)$$

$$1{,}500 + 5x = 2{,}400 - 8x$$

$$13x = 900$$

$$x = 69\frac{3}{13} \text{ miles/hour (wind speed)}$$

$69\frac{3}{13}$ miles/hour
_____

Check: $5(300 + x) = 8(300 - x)$

$$5\left(300 + \frac{900}{13}\right) = 8\left(300 - \frac{900}{13}\right)$$

$$5\left(\frac{3{,}900}{13} + \frac{900}{13}\right) = 8\left(\frac{3{,}900}{13} - \frac{900}{13}\right)$$

$$5\left(\frac{4{,}800}{13}\right) = 8\left(\frac{3{,}000}{13}\right)$$

$$\frac{24{,}000}{13} = \frac{24{,}000}{13}$$

2. Not counting time on the roof and the ground, an evacuation helicopter carrying fire victims from the roof of a condominium to a hospital 30 miles away can make the round trip in 30 minutes. The helicopter flies five miles with the wind in the same time that it flies two miles against the wind. What is the wind speed?

Let a = air speed (in miles/hour) and w = wind speed (in miles/hour). Then

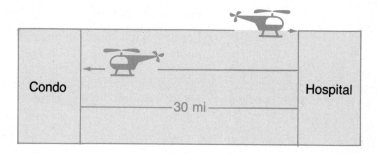

Wind direction	Ground speed (miles/hour)	Time $t = \dfrac{d}{r}$ (hours)	Distance (miles)
Tail wind	$a + w$	$\dfrac{5}{(a + w)}$	5
Head wind	$a - w$	$\dfrac{2}{(a - w)}$	2

And

Wind direction	Ground speed (miles/hour)	Time $t = \dfrac{d}{r}$ (hours)	Distance (miles)
Tail wind	$a + w$	$\dfrac{30}{(a + w)}$	30
Head wind	$a - w$	$\dfrac{30}{(a - w)}$	30

Form and solve an equation for a (air speed):

$$\frac{5}{(a + w)} = \frac{2}{(a - w)}$$

$$5(a - w) = 2(a + w)$$

$$5a - 5w = 2a + 2w$$

$$3a - 7w = 0$$

$$3a = 7w$$

$$*a = \left(\frac{7}{3}\right)(w)$$

Form and solve an equation for w (wind speed):

$$\frac{30}{a + w} + \frac{30}{a - w} = \frac{1}{2}$$

Substitute $\left(\frac{7}{3}\right)(w)$ for a:

$$\frac{30}{\left[\left(\frac{7}{3}\right)(w) + w\right]} + \frac{30}{\left[\left(\frac{7}{3}\right)(w) - w\right]} = \frac{1}{2}$$

$$\frac{30}{\left[\left(\frac{10}{3}\right)(w)\right]} + \frac{30}{\left[\left(\frac{4}{3}\right)(w)\right]} = \frac{1}{2}$$

$$\frac{9}{w} + \frac{90}{(4w)} = \frac{1}{2}$$

$$(4w)\left(\frac{9}{w}\right) + (4w)\left(\frac{90}{4w}\right) = (4w)\left(\frac{1}{2}\right)$$

$$36 + 90 = 2w$$

$$126 = 2w$$

$$63 = w$$

$$w = 63 \text{ miles/hour (wind speed)}$$

$$a = \frac{7}{3}w = \frac{7}{3} \cdot 63 = 147 \text{ miles/hour (air speed)}$$

Air speed: 147 miles/hour
Wind speed: 63 miles/hour

Check 1: $\dfrac{5}{a + w} = \dfrac{2}{a - w}$

$$\frac{5}{147 + 63} = \frac{2}{147 - 63}$$

$$\frac{5}{210} = \frac{2}{84}$$

$$\frac{1}{42} = \frac{1}{42}$$

Check 2: $\dfrac{30}{a + w} + \dfrac{30}{a - w} = \dfrac{1}{2}$

$$\frac{30}{147 + 63} + \frac{30}{147 - 63} = \frac{1}{2}$$

$$\frac{30}{210} + \frac{30}{84} = \frac{1}{2}$$

$$\frac{1}{7} + \frac{5}{14} = \frac{1}{2}$$

$$\frac{2}{14} + \frac{5}{14} = \frac{1}{2}$$

$$\frac{7}{14} = \frac{1}{2}$$

$$\frac{1}{2} = \frac{1}{2}$$

3. A private plane, flying with a tail wind, is used by several land developers to fly to a site 500 miles away. The journey takes 2.5 hours. The return flight with a head wind takes 2.5 hours longer. Find the air speed of the plane and the wind speed.

Let a = air speed (in miles/hour) and w = wind speed (in miles/hour). Then

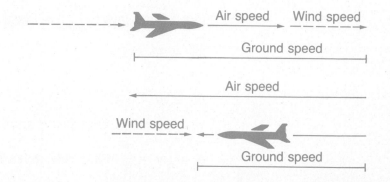

Wind direction	Ground speed (miles/hour)	Time (hours)	Distance $d = rt$ (miles)
Tail wind	$a + w$	2.5	$2.5(a + w)$
Head wind	$a - w$	5	$5(a - w)$

1. $2.5(a + w) = 500$

2. $5(a - w) = 500$

$$a + w = 200$$
$$+a - w = 100$$

$$2a = 300$$

$$a = 150 \text{ miles/hour (air speed)}$$

$$a + w = 200$$
$$150 + w = 200$$
$$w = 50 \text{ miles/hour (wind speed)}$$

Air speed: **150 miles/hour**
Wind speed: **50 miles/hour**

Check 1: $2.5(a + w) = 500$
$2.5(150 + 50) = 500$
$2.5(200) = 500$
$500 = 500$

Check 2: $5(a - w) = 500$
$5(150 - 50) = 500$
$5(100) = 500$
$500 = 500$

4. Flying with a tail wind, a helicopter reached a base 400 miles away in four hours. After minor repairs were made, the return trip with a head wind took five hours. Find the air speed of the helicopter and the wind speed.

Let a = air speed (in miles/hour) and w = wind speed (in miles/hour). Then

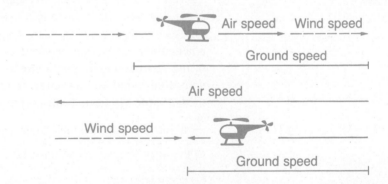

Wind direction	Ground speed (miles/hour)	Time (hours)	Distance $d = rt$ (miles)
Tail wind	$a + w$	4	$4(a + w)$
Head wind	$a - w$	5	$5(a - w)$

1. $4(a + w) = 400$

2. $5(a - w) = 400$

$a + w = 100$
$+ \ a - w = \ \ 80$

$$2a \qquad = 180$$
$$a = 90 \text{ miles/hour (air speed)}$$

$$4(a + w) = 400$$
$$4(90 + w) = 400$$
$$360 + 4w = 400$$
$$4w = 40$$
$$w = 10 \text{ miles/hour (wind speed)}$$

Air speed: **90 miles/hour**
Wind speed: **10 miles/hour**

Check 1: $4(a + w) = 400$
 $4(90 + 10) = 400$
 $4(100) = 400$
 $400 = 400$

Check 2: $5(a - w) = 400$
 $5(90 - 10) = 400$
 $5(80) = 400$
 $400 = 400$

Challenge

5. Two convicts have planned an escape from prison that involves a getaway plane that will touch down at a nearby airport at a prearranged time for only as long as it takes the convicts to leap aboard. The plan also requires a helicopter connection between the prison and the airport, and this part of the scheme may not be going according to the convicts' plan. Flying with a tail wind and an enforcer for the cons, the helicopter has made the five-mile trip from the airport to the prison in the fastest time possible: $\frac{1}{12}$ hour. The convicts and their accomplice then decide that the return to the airport rendezvous must take place within $\frac{1}{10}$ hour for the plan to be successful (the longer the rendezvous plane remains on the ground waiting for the convicts, the more likely that it will be disabled by police sharpshooters). The helicopter pilot tells the convicts that a six-minute trip is impossible because the helicopter will encounter a head wind of 15 miles/hour, and that the trip will take $\frac{1}{6}$ hour. The getaway plane will land at the airport 6 minutes after the convicts leave prison by helicopter. The convicts force the pilot to take them to the airport anyway. Find the wind speed and the air speed of the helicopter. Are the convicts smart if the getaway plane can be on the ground for only 2 minutes before being disabled?

Let a = air speed (in miles/hour) and w = wind speed (in miles/hour). Then

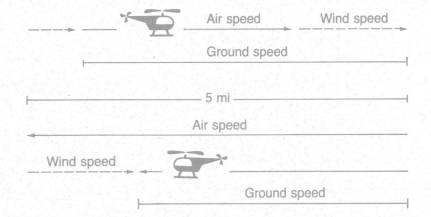

Wind direction	Ground speed (miles/hour)	Time (hours)	Distance $d = rt$ (miles)
Tail wind	$a + w$	$\dfrac{1}{12}$	$\left(\dfrac{1}{12}\right)(a + w)$
Head wind	$a - w$	$\dfrac{1}{6}$	$\left(\dfrac{1}{6}\right)(a - w)$

1. $\left(\dfrac{1}{12}\right)(a + w) = 5$

2. $\left(\dfrac{1}{6}\right)(a - w) = 5$

$$a + w = 60$$
$$+\; a - w = 30$$
$$2a\qquad = 90$$

$a = 45$ miles/hour (air speed)

$a + w = 60$

$45 + w = 60$

$w = 15$ miles/hour (wind speed)

No, the pilot is right. It will take ten minutes to return to the airport. In the four-minute time difference, the escape plane can be disabled.

Air speed: 45 miles/hour
Wind speed: 15 miles/hour

Check 1: $\left(\dfrac{1}{12}\right)(a + w) = 5$

$\left(\dfrac{1}{12}\right)(45 + 15) = 5$

$$\left(\frac{1}{12}\right)(60) = 5$$

$$5 = 5$$

Check 2: $\left(\frac{1}{6}\right)(a - w) = 5$

$$\left(\frac{1}{6}\right)(45 - 15) = 5$$

$$\left(\frac{1}{6}\right)(30) = 5$$

$$5 = 5$$

STUDY GUIDE 11

Mixtures

TERMS AND CONCEPTS

Introductory Precepts

If you sold 20 pounds of cashew nuts for $1.50 per pound and ten pounds of peanuts at 75¢ per pound, then you should receive $30 for the cashews and $7.50 for the peanuts for a total of $37.50. Suppose that few people would buy the peanuts, but many people would buy a mixture of peanuts and cashews. Your goal is to make the same profit with a mixture that you would make by selling the nuts separately. At what price per pound would you sell the 30-pound mixture in order to receive $37.50?

To determine the price per pound, divide the value of the mixture by the total pounds: $37.50 ÷ 30 = $1.25 per pound.

The sum of the values of the original ingredients must equal the value of the mixture: $(20)(\$1.50) + 10(\$.75) = 30(\$1.25)$.

LEVELS OF COMPREHENSION

STEP 1   Read the problem.

STEP 2   Choose the variable(s).

STEP 3   Form the equation.

STEP 4   Solve the equation.

STEP 5   Check the equation.

MODEL PROBLEM 1

A hood ornament for an expensive car is to be made of gold and silver. Suppose that gold sells at $400 per ounce on the world market, and silver sells at $10 per ounce. How many ounces of gold must be combined with silver to obtain 18 ounces of an alloy worth $270 per ounce?

READ THE PROBLEM

After reading the problem, give the answers to the following statements in the spaces provided.

Gold is selling at _____ $400 _____ per ounce on the world market. Silver is selling at _____ $10 _____ per ounce. The alloy weighs _____ 18 _____ ounces and sells for _____ $270 _____ per ounce.

1. You know the most information about the alloy and the least about the number of ounces of

   gold,   silver,   gold and silver

   _____ **Gold and silver** _____

2. If there are n ounces of gold and two ounces of silver, then the alloy will weigh

   $(n + 2)$ ounces, $(n - 2)$ ounces, $(2n)$ ounces

   _____ **$(n + 2)$ ounces** _____

3. The alloy is to weigh

   18 ounces,   20 ounces, $(n + 2)$ ounces

   _____ **18 ounces** _____

4. If n = number of ounces of gold, then the number of ounces of silver will be represented by

   $n + 18$, $18 + n$, $18 - n$, $n - 18$

   _____ **$18 - n$** _____

5. The value of n ounces of gold at $400 per ounce is

   $400n$, $400 - n$, $400 \div n$,   none of these

   _____ **$400n$** _____

6. The value of $(18 - n)$ ounces of silver at $10 per ounce is

   $(18 - n) \cdot \$10$, $\$10 \cdot (n + 18)$, $(18 - n) \div 10$

   _____ **$(18 - n) \cdot \$10$** _____

7. The value of the silver plus the value of the gold should equal the value of the

   alloy,   gold,   silver,   none of these

   _____ **alloy** _____

Sometimes a diagram can help form the equation:

? oz		? oz		18 oz
gold	+	silver	=	alloy
$400/oz		$10/oz		$270/oz

CHOOSE THE VARIABLE(S)

Let n = the number of ounces of gold.

Frequently a chart helps solve the problem. This mixture problem follows this form.

Material	Number of ounces	Price per ounce	Value
Gold	n	$400	400n$
Silver	18 − n	$ 10	$10(18 − n)
Alloy	18	$270	$270(18)

FORM THE EQUATION

Application Level

$400n + $10(18 − n) = $270(18)

SOLVE THE EQUATION

$400n + $10(18 − n) = $270(18)
$$400n + 180 - 10n = \$4{,}860$$

$390n + 180 = 4,860$
$$390n = 4{,}680$$

$n = \underline{\ 12\ }$ ounces (amount of gold)

$18 - n = \underline{\ 6\ }$ ounces (amount of silver)   **12 ounces**

CHECK THE EQUATION

$400n + $10(18 − n) = $270(18)

400(12) + 10(18 − 12) = 270(18)

$$4{,}800 + 60 = 4{,}860$$

$$\$4{,}860 = \$4{,}860$$

ACTIVITY EXTENSION

If you had let n = number of ounces of silver, what would the resulting equation have been?

$10($n$) + $400(18 − n) = $270(18)

MODEL PROBLEM 2

Suppose gold costs $60 per ounce and silver costs $20 per ounce. Forty ounces of an alloy of gold and silver are made. Could a profit be made if the alloy is sold at $25 per ounce?

READ THE PROBLEM

After reading the problem, give the answers to the following statements in the spaces provided.

Literal Level

1. More information is known about

   gold,   silver,   alloy of gold and silver

   <u>alloy of gold and silver</u>

2. The number of ounces of alloy of gold and silver is __<u>40</u>__.

3. The alloy is to be sold at __<u>$25</u>__ per ounce.

Interpretive Level

4. If n = the number of ounces of gold used, then the number of ounces of silver used is

   $40 + n$, $40 - n$,   40, $25n$

   <u>40 − n</u>

Sometimes a diagram can help form the equation.

? oz		? oz		40 oz
gold	+	silver	=	alloy
$60/oz		$20/oz		$25/oz

CHOOSE THE VARIABLE(S)

Let n = number of ounces of gold.

Frequently a chart helps solve the problem. This mixture problem follows this form.

Material	Number of ounces	Price per ounce	Value
Gold	n	$60	<u>$60n</u>
Silver	$40 - n$	<u>$20</u>	$20(40 − n)$
Alloy	<u>40</u>	$25	$25(40)$

FORM THE EQUATION

$60n + $20(40 - n) = $25(40)$

SOLVE THE EQUATION

$60n + $20(40 - n) = $25(40)$

$60n + 800 - 20n = \underline{\quad 1,000 \quad}$

$\underline{\quad 40n \quad} + 800 = 1,000$

$40n = 200$

$n = \underline{\quad 5 \quad}$ ounces (amount of gold)

$40 - n = \underline{\quad 35 \quad}$ ounces (amount of silver)

CHECK THE EQUATION

$60n + $20(40 - n) = $25(40)$

$60(\underline{\ 5\ }) + 20(40 - \underline{\ 5\ }) = 24(40)$

$\underline{\ 300\ } + 20(\underline{\ 35\ }) = 1,000$

$300 + \underline{\ 700\ } = 1,000$

$1,000 = $1,000$

Yes
Gold: **5 ounces**
Alloy: **35 ounces**

MODEL PROBLEM 3

Three sedans and two station wagons sell for $66,000. Four sedans and five station wagons sell for $123,000. Prices of each are uniform. Find the price of each.

READ THE PROBLEM

After reading the problem, give the answers to the following statements in the spaces provided.

$\underline{\quad \textbf{Three} \quad}$ sedans and $\underline{\ \textbf{two}\ }$ station wagons sell for $66,000. Four sedans and five station wagons sell for $\underline{\ \textbf{\$123,000}\ }$. Prices are $\underline{\ \textbf{uniform}\ }$.

Solve problems of this type by using *one* variable or *two* variables. Sometimes a diagram can help form the equation.

Cost of [sedan][sedan][sedan] + [wagon][wagon] = $66,000

Cost of [sedan][sedan][sedan][sedan] + [wagon][wagon][wagon][wagon][wagon] = $123,000

The one-variable method does not lend itself to this type of problem.

CHOOSE THE VARIABLE(S)

Let x = the price of the sedan (in dollars).

Let y = the price of the station wagon (in dollars).

} Two-variable method

Frequently a chart helps solve the problem. This mixture problem follows this form.

Car	Number	Price	Value	Total	Grand Total
Sedan	3	x	$3x$	$ 66,000	
Station Wagon	2	y	$2y$		$189,000
Sedan	4	x	$4x$	$123,000	
Station Wagon	5	y	$5y$		

Application Level

FORM THE EQUATIONS

1. $3x + 2y = 66,000$
2. $4x + 5y = 123,000$

SOLVE THE EQUATIONS

1. $3x + 2y = 66,000$
2. $4x + 5y = 123,000$

$$-12x - 8y = -264,000$$

$$+12x + 15y = 369,000$$

$$7y = 105,000$$

$y = \$15,000$ (price of station wagon)

$3x + 2y = 66,000$

$3x + 2(\underline{\ \ 15,000\ \ }) = 66,000$

$3x + \underline{\ \ 30,000\ \ } = 66,000$

$3x = 36,000$

$x = \underline{\ \ \$12,000\ \ }$ (price of sedan)

Price of sedan: **$12,000**

Price of station wagon: **$15,000**

CHECK THE EQUATION

$3x + 2y = 66,000$

$3(\underline{\ \ 12,000\ \ }) + 2(\underline{\ \ 15,000\ \ }) = 66,000$

$36,000 + \underline{\ \ 30,000\ \ } = 66,000$

$\underline{\ \ 66,000\ \ } = 66,000$

Name _____ Period _____

Teacher _____ Date _____ Grade _____

Mixtures Problems with Help

DIRECTIONS: Each of the following problems has been given a partial solution. Solve each problem by completing the given solution.

Note that if Ms. Jenner buys one more than twenty-two 22-cent stamps, her total cost will exceed $8.76.

1. Mr. Gleason bought eighteen 22-cent stamps and twenty-four 20-cent stamps. Ms. Jenner bought 100 2-cent stamps. How many 22-cent stamps can Ms. Jenner now buy without exceeding the amount Mr. Gleason spent?

Let x = the number of Ms. Jenner's 22-cent stamps.

Purchaser	Number	Each	Amount	Total
Gleason	18	22¢	$3.96	
	__24__	20¢	$4.80	$8.76
Jenner	100	__2¢__	$2.00	
	x	22¢	__$0.22x__	

$$\$2.00 + 0.22x \leq \$8.76$$
$$200 + 22x \leq 876$$
$$22x \leq 676$$
$$x \leq 30 \text{ (number of 22-cent stamps)} \quad \underline{\textbf{30 stamps}}$$

Check: $\$2.00 + 0.22x \leq \$8.76$
$$200 + 22x \cong 876$$
$$200 + 22(\underline{\textbf{30}}) \cong 876$$
$$200 + \underline{\textbf{660}} \cong 876$$
$$\underline{\textbf{860}} \leq 876$$

2. Three limes cost $1.00. Six lemons cost $1.50. How much should you sell three lemons and three limes for? (Use an arithmetic approach to solve this problem.)

Since six lemons cost $1.50, one lemon will cost $0.25. Therefore, three lemons will cost $0.75.

$\underline{\text{\$1.00}}$ (cost of limes)

\+ 0.75 (cost of lemons)

$\underline{\text{\$1.75}}$ (cost of limes and lemons) $\underline{\text{\$1.75}}$

Perhaps some students will solve this by the average method.

3. One kind of candy sells for $2.00 a pound and another kind sells for $5.00 a pound. How many pounds of each should be used to form a mixture of 60 pounds that will sell for $3.50 a pound?

Let x = the number of pounds of $2 candy.

x lb		$(60 - x)$ lb		60 lb
Candy 1	+	Candy 2	=	Candy 3
$2/lb		$5/lb		$3.50/lb

Composition	Number of pounds	Price per pound	Value of candy in cents
Candy 1	x	$2.00	$\underline{200x}$
Candy 2	$60 - x$	$5.00	$500(60 - x)$
Mixture	60	$3.50	$350(60)$

$200x + 500(60 - x) = 350(60)$

$200x + \underline{\dfrac{30{,}000 - 500x}{}} = 21{,}000$

$-300x = -9{,}000$

$x = \underline{30}$ pounds (amount of $2 candy)

$60 - x = 30$ pounds (amount of $5 candy) $\underline{\textbf{30 pounds of each}}$

Check: $200x + 500(60 - x) = 350(60)$

$200(\underline{30}) + 500(\underline{60 - 30}) = 21{,}000$

$6{,}000 + 500(\underline{30}) = 21{,}000$

$6{,}000 + \underline{15{,}000} = 21{,}000$

$\underline{21{,}000} = 21{,}000$

Some students will probably test the theory supporting this problem.

4. A grocer blends Ceylon tea selling at $1.50 per pound with orange pekoe tea selling at $2.50 per pound to make an interesting blend selling at $2.00 per pound. How many pounds of each kind should be used to make a mixture of 100 pounds for a hotel?

Let n = the number of pounds of Ceylon tea.

Tea	Price per pound	Number of pounds	Value in cents
Ceylon	$1.50	n	150(n)
Pekoe	$2.50	$\underline{100 - n}$	250(100 − n)
Mixture	$2.00	100	$\underline{200(100)}$

$150n + 250(100 - n) = 200(100)$

$150n + \underline{\dfrac{25{,}000 - 250n}{}} = 20{,}000$

$-100n = -5{,}000$

$n = \underline{50}$ pounds (amount of Ceylon tea)

$100 - n = \underline{50}$ pounds (amount of pekoe tea)

Ceylon tea: **50 pounds**
Pekoe tea: **50 pounds**

Check: $150n + 250(100 - n) = 200(100)$

$150(50) + 250(\underline{\dfrac{100 - 50}{}}) = 20{,}000$

$7{,}500 + 250(\underline{50}) = 20{,}000$

$7{,}500 + \underline{12{,}500} = 20{,}000$

$\underline{20{,}000} = 20{,}000$

5. The owner of a candy store can sell peppermint stick candy and not lemon. If peppermint sticks sell for $3.00 a pound and lemon candy for $4.00 a pound, how many pounds of each should be used in a two-color mixture of 40 pounds to be sold at $3.50 per pound?

Let n = the number of pounds of peppermint.

Candy	Price per pound	Number of pounds	Value in cents
Mint	$3.00	n	300(n)
Lemon	$4.00	$\underline{40 - n}$	400(40 − n)
Mixture	$3.50	40	350(40)

$300n + 400(40 - n) = 350(40)$

$300n + 16{,}000 - 400n = \underline{14{,}000}$

$-100n = -2{,}000$

$n = \underline{\textbf{20 pounds}}$ (amount of peppermint candy)

$40 - n = \underline{\textbf{20 pounds}}$ (amount of lemon candy)

20 pounds of each candy

Check: $300n + 400(40 - n) = 350(40)$

$300(20) + 400(\underline{\hspace{0.3cm}40 - 20\hspace{0.3cm}}) = 14,000$

$6,000 + 400(\underline{\hspace{0.3cm}20\hspace{0.3cm}}) = 14,000$

$6,000 + 8,000 = 14,000$

$\underline{\hspace{0.3cm}14,000\hspace{0.3cm}} = 14,000$

No average here!

6. A five-pound box of Valentine's candy will sell for $20. It was made by mixing chocolates worth $5.00 per pound with chocolate fruit creams worth $2.00 per pound. How many pounds of each kind were used?

Let $n =$ the number of pounds of $5 chocolates.

Candy	Price per pound	Number of pounds	Value in cents
Chocolates	$5.00	n	$500n$
Fruit Creams	$2.00	$5 - n$	$200(5 - n)$
Valentine mixture	—	5	2,000

$500n + 200(\underline{\hspace{0.3cm}5 - n\hspace{0.3cm}}) = 2,000$

$500n + 1,000 - \underline{\hspace{0.3cm}200n\hspace{0.3cm}} = 2,000$

$300n + \underline{\hspace{0.3cm}1,000\hspace{0.3cm}} = 2,000$

$\underline{\hspace{0.3cm}300n\hspace{0.3cm}} = 1,000$

$n = \underline{\hspace{0.5cm}3\frac{1}{3} \text{ pounds}\hspace{0.5cm}}$ (amount of $5 chocolates)

$5 - n = \underline{\hspace{0.5cm}1\frac{2}{3} \text{ pounds}\hspace{0.5cm}}$ (amount of $2 chocolate fruit creams)

$5 chocolates: $3\frac{1}{3}$ pounds

$2 chocolate fruit creams: $1\frac{2}{3}$ pounds

Check: Use fraction

$500n + 200(5 - n) = 2,000$

$500\left(\dfrac{10}{3}\right) + 200\left(5 - \dfrac{10}{3}\right) = 2,000$

$\dfrac{5,000}{3} + 1,000 - \dfrac{2,000}{3} = 2,000$

$\dfrac{3,000}{3} + 1,000 = \underline{\hspace{0.3cm}2,000\hspace{0.3cm}}$

$\underline{\hspace{0.3cm}1,000\hspace{0.3cm}} + 1,000 = 2,000$

$\underline{\hspace{0.3cm}2,000\hspace{0.3cm}} = 2,000$

7. How many pounds of almonds worth $2.50 per pound must be mixed with 12 pounds of walnuts selling at $4.00 per pound to produce a mixture that can be sold for $3.00 per pound?

Let n = the number of pounds of almonds.

Nuts	Number of pounds	Price per pound	Value in cents
Almonds	n	$2.50	$250n$
Walnuts	12	$4.00	12(400)
Mixture	$n + 12$	$3.00	$300(n + 12)$

$250n + 12(400) = $ __$300(12 + n)$__

$250n + 4,800 = $ __$3,600 + 300n$__

__$-50n$__ $= -1,200$

$n = $ __24 pounds__ (almonds)   __24 pounds__

Check: $250n + 12(400) = 300(12 + n)$

$250(24) + 12(400) = 300($ __$12 + 24$__ $)$

$6,000 + 4,800 = 300($ __36__ $)$

$10,800 = $ __10,800__

Challenge

8. A seed dealer wishes to combine 100 pounds of ground-cover seed selling for $3.00 per pound with 200 pounds of clover seed selling for $5.00 per pound to make a mixture of 300 pounds. How much should he charge for each pound of the mixture in order to earn the same profit as if the two had been sold separately?

Let x = the cost of the mixture per pound (in dollars).

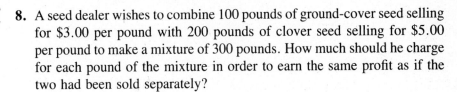

Seed	Number of pounds	Price per pound	Value in cents
Ground cover	100	$3.00	100(300)
Clover	200	$5.00	200(500)
Mixture	300	x	$300x$

$100(300) + 200(500) = 300x$

__$30,000 + 100,000$__ $= 300x$

$130,000 = $ __$300x$__

$433\frac{1}{3} = x$

__$\$4.33\frac{1}{3}$__ (cost per pound) $= x$ __$\$4.33\frac{1}{3}$ per pound__

$$x = \frac{130,000}{300}$$

Check: $100(\underline{300}) + 200(\underline{500}) = 300x$

$30,000 + \underline{100,000} = 300\left(\dfrac{130,000}{300}\right)$

$\underline{130,000} = 130,000$

Name _____ Period _____

Teacher _____ Date _____ Grade _____

Mixtures Problems

DIRECTIONS: Use the five levels of comprehension to solve each of the problems in the spaces provided. Write your answers in the blank to the right after each problem.

1. A grocer marks sundae toppings such that eight strawberry toppings and three chocolate toppings cost $22 and four strawberry toppings and seven chocolate toppings also cost $22. Find the price of each strawberry topping and each chocolate topping. (Use two variables.)

   Let s = price of strawberry topping (in dollars).

   Let c = price of chocolate topping (in dollars).

	Number	Price	Value	Total
Strawberry	8	s	$8s$	
				$22
Chocolate	3	c	$3c$	
Strawberry	4	s	$4s$	
				$22
Chocolate	7	c	$7c$	

$$
\begin{aligned}
&1. \quad 8s + 3c = \$22 \\
&2. \quad \underline{4s + 7c = \$22} \\
\end{aligned}
$$

$$
\begin{aligned}
8s + 3c &= 22 \\
+-8s - 14c &= -44 \\
\hline
-11c &= -22
\end{aligned}
$$

$$c = \$2$$

$$8s + 3c = 22$$
$$8s + 3(2) = 22$$
$$8s + 6 = 22$$
$$8s = 16$$
$$s = \$2$$

$2 each

Check: $8s + 3c = 22$

$8(2) + 3(2) = 22$

$16 + 6 = 22$

$\$22 = \$22$

2. At the fruit market, eight kiwis and two nectarines cost $5.98. Four kiwis and seven nectarines cost $4.37. What is the price of each? (Use two variables.)

Let k = the price of each kiwi (in dollars).

Let n = the price of each nectarine (in dollars).

	Number	Price	Value	Total
Kiwis	8	k	$8k$	
				$\$5.98$
Nectarines	2	n	$2n$	
Kiwis	4	k	$4k$	
				$\$4.37$
Nectarines	7	n	$7n$	

1. $8k + 2n = \$5.98$
2. $4k + 7n = \$4.37$

$$8k + 2n = \$5.98$$
$$+ -8k - 14n = -8.74$$

$$-12n = -2.76$$
$$n = \$0.23 \text{ (price of a nectarine)}$$

$8k + 2n = 5.98$

$8k + 2(0.23) = 5.98$

$8k + 0.46 = 5.98$

$8k = 5.52$

$k = \$0.69 \text{ (price of a kiwi)}$

Nectarine: **$0.23**
Kiwi: **$0.69**

Check: $8k + 2n = \$5.98$

$8(0.69) + 2(0.23) = \$5.98$

$\$5.52 + 0.46 = \$5.98$

$\$5.98 = \$5.98$

3. A florist sells long-stemmed red roses at $35 per dozen and pink sweet-heart roses at $10 per dozen. The florist sold 20 dozen roses totaling $450. How many dozens of each rose did the florist sell?

Let x = the number of dozens of red roses.

Roses	Number of dozens	Price per dozen	Value in dollars	Value in cents	Total in cents
Red	x	$35	$35x	3,500x	45,000
Pink sweetheart	20 − x	$10	$10(20 − x)	1,000(20 − x)	

$3,500x + 1,000(20 - x) = 45,000$

$3,500x + 20,000 - 1,000x = 45,000$

$2,500x = 25,000$

$x = 10$ (number of dozens of red roses)

$20 - x = 10$ (number of dozens of pink sweetheart roses)

Red roses: **10 dozen**
Pink roses: **10 dozen**

Check: $3,500x + 1,000(20 - x) = 45,000$

$3,500(10) + 1,000(20 - 10) = 45,000$

$35,000 + 1,000(10) = 45,000$

$35,000 + 10,000 = 45,000$

$45,000 = 45,000$

4. The PTA serves refreshments at all meetings. The social chairperson buys stale cookies at $1 per dozen and freshly made brownies for $3 per dozen. If the chairperson spends $26 for ten dozen of the two items mixed together, how many dozens of each are purchased? (Use two variables.)

Let s = the number of dozens of stale cookies.

Let b = the number of dozens of brownies.

Cookies	Number of dozens	Price per dozen in cents	Total cost in cents
Brownies	b	300	300b
Stale	s	100	100s
Mixture	10	—	2,600

1. $s + b \qquad = \qquad 10$

2. $\underline{100s + 300b \quad = \quad 2{,}600}$

$\qquad -100s - 100b = -1{,}000$

$\qquad \underline{+100s + 300b = \quad 2{,}600}$

$\qquad\qquad\qquad 200b = 1{,}600$

$\qquad b = 8$ dozen (brownies)

$\qquad s + b = 10$

$\qquad s + 8 = 10$

$\qquad s = 2$ dozen (stale cookies)

Brownies: 8 dozen

Stale cookies: 2 dozen

Check: $s + b = 10$

$\qquad\qquad 2 + 8 = 10$

$\qquad\qquad 10 = 10$

5. A senator entertains often. To some, she serves caviar costing $35 per ounce. To others, she serves caviar spread costing $9 per ounce. She served altogether 90 ounces of caviar and caviar spread at two parties, at a total cost of $2,370. How many ounces of each did she serve?

Let c = the number of ounces of caviar.

	Number of ounces	Cost per ounce	Total
Caviar	c	$35	$35c
Caviar spread	$90 - c$	$9	$9(90 - c)$
Grand total	90	—	$2,370

$35c + \$9(90 - c) = \$2{,}370$

$35c + 810 - 9c = 2{,}370$

$26c = 1{,}560$

$c = 60$ ounces (caviar)

$90 - c = 30$ ounces (caviar spread)

Caviar: 60 ounces

Caviar spread: 30 ounces

Check: $\$35c + \$9(90 - c) = \$2{,}370$

$\qquad\qquad 35(60) + 9(90 - 60) = 2{,}370$

$\qquad\qquad 2{,}100 + 810 - 540 = 2{,}370$

$\qquad\qquad 2{,}910 - 540 = 2{,}370$

$\qquad\qquad 2{,}370 = 2{,}370$ (dollars)

6. A dock worker pays $30 for 10 pounds of seafood. It is made of two kinds of shrimp: Large shrimp sell for $5 per pound, and popcorn shrimp sell for $1 per pound. How many pounds of each kind were in the mixture?

Let x = the number of pounds of large shrimp.

Seafood	Number of pounds	Price per pound	Value in cents
Large shrimp	x	$5.00	500x
Popcorn shrimp	10 − x	$1.00	100(10 − x)
Mixture	10	—	3,000

500x + 100(10 − x) = 3,000

500x + 1,000 − 100x = 3,000

400x = 2,000

x = 5 pounds (large shrimp)

10 − x = 5 pounds (popcorn shrimp)

Large shrimp: **5 pounds**
Popcorn shrimp: **5 pounds**

Check: 500x + 100(10 − x) = 3,000

500(5) + 100(10 − 5) = 3,000

2,500 + 100(5) = 3,000

2,500 + 500 = 3,000

3,000 = 3,000

7. A grocer sells coffee from Brazil for $3.00 per pound and coffee from Colombia for $4.00 per pound. How many pounds of each should be used in order to sell the blend of 100 pounds for $3.50 per pound?

Let b = the number of pounds of Brazil coffee.

Coffee	Number of pounds	Price per pound	Value in cents
Brazil	b	$3	300b
Colombia	100 − b	$4	400(100 − b)
Mixture	100	—	100(350)

300b + 400(100 − b) = 100(350)

300b + 40,000 − 400b = 35,000

−100b = −5,000

b = 50 pounds (Brazil coffee)

100 − b = 50 pounds (Colombia coffee)

Brazil coffee: **50 pounds**
Colombia coffee: **50 pounds**

Check: $300b + 400(100 − b) = 100(350)$

$300(50) + 400(100 − 50) = 100(350)$

$15{,}000 + 400(50) = 35{,}000$

$15{,}000 + 20{,}000 = 35{,}000$

$35{,}000 = 35{,}000$

Challenge

8. A nursery can sell pansies for \$8 per dozen, snapdragons for \$12 per dozen, and petunias for \$5 per dozen. How many snapdragons and petunias did Mr. Cheng buy if he purchased 12 dozen plants, two dozen of which were pansies, and spent \$122 in all?

Let n = the number of dozens of snapdragons.

Flowers	Number of dozens	Price per dozen	Value in cents
Pansies	2	\$8	2(800)
Snapdragons	n	\$12	1,200n
Petunias	10 − n	\$5	500(10 − n)

$2(800) + 1{,}200n + 500(10 − n) =$
$12{,}200$

$1{,}600 + 1{,}200n + 500(10 − n) =$
$12{,}200$

$16 + 12n + 5(10 − n) = 122$

$16 + 12n + 50 − 5n = 122$

$7n + 66 = 122$

$7n = 56$

n = 8 dozen (snapdragons)

10 − n = 2 dozen (petunias)

Snapdragons: **8 dozen**
Petunias: **2 dozen**

Check: $2(800) + 1{,}200n + 500(10 − n) = 12{,}200$

$1{,}600 + 1{,}200n + 500(10 − n) = 12{,}200$

$16 + 12n + 5(10 − n) = 122$

$16 + 12(8) + 5(10 − 8) = 122$

$16 + 96 + 5(2) = 122$

$16 + 96 + 10 = 122$

$122 = 122$

STUDY GUIDE 12

Solutions

TERMS AND CONCEPTS

Because scientists, pharmacists, and other professionals experiment with solutions, they must understand what the term *percent* means. *Per* means each and *cent* means hundred. One hundred percent of anything means all of it. Fifty percent of any quantity is $\frac{1}{2}$ or 0.50 times the quantity. The amount of pure salt in 20 ounces of a 50 percent solution of salt and water is 0.50(20) or ten ounces. A farmer's milk must test to have a certain percent of butterfat. The amount of butterfat in x pounds of milk testing 7 percent butterfat is $0.07(x)$ or $0.07x$ pounds. The amount of pure chlorine in $(100 - x)$ ounces of a 25-percent solution of chlorine in water is $0.25(100 - x)$ ounces.

You may form the equation for a solutions problem involving Element A and Element B in two ways. You may use the percents of Element A in the equation, or you may use the percents of Element B in the equation. For example, if iodine and baby oil are used in a solution, one equation may be formed using the percents of iodine. In other words, the iodine content in the original solution plus or minus the iodine content in a second solution should equal the iodine content in the final solution. The other equation would use the percents of baby oil in the problem. In other words, the baby oil content in the original solution plus or minus the baby oil content in the second solution should equal the baby oil content in the final solution.

It's extremely critical to remember that in solving solutions problems *all percents* in a given equation must represent the same element in the solution.

LEVELS OF COMPREHENSION

STEP 1 Read the problem.

STEP 2 Choose the variable(s).

STEP 3 Form the equation.

STEP 4 Solve the equation.

STEP 5 Check the equation.

MODEL PROBLEM 1

Nicotinic acid is prescribed at a clinic for health problems. A pharmacist has 20 ounces of nicotinic acid compound testing 50 percent nicotinic acid. How much pure nicotinic acid must be added to the original compound in order to produce a compound that is 60 percent nicotinic acid?

READ THE PROBLEM

After reading the problem, give the answers to the following statements or questions in the spaces provided.

Literal Level

There are ___20___ ounces of a nicotinic acid solution. This solution tests __50 percent__ nicotinic acid. Enough ___pure___ (100 percent) nicotinic acid must be added to this solution in order for it to test __60 percent__ nicotinic acid.

Interpretive Level

1. If you let x = number of ounces of pure nicotinic acid to be added to the original 20 ounces of nicotinic acid solution, then the new solution would contain

   $(20 - x)$ ounces, $(20 + x)$ ounces,
   $20x$ ounces, $(x - 20)$ ounces

   _____
   (20 + x) ounces

2. The pure nicotinic acid in the original solution is

   $0.50(20)$ ounces, $0.05(20)$ ounces,
   $(0.50 + 20)$ ounces, $0.20(0.50)$ ounces

   _____
   0.50(20) ounces

3. If x ounces of pure nicotinic acid are added to the original solution, then the final solution will contain how many ounces of nicotinic acid?

   $[0.50(20) + x]$ ounces, $(0.50x)$ ounces,
   $[0.50(x) + 20]$ ounces, $0.50(20)$ ounces

   _____
   [0.50(20) + x] ounces

4. The number of ounces of pure nicotinic acid in the final solution will be equivalent to the 60 percent pure nicotinic acid of the $(20 + x)$-ounce solution and should be equated to

   $0.60[(20 + x)]$ ounces, $0.06(20 - x)$ ounces,
   $160(20 + x)$ ounces, $0.20(60)$ ounces

   _____
   0.60[(20 + x)] ounces

CHOOSE THE VARIABLE(S)

Let x = the number of ounces of pure acid to be added.

Sometimes a diagram can help form the equation.

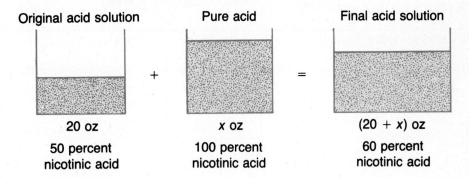

Original acid solution		Pure acid		Final acid solution
20 oz	+	x oz	=	(20 + x) oz
50 percent nicotinic acid		100 percent nicotinic acid		60 percent nicotinic acid

A tabular arrangement may help solve the equation.

Kind of solution	Number of ounces	Part (percent) of pure nicotinic acid	Number of ounces of pure nicotinic acid
Original	20 oz	50 percent	0.50(20) oz
Nicotinic acid to be added	x oz	100 percent	1.00 · x oz
Final solution	(20 + x) oz	60 percent	0.60(20 + x) oz

The resulting equation, yielding nicotinic acid content, will lead to the solution of the problem. Multiplication by 100 will eliminate the decimal.

FORM THE EQUATION

Application Level

$0.50(20) + 1.00x = 0.60(20 + x)$

SOLVE THE EQUATION

$0.50(20) + 1.00x = 0.60(20 + x)$

$50(20) + 100x = \underline{60(20 + x)}$

$1,000 + 100x = 1,200 + 60x$

$40x = \underline{200}$

$x = \underline{5}$ ounces (amount of pure acid to be added) $\underline{5\text{ ounces}}$

CHECK THE EQUATION

$0.50(20) + 1.00(x) = 0.60(20 + x)$

$0.50(20) + \underline{1.00(5)} = 0.60(20 + 5)$

$10 + 5 = 0.60(25)$

$\underline{15} = 15$

If 100 percent pure nico-
tinic acid is added to a
nicotinic acid compound
that is not 100 percent nicotinic acid, the nicotinic
acid content in the final
compound will increase.
With students, discuss
possibilities if other per-
centages of nicotinic acid
are added to the original
compound.

ACTIVITY EXTENSION

1. Could you, by adding x ounces of pure nicotinic acid, reduce the nicotinic acid content of the final solution to 20 percent nicotinic acid?

yes,   no,   maybe

No

2. In the problem, as more pure nicotinic acid is added to the 20-ounce solution testing 50 percent nicotinic acid, the percentage of pure nicotinic acid in the final solution

increases,   decreases,   stays the same

Increases

3. In order to reduce the final solution's nicotinic acid content to a solution testing 20 percent pure nicotinic acid, you would not add more

chlorine,   pure nicotinic acid,   iodine,   any of these

Pure nicotinic acid

MODEL PROBLEM 2

In nursing the injured in a disaster area, a Red Cross volunteer uses a saline solution of salt and water that is 10 percent salt and weighs 50 pounds. How much water must be added to produce a solution that is 2 percent salt?

READ THE PROBLEM

After reading the problem, give the answers to the following statements in the spaces provided.

Literal Level

The solution contains salt and ____**water**____ and weighs __**50**__ pounds. The solution is __**10 percent**__ salt. Enough ____**water**____ will be added to the solution to lower the salt content of the final solution to __**2 percent**__.

Interpretive Level

1. The original solution contains how many pounds of salt?

0.10(500) pounds,   0.1(50) pounds,
100(50) pounds,   100 pounds

0.1(50) pounds

2. If x is the number of pounds of water to be added, then the final solution will contain

(50 + x) pounds,   (50 − x) pounds,

(50x) pounds, $\dfrac{50}{x}$ pounds

<u>(50 + x) pounds</u>

3. The salt content of the final solution will be

0.02(50 + x) pounds,   0.02(50 − x) pounds,
0.02(x − 50) pounds,   0.02(50) pounds

<u>0.02(50 + x) pounds</u>

CHOOSE THE VARIABLE(S)

Let x = the number of pounds of water to be added.

Sometimes a diagram can help form the equation.

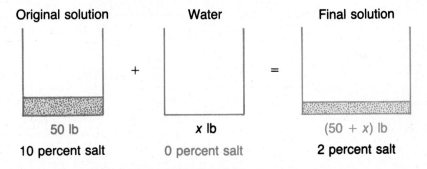

Original solution		Water		Final solution
50 lb	+	x lb	=	(50 + x) lb
10 percent salt		0 percent salt		2 percent salt

A tabular arrangement may help solve the equation.

Kind of solution	Number of pounds	Part (percent) pure salt	Number of pounds pure salt
Original	50 lb	10 percent	0.10(50) lb
Water to be added	x lb	0 percent	0(x) lb
New solution	(50 + x) lb	2 percent	0.02(50 + x) lb

The resulting equation, yielding salt content, will lead to the solution of the problem. Multiplication by 100 will eliminate the decimal. With x being the number of pounds of water added, which of the following is the equation yielding salt content for the problem?

0.10(50) + 0 · x = 0.02(50 + x)
0.10(50) + x = 0.02(50 + x)
0.10(50) + 1 · x = 0.02(50 + x)
None of these

<u>0.10(50) + 0 · x = 0.02(50 + x)</u>

FORM THE EQUATION

0.10(50) + 0 percent x = 0.02(50 + x)

SOLVE THE EQUATION

$0.10(50) + 0 \text{ percent } x = 0.02(50 + x)$

$0.10(50) + 0 = \underline{\dfrac{0.02(50 + x)}{}}$

$10(50) = \underline{\dfrac{2(50 + x)}{}}$

$500 = \underline{\dfrac{100 + 2x}{}}$

$400 = \underline{\dfrac{2x}{}}$

$\underline{\dfrac{200}{}}$ pounds (amount of water to be added) $= x$ **200 pounds**

CHECK THE EQUATION

$0.10(50) + 0 \text{ percent } x = 0.02(50 + x)$

$0.10(50) + 0 = \underline{\dfrac{0.02(50 + 200)}{}}$

$5 + 0 = \underline{\dfrac{0.02(250)}{}}$

$5 = \underline{\dfrac{5}{}}$

ACTIVITY EXTENSION

Write an equation that will yield the water content for the problem.

$$0.90(50) + 1.00x = 0.98(50 + x)$$

MODEL PROBLEM 3

In a vat there are 200 pounds of a solution of blue dye and water that is 15 percent water. How much water must be extracted in order to increase the dye content to 95 percent?

READ THE PROBLEM

After reading the problem, give the answers to the following statements in the spaces provided.

Literal Level

The vat contains __200 pounds__ of a solution of blue dye and water. The water content is __15 percent__. The blue dye content is __85 percent__. In order for the final solution to be __95 percent__ blue dye, __x pounds of water__ are to be extracted.

Interpretive Level

1. The original solution of 200 pounds contains how many pounds of water?

   3 pounds,   30 pounds,   300 pounds,   0.3 pounds

   30 pounds

2. If x is the number of pounds of water extracted, then the final solution contains

$(200 + x)$ pounds, $(x - 200)$ pounds,
$(200 - x)$ pounds, $200x$ pounds

<u>**$(200 - x)$ pounds**</u>

3. The final solution will have an increased content of blue dye represented by

$0.95(200 - x)$ pounds, $0.95(x - 200)$ pounds,
$0.95(200)$ pounds,   none of these

<u>**$0.95(200 - x)$ pounds**</u>

CHOOSE THE VARIABLE(S)

Let x = the number of pounds of water to be extracted.

Sometimes a diagram can help form the equation.

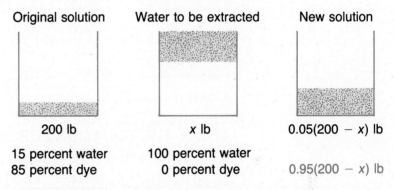

Original solution	Water to be extracted	New solution
200 lb	x lb	$0.05(200 - x)$ lb
15 percent water	100 percent water	
85 percent dye	0 percent dye	$0.95(200 - x)$ lb

A tabular arrangement may help solve the problem.

Kind of solution	Number of pounds	Part (percent) water	Number of pounds of water
Original	200 lb	<u>15 percent</u>	0.15(200) lb
Water to be ex- tracted	<u>x lb</u>	100 percent	1x lb
New solution	<u>200 − x lb</u>	5 percent	0.05(200 − x) lb

FORM THE EQUATION

Which equation below emphasizes blue dye content?

Application Level

$0.85(200) - 0 \cdot x = 0.95(200 - x)$
$0.15(200) - 1 \cdot x = 0.05(200 - x)$

<u>**$0.85(200) - 0 \cdot x = 0.95(200 - x)$**</u>

Is the other equation correct for determining water content?   **Yes**

SOLVE THE EQUATION FOR BLUE DYE

$$0.85(200) - 0 = 0.95(200 - x)$$

$$85(200) = 95(200 - x)$$

$$\underline{17{,}000} = 19{,}000 - 95x$$

$$-2{,}000 = \underline{-95x}$$

$$\underline{21.05} \cong x$$

$21\dfrac{1}{19}$ pounds (amount of water to be extracted) = x $21\dfrac{1}{19}$ **pounds**

CHECK THE EQUATION

$$0.85(200) - 0 = 0.95(200 - x)$$

$$85(200) = 95\left(200 - 21\dfrac{1}{19}\right)$$

$$85(200) = 19{,}000 - \left(\dfrac{400}{19} \cdot 95\right)$$

$$\underline{17{,}000} = 19{,}000 - 2{,}000$$

$$17{,}000 = \underline{17{,}000}$$

SOLVE THE EQUATION FOR WATER

$$0.15(200) - 1 \cdot x = 0.05(200 - x)$$

$$15(200) - 100x = \underline{5(200 - x)}$$

$$3{,}000 - 100x = \underline{1{,}000 - 5x}$$

$$-95x = \underline{-2{,}000}$$

$$x \cong \underline{21.05} \text{ pounds}$$

$x = 21\dfrac{1}{19}$ pounds (amount of water to be extracted) $21\dfrac{1}{19}$ **pounds**

CHECK THE EQUATION

$$0.15(200) - 1 \cdot x = 0.05(200 - x)$$

$$15(200) - 100\left(21\dfrac{1}{19}\right) = 5\left(200 - 21\dfrac{1}{19}\right)$$

$$15(200) - \left(100 \cdot \dfrac{400}{19}\right) = 5\left(200 - \dfrac{400}{19}\right)$$

$$3{,}000 - \dfrac{40{,}000}{19} = 1{,}000 - \dfrac{2{,}000}{19}$$

$$57{,}000 - 40{,}000 = \underline{19{,}000 - 2{,}000}$$

$$17{,}000 = \underline{17{,}000}$$

Name _____ Period _____

Teacher _____ Date _____ Grade _____

Solutions Problems with Help

DIRECTIONS: Each of the following problems has been given a partial solution. Solve each problem by completing the given solution.

1. How much camphor must be added to a pound of crystalline compound that is 90 percent camphor to make a new compound that is 98 percent camphor?

Let x = the number of pounds of camphor to be added.

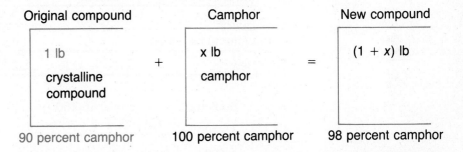

Kind of solution	Amount	Percent camphor	Number of pounds of camphor
Original	1 lb	90 percent	0.90(1) lb
Camphor to be added	x lb	100 percent	1.00(x) lb
New	(1 + x) lb	98 percent	0.98(1 + x) lb

$$0.90(1) + x = \underline{0.98(1 + x)}$$
$$\underline{90 + 100x = 98(1 + x)}$$

$$90 + 100x = 98 + 98x$$
$$2x = \underline{8}$$
$$x = \underline{4} \text{ pounds (amount of camphor to be added)}$$

4 pounds

Check: $0.90(1) + x = 0.98(1 + x)$

$0.90(1) + 4 = \underline{0.98(1 + 4)}$

$90(1) + 400 = \underline{98(5)}$

$90 + 400 = \underline{490}$

$490 = \underline{490}$

2. Tuna is sometimes packed in a brine (salt) solution. How many pounds of water must be added to 100 pounds of a 15 percent solution of salt and water to reduce it to a 10 percent solution of salt?

Let x = the number of pounds of water to be added.

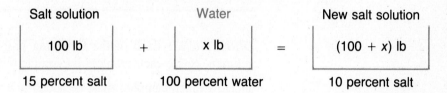

Kind of solution	Amount of solution	Percent salt	Number of pounds of salt
Original	100 lb	15 percent	0.15x lb
Water to be added	x lb	0 percent	0 · x lb
New	(100 + x) lb	10 percent	0.10(100 + x) lb

$$0.15(100) + 0 \cdot x = 0.10(100 + x)$$
$$15(100) = \underline{10(100 + x)}$$
$$1{,}500 = 1{,}000 + 10x$$
$$500 = \underline{10x}$$
$$\underline{50} \text{ pounds (amount of water to be added)} = x \qquad \underline{50 \text{ pounds}}$$

Check: $0.15(100) + 0 \cdot x = \underline{0.10(100 + x)}$
$$15(100) + 0 \cdot 50 = \underline{10(100 + 50)}$$
$$1{,}500 + 0 = \underline{10(150)}$$
$$1{,}500 = \underline{1{,}500}$$

3. How many quarts of solvent containing 50 percent acetone must be added to 20 quarts of solvent containing 4 percent acetone to produce a mixture containing 20 percent acetone?

Let x = the number of quarts of solvent containing 50 percent acetone to be added.

Original solvent   Solvent   New solvent

20 qt   +   x qt   =   (20 + x) qt

4 percent   50 percent   20 percent
acetone   acetone   acetone

Kind of solution	Quarts of solvent	Percent acetone	Quarts of acetone
Original solvent	20 qt	4 percent	0.04(20) qt
Solvent to be added	x qt	50 percent	0.50(x) qt
New solvent	(20 + x) qt	20 percent	0.20(20 + x) qt

$0.04(20) + 0.50x = 0.20(20 + x)$

$4(20) + 50x = 20(20 + x)$

$80 + 50x = 400 + 20x$

$30\,x = 320$

$x = \dfrac{10\frac{2}{3}}{}$ quarts (amount of 50 percent acetone-containing solvent to be added) $x \cong 10.67$

$$10\frac{2}{3} \text{ quarts}$$

Since $10\frac{2}{3} \neq 10.67$, these results are expected.

Check: (using decimal)

$0.04(20) + 0.50x = 0.20(20 + x)$

$4(20) + 50(10.67) = 20(20 + 10.67)$

$80 + 533.50 = 400 + 213.40$

$613.50 \neq 613.40$

Check: (using fraction)

$0.04(20) + 0.50x = 0.20(20 + x)$

$4(20) + 50x = 20\left(20 + \dfrac{32}{3}\right)$

$80 + 50\left(\dfrac{32}{3}\right) = 400 + \dfrac{640}{3}$

$80 + \dfrac{1{,}600}{3} = 400 + \dfrac{640}{3}$

$240 + 1{,}600 = 1{,}200 + 640$

$1{,}840 = 1{,}840$

4. If the radiator of an automobile contains 5 quarts of a solution of alcohol and water (10 percent alcohol), how much alcohol must be added to produce a 25 percent alcohol solution?

Let x = the number of quarts of alcohol to be added.

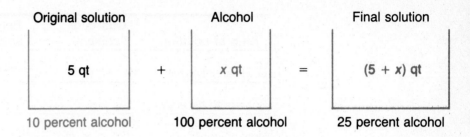

Kind of solution	Amount of solution	Percent alcohol	Quarts of alcohol
Original	5 qt	<u>10 percent</u>	0.10(5) qt
Alcohol to be added	x qt	100 percent	<u>1.00(x) qt</u>
Final	<u>(5 + x) qt</u>	25 percent	0.25(5 + x) qt

$$0.10(5) + 1 \cdot x = \underline{0.25(5 + x)}$$
$$10(5) + 100x = \underline{25(5 + x)}$$
$$50 + 100x = \underline{125 + 25x}$$
$$75x = \underline{75}$$
$$x = \underline{1} \text{ quart (amount of alcohol to be added)} \quad \underline{1 \text{ quart}}$$

Check:
$$0.10(5) + 1 \cdot x = \underline{0.25(5 + x)}$$
$$10(5) + 100x = \underline{25(5 + x)}$$
$$50 + 100 \cdot 1 = \underline{25(5 + 1)}$$
$$50 + 100 = \underline{25(6)}$$
$$150 = \underline{150}$$

5. A chemist has one solution that is 40 percent pure glycoside and another solution that is 80 percent pure glycoside. How many pounds of each solution must be used to produce 100 pounds of a solution that is 60 percent glycoside?

Let n = the number of pounds of solution that is 40 percent glycoside.

Let $100 - n$ = the number of pounds of solution that is 80 percent glycoside.

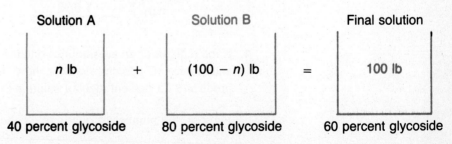

Kind of solution	Amount of solution	% Glycoside	Pounds of glycoside
Solution A	n lb	40%	0.40(n) lb
Solution B	(100 − n) lb	80%	0.80(100 − n) lb
Final solution	100 lb	60%	0.60(100) lb

$$0.40n + 0.80(100 - n) = \underline{0.60(100)}$$
$$40n + 80(100 - n) = \underline{60(100)}$$
$$40n + 8,000 - 80n = \underline{6,000}$$
$$-40n = \underline{-2,000}$$
$$n = \underline{50} \text{ pounds (amount of glycoside solution)}$$
$$100 - n = \underline{50} \text{ pounds (amount of 80 percent glycoside solution)}$$

50 pounds of each

Check: $\underline{0.40n + 0.80(100 - n) = 0.60(100)}$

$$\frac{40n + 80(100 - n)}{} = 60(100)$$
$$40 \cdot 50 + 80(100 - 50) = 60(100)$$
$$2,000 + 80(50) = 6,000$$
$$2,000 + 4,000 = 6,000$$
$$\underline{6,000} = 6,000$$

6. Three ounces of merthiolate solution containing 50 percent alcohol lose $\frac{1}{8}$ ounce of alcohol by evaporation. What percent of the remaining solution is alcohol?

Let x = the part of the final solution that is alcohol (percent).

Original solution		Alcohol		Final solution
3 oz	−	$\frac{1}{8}$ oz	=	$\left(3 - \frac{1}{8}\right)$ oz
50 percent alcohol		? percent alcohol		? percent alcohol

Kind of solution	Amount of solution	% Alcohol	Ounces of alcohol
Original solution	3 oz	50 percent	0.50(3) oz
Alcohol lost	$\frac{1}{8}$ oz	100 percent	$1.00\left(\frac{1}{8}\right)$ oz
Final solution	$\left(3 - \frac{1}{8}\right)$ oz	x percent	$x\% \left(3 - \frac{1}{8}\right)$ oz

$$0.50(3) - \frac{1}{8} = x\left(3 - \frac{1}{8}\right)$$

$$1.5 - 0.125 = \underline{2\frac{7}{8}x}$$

$$1.375 = \frac{23}{8}x$$

$$1\frac{3}{8} = \frac{23}{8}x$$

$$\frac{11}{8} = \frac{23}{8}x$$

$$11 = \underline{23x}$$

$$\underline{\frac{11}{23}} = x \text{ (part of final solution that is alcohol)}$$

$$\frac{11}{23} \cong \underline{47.8 \text{ percent}} \text{ (part of final solution that is alcohol)}$$

$$\underline{47.8 \text{ percent}}$$

Check: (using decimal)

$$0.50(3) - \frac{1}{8} = x\left(3 - \frac{1}{8}\right)$$

$$1.5 - 0.125 = \underline{0.478(2.875)}$$

$$\underline{1.375} \neq 1.37425$$

Check: (using fraction)

$$0.50(3) - \frac{1}{8} = x\left(3 - \frac{1}{8}\right)$$

$$\frac{3}{2} - \frac{1}{8} = \underline{2\frac{7}{8}x}$$

$$\frac{3}{2} - \frac{1}{8} = \frac{23}{8} \cdot \frac{11}{23}$$

$$\frac{12}{8} - \frac{1}{8} = \underline{\frac{11}{8}}$$

$$\frac{11}{8} = \underline{\frac{11}{8}}$$

Since $\frac{11}{23} \neq .478$, these results are expected.

Challenge

7. Shortly before a violent windstorm, public emergency officials were summoned to a plant that had 1,000 gallons of muriatic acid stored in a temporary tank. In anticipation of tank breakage, evacuation took place. The officials knew the storm was to hit in 70 minutes. If the muriatic acid could be pumped into a large sturdy tank at the rate of 50.5 gallons

per minute and at the same time water could be combined with it at a rate of 5,000 gallons per minute, in how many minutes would the solution be reduced to 1 percent muriatic acid? Was there enough time?

Point out that 50.5 gallons per minute times 20 (minutes) are equal to 1,010 gallons.

Let x = the number of minutes.

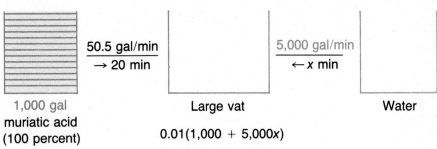

1,000 gal
muriatic acid
(100 percent)

Large vat

$0.01(1,000 + 5,000x)$

Water

Point out that 50.5 gallons per minute times 19.8 (minutes) are equal to 999.9 gallons.

$$1,000 = 0.01\,(1,000 + 5,000x)$$
$$1,000 = \underline{\quad 10 + 50x \quad}$$
$$990 = \underline{\quad 50x \quad}$$
$$\underline{\textbf{19.8 minutes}} = x \cong 20 \text{ minutes} \qquad\qquad \underline{\textbf{19.8 minutes; Yes}}$$

Check: $1,000 = 0.01(1,000 + 5,000x)$
$$1,000 = 0.01\,[1,000 + 5,000(19.8)]$$
$$1,000 = \underline{\quad \textbf{0.01 [1,000 + 99,000]} \quad}$$
$$1,000 = \underline{\quad \textbf{0.01(100,000)} \quad}$$
$$1,000 = \underline{\quad \textbf{1,000} \quad}$$

Name _____ Period _____

Teacher _____ Date _____ Grade _____

Solutions Problems

DIRECTIONS: Use the five levels of comprehension to solve each of the problems in the space provided. Write your answers in the blank to the right after each problem.

1. A plastics manufacturer has vinegar testing 28 percent acetic acid and vinegar testing 20 percent acetic acid. How many quarts of each must he use to produce 100 quarts of vinegar testing 25 percent acetic acid?

   Let n = the number of quarts of vinegar testing 28 percent acetic acid.

   Original A   Original B   Final mixture

   n qt   + $(100 - n)$qt   =   100 qt

   28 percent acetic acid   20 percent acetic acid   25 percent acetic acid

Kind of solution	Amount (quarts)	Percent acetic acid	Acetic acid (quarts)
Original A	n qt	28 percent	$0.28n$ qt
Original B	$100 - n$ qt	20 percent	$0.20(100 - n)$ qt
Final mixture	100 qt	25 percent	$0.25(100)$ qt

   $0.28n + 0.20(100 - n) = 0.25(100)$

   $28n + 20(100 - n) = 25(100)$

   $28n + 2{,}000 - 20n = 2{,}500$

   $8n = 500$

   $n = 62\frac{1}{2}$ or 62.5 quarts (amount testing 28 percent acetic acid)

   $100 - n = 37\frac{1}{2}$ or 37.5 quarts (amount testing 20 percent acetic acid)

   Original A: **62.5 quarts**
   Original B: **37.5 quarts**

Check: (using decimal)

$$0.28n + 0.20(100 - n) = 0.25(100)$$
$$28n + 20(100 - n) = 25(100)$$
$$28(62.5) + 20(100 - 62.5) = 25(100)$$
$$1,750 + 20(37.5) = 2,500$$
$$1,750 + 750 = 2,500$$
$$2,500 = 2,500$$

Since $62\frac{1}{2} = 62.5$, these results are expected.

Check: (using mixed number)

$$0.28n + 0.20(100 - n) = 0.25(100)$$
$$28n + 20(100 - n) = 25(100)$$
$$28\left(62\frac{1}{2}\right) + 20\left(100 - 62\frac{1}{2}\right) = 25(100)$$
$$28\left(\frac{125}{2}\right) + 20\left(\frac{75}{2}\right) = 2,500$$
$$\frac{3,500}{2} + \frac{1,500}{2} = 2,500$$
$$3,500 + 1,500 = 5,000$$
$$5,000 = 5,000$$

2. How many pounds of a solution that is 75 percent pure chemical insecticide must be mixed with 16 pounds of a solution that is 25 percent pure chemical insecticide to produce a solution that reflects 30 percent pure chemical insecticide?

Let x = the number of pounds of Solution 1.

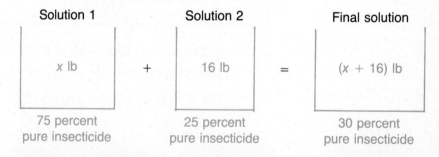

Kind of solution	Amount (pounds)	Percent pure insecticide	Insecticide (pounds)
Solution 1	x lb	75 percent	$0.75x$ lb
Solution 2	16 lb	25 percent	0.25(16) lb
Final solution	$x + 16$ lb	30 percent	$0.30(x + 16)$ lb

$$0.75x + 0.25(16) = 0.30(x + 16)$$

$$75x + 25(16) = 30(x + 16)$$

$$75x + 400 = 30x + 480$$

$$45x = 80$$

$$x = 1\frac{7}{9} \text{ pounds (Solution 1)}$$

$$x \cong 1.78 \text{ pounds (Solution 1)}$$

$1\frac{7}{9}$ pounds; 1.78 pounds

Since $1\frac{7}{9} \neq 1.78$, these results are expected.

Check: (using decimal)

$$0.75x + 0.25(16) = 0.30(x + 16)$$

$$75x + 25(16) = 30(x + 16)$$

$$75(1.78) + 400 = 30(1.78 + 16)$$

$$133.5 + 400 = 30(17.78)$$

$$533.5 \neq 533.40$$

Check: (using mixed number)

$$0.75x + 0.25(16) = 0.30(x + 16)$$

$$75x + 25(16) = 30(x + 16)$$

$$75\left(\frac{16}{9}\right) + 25(16) = 30\left(\frac{16}{9} + 16\right)$$

$$\frac{1,200}{9} + 400 = \frac{480}{9} + 480$$

$$1,200 + 3,600 = 480 + 4,320$$

$$4,800 = 4,800$$

3. A solution of turpentine and alcohol contains 15 ounces of turpentine and 45 ounces of alcohol. How much pure turpentine must be added to produce a solution that is 75 percent turpentine?

Let x = the number of ounces of pure turpentine to be added.

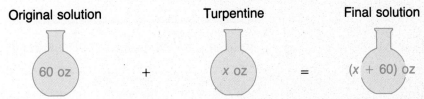

Original solution   Turpentine   Final solution

60 oz   +   x oz   =   (x + 60) oz

$\frac{15}{60} = \frac{1}{4}$ = 25 percent turpentine   100 percent turpentine   75 percent turpentine

$\frac{45}{60} = \frac{3}{4}$ = 75 percent alcohol

Kind of solution	Amount (ounces)	Percent turpentine	Turpentine content (ounces)
Original solution	60 oz	25 percent	0.25(60) oz
Turpentine	x oz	100 percent	1 · x oz
Final solution	60 + x oz	75 percent	0.75(60 + x) oz

$0.25(60) + 1 \cdot x = .75(60 + x)$

$15 + x = 45 + .75x$

$.25x = 30$

$x = 120$ 120 ounces

Check: $0.25(60) + 1 \cdot x = 0.75(60 + x)$

$\frac{1}{4}(60) + 120 = 0.75(60 + 120)$

$15 + 120 = 0.75(180)$

$135 = 135$

4. A solution contains 48 quarts of acetic acid and 32 quarts of water. How many quarts of water must be evaporated to produce a solution that is 80 percent acetic acid?

Let x = the number of quarts of water to be evaporated.

Original solution   Water   Final solution

80 qt   −   x qt   =   (80 − x) qt

60 percent acetic acid   100 percent water   80 percent acetic acid
40 percent water

Kind of solution	Amount (quarts)	Percent acetic acid	Acetic acid content (quarts)
Original solution	80 qt	60 percent	0.60(80) qt
Water	x qt	0 percent	0 qt
Final solution	(80 − x) qt	80 percent	0.80(80 − x) qt

$0.60(80) - 0 \cdot x = 0.80(80 - x)$

$60(80) = 80(80 - x)$

$4{,}800 = 6{,}400 - 80x$

$-1{,}600 = -80x$

20 quarts (amount of water to be evaporated) $= x$

20 quarts

Check: $0.60(80) - 0 \cdot x = 0.80(80 - x)$

$0.60(80) = 0.80(80 - x)$

$0.60(80) = 0.80(80 - 20)$

$0.60(80) = 0.80(60)$

$48 = 48$

5. Ninety pounds of an analgesic contain 15 percent salicylic acid. How much pure salicylic acid must be added to make a compound that is 85 percent salicylic acid?

Let $x =$ the number of pounds of salicylic acid to be added.

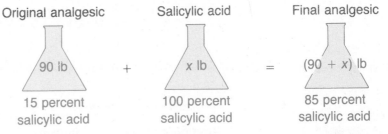

Kind of solution	Amount (pounds)	Percent salicylic acid	Salicylic acid content (pounds)
Original analgesic	90 lb	15 percent	0.15(90) lb
Salicylic acid	x lb	100 percent	1 · x lb
Final analgesic	90 + x lb	85 percent	0.85(90 + x) lb

$0.15(90) + 1 \cdot x = 0.85(90 + x)$

$15(90) + 100x = 85(90 + x)$

$1{,}350 + 100x = 7{,}650 + 85x$

$15x = 6{,}300$

$x = 420$ pounds (amount of salicylic acid to be added)

420 pounds

Check: $0.15(90) + 1 \cdot x = 0.85(90 + x)$

$13.5 + 420 = 0.85(90 + 420)$

$433.5 = 0.85(510)$

$433.5 = 433.5$

An excellent math student could penetrate this problem by seeing that three ounces of cream added to two ounces of cream would be five ounces of cream in a ten-ounce formula!

6. A hair stylist used four ounces of peroxide, two ounces of cream bleach, and one ounce of powder bleach as a formula for seven ounces of bleach. How many ounces of cream bleach must be added to obtain a formula that tests 50 percent cream?

Let x = the number of ounces of cream to be added.

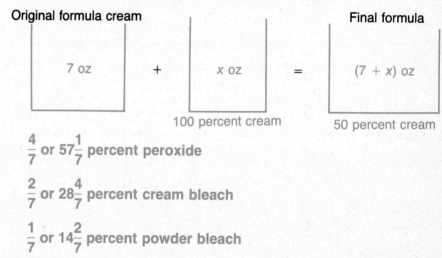

Original formula cream

7 oz   + x oz   = $(7 + x)$ oz

100 percent cream   50 percent cream

Final formula

$\frac{4}{7}$ or $57\frac{1}{7}$ percent peroxide

$\frac{2}{7}$ or $28\frac{4}{7}$ percent cream bleach

$\frac{1}{7}$ or $14\frac{2}{7}$ percent powder bleach

Kind of formula	Amount (ounces)	Percent cream	Cream content (ounces)
Original formula	7 oz	$28\frac{4}{7}$ percent	$0.28\frac{4}{7}(7)$ oz
Cream	x oz	100 percent	$1 \cdot x$ oz
Final formula	$7 + x$ oz	50 percent	$0.50(7 + x)$ oz

$0.28\frac{4}{7}(7) + 1 \cdot x = 0.50(7 + x)$

$28\frac{4}{7}(7) + 100x = 50(7 + x)$

$\frac{200}{7}(7) + 100x = 350 + 50x$

$200 + 100x = 350 + 50x$

$50x = 150$

$x = 3$ ounces (amount of cream to be added)   <u>3 ounces</u>

Check: $0.28\frac{4}{7}(7) + 1 \cdot x = 0.50(7 + x)$

$0.28\frac{4}{7}(7) + 1 \cdot 3 = 0.50(7 + x)$

$\frac{2.0}{7}(7) + 1 \cdot 3 = 0.50(7 + 3)$

$2 + 3 = 0.50(10)$

$5 = 5$

Challenge

7. Use of chlorine was suspended at a water treatment center and a test of chlorine dioxide ordered after a 1,900 gallon tank of chlorine developed a bulge. Chlorine dioxide contains about 10% chlorine and the rest is water. How many gallons of water should be combined with 1,900 gallons of chlorine to make chlorine dioxide testing 10% chlorine?

Let x = the number of gallons of water to be combined with 1,900 gallons of chlorine.

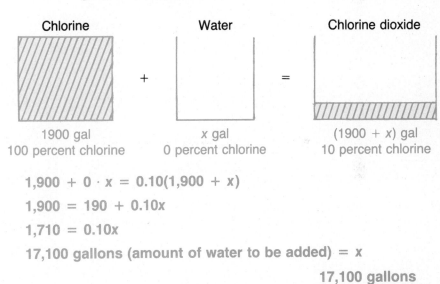

Chlorine	Water	Chlorine dioxide
1900 gal	x gal	$(1900 + x)$ gal
100 percent chlorine	0 percent chlorine	10 percent chlorine

$1{,}900 + 0 \cdot x = 0.10(1{,}900 + x)$

$1{,}900 = 190 + 0.10x$

$1{,}710 = 0.10x$

17,100 gallons (amount of water to be added) $= x$

                                                                                          17,100 gallons

Check: $1{,}900 + 0 \cdot x = 0.10(1{,}900 + x)$

$1{,}900 + 0 = 0.10(1{,}900 + 17{,}100)$

$1{,}900 = 0.10(19{,}000)$

$1{,}900 = 1{,}900$

STUDY GUIDE 13

Geometry

TERMS AND CONCEPTS

Introductory Precepts

Emphasize that the trian-
gle is the most important
plane figure.

A *triangle* is a geometric figure formed by three segments joining three points not on a line. Each of the three points is a *vertex* of the triangle. The vertices of the triangle identified as $\triangle ABC$ are A, B, and C. The angles of $\triangle ABC$ are $\angle A$, $\angle B$, and $\angle C$.

Complementary angles are two angles, the sum of whose measures is 90°.

Supplementary angles are two angles, the sum of whose measures is 180°.

In any triangle, the sum of the measures of the three angles is 180°. The sides of $\triangle ABC$ are $\overline{AB}$, $\overline{BC}$, and $\overline{AC}$. The sum of the lengths of the three sides of any triangle is the *perimeter*.

The four common triangles and the number of equal sides and equal angles in each are listed in the following chart:

Type of triangle	Sides	Angles
Equilateral	Three equal sides	Three equal angles
Isosceles	At least two equal sides	At least two equal angles
Scalene	No equal sides	No equal angles
Right	Two or no two equal sides	Two or no two equal angles (one of the three angles must be 90°)

The *vertex angle* of an isosceles triangle is formed by the two sides of equal length. The longest side of a right triangle lies opposite the 90° angle and is called the *hypotenuse*. The *Pythagorean Theorem* states that in a right triangle, the square of the hypotenuse is equal to the sum of the squares of the other two sides ($a^2 + b^2 = c^2$).

Classification of quadrila-
terals is an appropriate
topic if time permits.

A *quadrilateral* is a geometric figure formed by four segments joining four points. A *rectangle* has four sides and four right angles. The opposite sides are equal in length. A *square* is a rectangle with four right angles and all sides equal in length. Other geometric figures include a pentagon (five sides), hexagon (six sides), and octagon (eight sides). A figure is *regular* if all sides are equal and all angles are equal. The equilateral triangle, the square, the pentagon, the hexagon, and the octagon are examples of regular figures.

A *perimeter* is the distance around a geometric figure. To find the perimeter of any figure, find the sum of the lengths of its sides. *Area* is the number of square units contained by the figure. Make sure that all measures are in the same unit.

LEVELS OF COMPREHENSION

STEP 1   Read the problem.

STEP 2   Choose the variable(s).

STEP 3   Form the equation.

STEP 4   Solve the equation.

STEP 5   Check the equation.

MODEL PROBLEM 1

Two angles are complementary. One angle is twice as large as the other. Find the number of degrees in each angle.

READ THE PROBLEM

After reading the problem, give the answers to the following statements in the spaces provided.

Literal Level

One angle is ___two___ times as large as the other. The sum of their measures is ___90°___ .

Interpretive Level

1. The angles could be represented by

x and $2x$, $\frac{1}{2}x$ and x, $5x$ and $10x$,   any of these

Any of these

2. The simplest representation of the two angles is

x and $2x$, $\frac{1}{2}x$ and x, $5x$ and $10x$,   none of these

<u> $x + 2x$ </u>

3. The sum of the measures of the two angles is

180,   90,   60,   30

<u>   90   </u>

CHOOSE THE VARIABLE(S)

Sometimes a diagram can help form the equation.

Let $x =$ the number of degrees in one angle.
Then $2x =$ the number of degrees in its complement.

Application Level

FORM THE EQUATION

$x + 2x = 90$

SOLVE THE EQUATION

$x + 2x = 90$

<u> 3x </u> $= 90$

$x = $ <u> 30° </u> (one angle)

$2x = $ <u> 60 </u> (its complement)

One angle: 30°
Its complement: 60°

CHECK THE EQUATION

$x + 2x = 90$

$30 + 2$ <u> (30) </u> $= 90$

$30 + $ <u> 60 </u> $= 90$

<u> 90 </u> $= 90$

ACTIVITY EXTENSION

Suppose two angles are supplementary with one angle twice the other angle.

1. What equation would lead to the solution? <u> $x + 2x = 180$ </u>

2. What would the number of degrees be for each
of the two angles?

$x + 2x = 180$

<u> 3x </u> $= 180$

$x = $ <u> 60 </u> (number of degrees in one angle)

$2x = 120$ (number of degrees in supplement)

One angle: 60°
Its supplement: 120°

MODEL PROBLEM 2

One angle of a triangle is 8° more than the second angle. The third angle is 68° less than the second angle. Find the number of degrees in each angle.

READ THE PROBLEM

After reading the problem, give the answers to the following statements in the spaces provided.

Literal Level

The first angle is ___8°___ more than the second angle. The third angle is ___68° less than___ the second angle. The sum of the measures of all three angles is ___180°___.

CHOOSE THE VARIABLE(S)

Interpretive Level

Sometimes a diagram can help form the equation.

Let n = the measure of the second angle (in degrees). Then $n + 8$ = the measure of the first angle (in degrees), and ___$n - 68$___ = the measure of the third angle (in degrees).

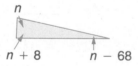

$$n$$
$$n + 8 \qquad n - 68$$

FORM THE EQUATION

Application Level

$$n + (n + 8) + (n - 68) = 180$$

SOLVE THE EQUATION

$$n + (n + 8) + (n - 68) = 180$$
$$\underline{3n - 60} = 180$$
$$\underline{3n} = 240$$
$$n = \underline{80°} \quad \text{(the measure of the second angle)}$$
$$n + 8 = \underline{88°} \quad \text{(the measure of the first angle)}$$
$$n - 68 = 12° \quad \text{(the measure of the third angle)}$$

Second angle: **80°**
First angle: **88°**
Third angle: **12°**

CHECK THE EQUATION

$n + (n + 8) + (n - 68) = 180$

$80 + (80 + 8) + (80 - 68) = 180$

$80 + 88 + \underline{\quad 12 \quad} = 180$

$180 = 180$

MODEL PROBLEM 3

If the perimeter of an equilateral triangle is 24 inches, find the length of a side of the triangle.

READ THE PROBLEM

After reading the problem, give the answers to the following statements in the spaces provided.

The triangle has three sides of the same ___**length**___. Its perimeter is ___**24 inches**___.

1. An arithmetic solution to this problem is

   possible,   impossible   **Possible**

2. The perimeter divided by three should equal

   the length of each side,   1, $\frac{1}{3}$,   none of these

                                                 The length of each side

CHOOSE THE VARIABLE(S)

Let s = the length of each side (in inches).

FORM THE EQUATION

$s + s + s = 24$

SOLVE THE EQUATION

$\underline{s + s + s} = 24$

$\underline{3s} = 24$

$s = 8$ inches (length of each side)

                                                        8 inches

CHECK THE EQUATION

$s + s + s = 24$

$8 + 8 + 8 = \underline{\quad 24 \quad}$

$24 = 24$

ACTIVITY EXTENSION

1. Is an equilateral triangle also isosceles?   <u>Yes</u>

2. Is an isosceles triangle also equilateral?   <u>No</u>

MODEL PROBLEM 4

Find the hypotenuse of a right triangle if the other two sides are six inches and eight inches.

READ THE PROBLEM

After reading the problem, give the answers to the following statements in the spaces provided.

Literal Level

A right triangle must have one angle of <u>90°</u>. The <u>hypotenuse</u> lies opposite the angle of 90°. The Pythagorean Theorem states that the square of the hypotenuse is equal to the <u>sum</u> of the squares of the other two sides.

CHOOSE THE VARIABLE(S)

Interpretive Level

Sometimes a diagram can help form the equation.

Let c = the length of the hypotenuse (in inches).

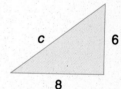

FORM THE EQUATION

Application Level

$c^2 = 6^2 + 8^2$

SOLVE THE EQUATION

$c^2 = 6^2 + 8^2$

$c^2 = \underline{\quad 36 \quad} + \underline{\quad 64 \quad}$

$c^2 = \underline{\quad 100 \quad}$

$c = \underline{\quad 10 \quad}$ inches (length of hypotenuse)   <u>10 inches</u>

The right triangle is basic to the study of trigonometry.

CHECK THE EQUATION

$c^2 = 6^2 + 8^2$

$10^2 = 36 + 64$

$\underline{100} = 36 + 64$

$\underline{100} = 100$

MODEL PROBLEM 5

The perimeter of a regular hexagon is 168 inches. Find the length of each side.

READ THE PROBLEM

After reading the problem, give the answers to the following statements in the spaces provided.

Literal Level

A hexagon has __six__ sides. If a hexagon is regular, __all or six__ sides are equal. The perimeter of a figure is the __sum__ of its sides.

CHOOSE THE VARIABLE(S)

Sometimes a diagram can help form the equation.

Interpretive Level

Let s = the length of each side of a hexagon (in inches).

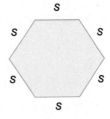

FORM THE EQUATION

Application Level

$s + s + s + s + s + s = \underline{168}$

SOLVE THE EQUATION

$s + s + s + s + s + s = 168$

$\underline{6s} = 168$

$s = \underline{28}$ inches (length of each side)

__28 inches__

CHECK THE EQUATION

$s + s + s + s + s + s = 168$

$28 + 28 + \underline{\hspace{0.3em}28\hspace{0.3em}} + 28 + 28 + 28 = 168$

$168 = \underline{\hspace{0.3em}168\hspace{0.3em}}$

MODEL PROBLEM 6

The perimeter of a rectangle is 72 feet. The length is 6 more than four times the width. Find the dimensions of the rectangle.

READ THE PROBLEM

After reading the problem, give the answers to the following statements in the spaces provided.

Literal Level

The perimeter of the rectangle is __72 feet__. The length is __6__ more than four times the __width__. The dimensions to be found are __length__ and width.

Interpretive Level

1. The length is longer than the

   perimeter,   width   __width__

2. The length is 6 more than four times the width. If w represents the width, then the length is represented by

   $4w + 6$, $6w + 4$, $6(4)$,   none of these   __$4w + 6$__

3. The sum of the four sides of the rectangle equals

   72,   27,   18,   none of these   __72__

CHOOSE THE VARIABLE(S)

Sometimes a diagram can help form the equation.

Let w = the width of the rectangle (in inches). Then $4w + 6$ = the length of the rectangle (in inches).

$$4w + 6$$

w [rectangle] w

$$4w + 6$$

FORM THE EQUATION

$w + (4w + 6) + w + (4w + 6) = \underline{\hspace{0.3em}72\hspace{0.3em}}$

SOLVE THE EQUATION

$w + (4w + 6) + w + (4w + 6) = 72$

$\underline{\quad 10w + 12 \quad} = 72$

$10w = 60$

$w = \underline{\quad 6 \quad}$ inches (width)

$4w + 6 = \underline{\quad 30 \quad}$ inches (length)

Width: **6 inches**

Length: **30 inches**

CHECK THE EQUATION

$w + (4w + 6) + w + (4w + 6) = 72$

$6 + (4 \cdot \underline{\quad 6 \quad} + 6) + 6 + (4 \cdot \underline{\quad 6 \quad} + 6) = 72$

$6 + (\underline{\quad 24 \quad} + 6) + 6 + (\underline{\quad 24 \quad} + 6) = 72$

$6 + \underline{\quad 30 \quad} + 6 + \underline{\quad 30 \quad} = 72$

$\underline{\quad 72 \quad} = 72$

ACTIVITY EXTENSION

1. Could you have arrived at the same solution set if you had used $w + (4w + 6) = 36$?

   Yes

   Why?   **Width + length = $\frac{1}{2}$ perimeter**

2. Could you have arrived at the same solution set if you had used $2w + 2(4w + 6) = 72$?

   Yes

   Why?   **2(length) + 2(width) = perimeter**

3. Could you have solved Model Problem 6 by using two equations and two variables?

   Yes

   Would the following two variables and equations lead to the solution?

   Let w = width (in inches) and n = length (in inches). Then,

   1. $n = 4w + 6$

   2. $\underline{2n + 2w = 72}$

      $n - 4w = 6$

      $\underline{2n + 2w = 72}$

      $n - 4w = 6$

      $\underline{+4n + 4w = 144}$

$$\underline{\dfrac{5n}{}} = 150$$

$n = 30$ inches (length)

$30 = 4w + 6$

$24 = \underline{\dfrac{4w}{}}$

6 inches (width) $= w$ ⟶ **Yes**

MODEL PROBLEM 7

The length of a rectangle exceeds the width by eight inches. If the length is increased by six inches and the width is decreased by one, then the area of the new rectangle formed is 36 square inches more than the area of the original rectangle. Find the dimensions of the original rectangle.

READ THE PROBLEM

After reading the problem, give the answers to the following statements in the spaces provided.

Literal Level

The length of the original rectangle is __8__ more than its width. To form a new rectangle, the length is increased by six and the width is decreased by __1__. The area of the new rectangle is then __36__ square inches more than the area of the original rectangle.

Interpretive Level

1. If w = width of original rectangle, then its length is represented by

   $8w,\quad \dfrac{8}{w},\quad w + 8,\quad$ none of these   __$w + 8$__

2. In the new rectangle, the width will be represented by

   $w + 1,\quad w - 1,\quad 1 - w,\quad$ none of these

   __$w - 1$__

3. In the new rectangle, the length will be represented by

   $(w + 8 + 6),\quad 14w,\quad w + 48,\quad$ none of these

   __$(w + 8 + 6)$__

4. The area of the new rectangle will be represented by

   $(w - 1)(w + 8 + 6),\quad (w + 14)w,\quad (1 - w)(w + 14),$
   none of these

   __$(w - 1)(w + 8 + 6)$__

5. The area of the original rectangle will be represented by

$w(8w)$, $(w + 8 + w)8$, $w(w + 8)$,   none of these

<u> $w(w + 8)$ </u>

CHOOSE THE VARIABLE(S)

Sometimes a diagram can help form the equation.

Let w = the width of the original rectangle (in inches). Then $w + 8$ = the length of the original rectangle (in inches), <u> $w - 1$ </u> = the width of the new rectangle (in inches), and $w + 8 + 6$ = the length of the new rectangle (in inches).

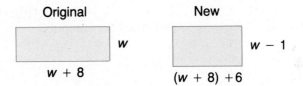

Original   New

w $w - 1$

$w + 8$ $(w + 8) + 6$

FORM THE EQUATION

Application Level

$w(w + 8) = (w - 1)(w + 14) - 36$

SOLVE THE EQUATION

The student can find the product $(w - 1) \cdot (w + 14)$ by the distributive property.

$w(w + 8) = (w - 1)(w + 14) - 36$

$w^2 + 8w = w^2 + 13w - 14 - 36$

<u>$8w = 13w - 50$</u>

$-5w = -50$

$w = $ <u> 10 </u> inches (width of the original rectangle)

$w + 8 = $ <u> 18 </u> inches (length of the original rectangle)

$w - 1 = $ <u> 9 </u> inches (width of the new rectangle)

$w + 14 = $ <u> 24 </u> inches (length of the new rectangle)

Width: **10 inches**
Length: **18 inches**

CHECK THE EQUATION

$w(w + 8) = (w - 1)(w + 14) - 36$

$10(10 + 8) = $ <u> $(10 - 1)$ </u> $(10 + 14) - 36$

$10(18) = (9)(24) - 36$

<u>180</u> $= 216 - 36$

$180 = 180$

ACTIVITY EXTENSION

Could the above problem be solved by using two equations and two variables?

Using w and n for the variables in the figures below, form the two equations:

1. $n = w + 8$

2. $(n + 6)(w - 1) - nw = 36$

To solve the two preceding equations for the dimensions of the original rectangle, first simplify:

1. $n = w + 8$

   $-w + n = 8$

2. $(n + 6)(w - 1) - nw = 36$

   $nw + 6w - n - 6 - nw = 36$

   $\underline{6w - n = 42}$

Add the equations:

1. $\quad -w + n = 8$

2. $\underline{+6w - n = 42}$

   $\quad 5w \qquad = 50$

   $w = \underline{\quad 10 \quad}$ inches (the width of the original rectangle)

   $n = w + 8$

   $n = 10 + 8$

   $n = \underline{\quad 18 \quad}$ inches (the length of the original rectangle)

Width: **10 inches**
Length: **18 inches**

Check: $n = w + 8$

$\qquad 18 = 10 + 8$

$\qquad 18 = 18$

Name _____ Period _____

Teacher _____ Date _____ Grade _____

Geometry Problems with Help

DIRECTIONS: Each of the following problems has been given a partial solution. Solve each problem by completing the given solution.

Remind students that the sum of the measures of the angles of any triangle is 180°.

1. One angle of a triangle is 20° larger than a second angle. The third angle is equal to the sum of the other two increased by 12. Find the number of degrees in each angle.

Third angle

$2m + 32$

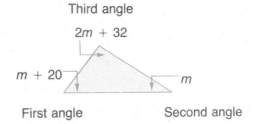

$m + 20$　　　　　　　　m

First angle　　　　　　　Second angle

Let $m = $ the measure of the second angle (in degrees).

$m + 20 = $ the measure of the first angle (in degrees)

$2m + 32 = $ the measure of the third angle (in degrees)

$m + (m + 20) + \underline{(2m + 32)} = 180$

　　$\underline{4m + 52 = 180}$

$4m = 128$

$m = \underline{32°}$ (the measure of the second angle)

$m + 20 = \underline{52°}$ (the measure of the first angle)

$2m + 32 = \underline{96°}$ (the measure of the third angle)

　　　　　　　　　　　Second angle: **32°**
　　　　　　　　　　　First angle: **52°**
　　　　　　　　　　　Third angle: **96°**

Check: $m + (m + 20) + (2m + 32) = 180$

　　　$\underline{32} + (\underline{32} + 20) + (2 \cdot \underline{32} + 32) = 180$

　　　$32 + \underline{52} + (64 + 32) = 180$

　　　$84 + \underline{96} = 180$

　　　$\underline{180} = 180$

2. A wire fence was built around a square field. On three sides the fence was made of four strands of wire. On one side, there were five strands

of wire. If 850 feet of wire was needed to build the fence, find the length of a side.

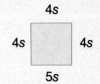

Let s = the length of the wire strand for a side of a fence (in feet).

$4s + 4s + 4s + \underline{5s} = 850$

$17s = \underline{850}$

$s = \underline{50}$ feet (length of wire strand for a side of a fence)

$\underline{\textbf{50 feet}}$

Check: $4s + 4s + 4s + \underline{5s} = 850$

$\qquad 4(50) + 4(50) + 4(50) + \underline{5(50)} = 850$

$\qquad 850 = 850$

3. The length of a rectangle is five less than two times the width. If the perimeter is 50 inches, find the length and the width.

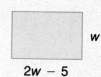

Let w = width (in inches).

$2w - 5$ = length (in inches)

$2w + 2(2w - 5) = 50$

$\underline{2w + 4w - 10} = 50$

$6w = \underline{60}$

$w = \underline{10}$ inches (width)

$2w - 5 = \underline{15}$ inches (length)

$\underline{\begin{array}{l}\text{Width: \textbf{10 inches}}\\ \text{Length: \textbf{15 inches}}\end{array}}$

Check: $2w + 2(2w - 5) = 50$

$\qquad (2 \cdot 10) + 2(2 \cdot 10 - 5) = 50$

$\qquad \underline{20} + 2 \underline{(15)} = 50$

$\qquad 20 + 30 = 50$

$\qquad \underline{50} = 50$

4. The area of a square is 144 square units. A rectangle whose length is 7 more than the width has the same area. What are the dimensions of the rectangle?

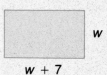

Let w = the width of the rectangle (in inches).

$w + 7$ = the length of the rectangle (in inches)

$w(w + 7) = 144$

$w^2 + 7w = 144$

$\underline{w^2 + 7w - 144} = 0$

$(w + 16)(w - 9) = 0$

Explain that -16 is a root of the equation but the dimensions of a rectangle or any other figure must be positive.

When the product of two numbers is zero, either or both can be zero. Therefore,

$$w + 16 = 0 \quad \text{or} \quad w - 9 = 0$$

Then $w = \underline{\ -16\ }$ or $w = \underline{\ 9\ }$ (the width of the rectangle)

$w + 7 = \underline{\ 16\ }$ (the length of the rectangle)

Width: 9 units
Length: 16 units

Check: $w(w + 7) = 144$

$9(9 + 7) = 144$

$9(16) = 144$

$\underline{\ 144\ } = 144$

5. Two angles of a triangle are complementary. One is 6° more than twice the other. Find the measure of each angle.

Let $n =$ the measure of the smaller angle (in degrees).

$2n + 6 =$ the measure of the larger angle (in degrees)

$n + (2n + 6) = 90$

$\underline{\ 3n + 6\ } = 90$

$\underline{\ 3n\ } = \underline{\ 84\ }$

$n = \underline{\ 28°\ }$ (the measure of the smaller angle)

$2n + 6 = \underline{\ 62°\ }$ (the measure of the larger angle)

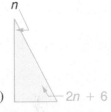

Smaller angle: 28°
Larger angle: 62°

Check: $n + (2n + 6) = 90$

$28 + (2 \cdot \underline{\ 28\ } + 6) = 90$

$28 + (\underline{\ 56\ } + 6) = 90$

$28 + \underline{\ 62\ } = 90$

$\underline{\ 90\ } = 90$

6. Each of the equal angles of an isosceles triangle is 12° less than the vertex angle. Find the measures of the angles of the triangle.

Let $n =$ the measure of the vertex angle (in degrees).

$n - 12 =$ the measure of each of the two equal angles (in degrees)

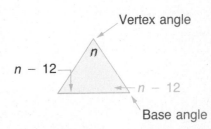

Vertex angle

$n - 12$

$n - 12$

Base angle

$n + (n - 12) + \underline{\quad \textbf{(n - 12)} \quad} = 180$

$3n - 24 = 180$

$\underline{\quad \textbf{3n} \quad} = 204$

$n = \underline{\quad \textbf{68°} \quad}$ (the measure of the vertex angle)

$n - 12 = \underline{\quad \textbf{56°} \quad}$ (the measure of each of the other angles)

Vertex angle: **68°**

Each of the other two angles: **56 °**

Check: $n + (n - 12) + (n - 12) = 180$

$68 + \underline{\quad \textbf{(68 - 12)} \quad} + \underline{\quad \textbf{(68 - 12)} \quad} = 180$

$68 + \underline{\quad \textbf{56} \quad} + \underline{\quad \textbf{56} \quad} = 180$

$\underline{\quad \textbf{180} \quad} = 180$

7. Tara's house is built on flat land. How long is a ladder that will reach a second-story window 12 feet above the ground if the foot of the ladder is five feet from the house?

Let $c =$ the length of the ladder (in feet).

$c^2 = \underline{\quad \textbf{5}^2 \quad} + 12^2$

$c^2 = \underline{\quad \textbf{25} \quad} + 144$

$c^2 = \underline{\quad \textbf{169} \quad}$

$c = \underline{\quad \textbf{13} \quad}$

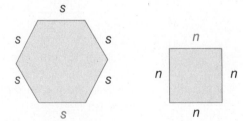

c 12 ft

5 ft

13 feet

Check: $c^2 = 5^2 + 12^2$

$\underline{\quad \textbf{13}^2 \quad} = 25 + 144$

$\underline{\quad \textbf{169} \quad} = 169$

8. The perimeter of a regular hexagon is 492 inches. What is the area of a square if its side is the same length as that of the regular hexagon?

Let $s =$ the length of one side of a regular hexagon (in inches).

s

$s \qquad s$

$s \qquad s$

s

n

$n \qquad n$

n

$s + s + s + s + s + s = 492$

$\underline{\quad \textbf{6s} \quad} = 492$

$s = \underline{\quad \textbf{82} \quad}$ inches (the side of a regular hexagon)

Let A = the area of the square (in square inches).

$A = \underline{\quad n^2 \quad}$

$A = \underline{\quad 82^2 \quad}$

$A = \underline{\quad 6,724 \quad}$ square inches (area of the square)

Area of the square: **6,724 square inches**

Check 1: $s + s + s + s + s + s = 492$

$82 + 82 + 82 + 82 + 82 + 82 = 492$

$\underline{\quad 492 \quad} = 492$

Check 2: $A = n^2$

$\underline{\quad 6,724 \quad} = 82^2$

$\underline{\quad 6,724 \quad} = 6,724$

Challenge

9. The area of a square is 144 square inches. The area of a rectangle is 144 square inches. What is the length of the rectangle if its width is nine inches?

Let n = the length of the rectangle.

s $A = 144$ $w = 9$ n

$A = n \cdot w$

$144 = n \cdot \underline{\quad 9 \quad}$

$\underline{\quad 16 \text{ inches} \quad} = n$ (the length of the rectangle)

Length: **16 inches**

Check: $A = nw$

$144 = \underline{\quad 16 \quad} \cdot 9$

$144 = 144$

Name _____ Period _____

Teacher _____ Date _____ Grade _____

Geometry Problems

DIRECTIONS: Use the five levels of comprehension to solve each of the problems in the space provided. Write your answers in the blank to the right after each problem.

1. The second angle of a triangle is 20° less than the measure of the first angle, and the third angle is 22° less than four times the first. What is the measure of each angle of the triangle?

Let n = the measure of the first angle (in degrees).

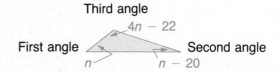

Third angle
$4n - 22$

First angle   Second angle
n $n - 20$

$n - 20$ = the measure of the second angle (in degrees)

$4n - 22$ = the measure of the third angle (in degrees)

$n + (n - 20) + (4n - 22) = 180$

$6n - 42 = 180$

$6n = 222$

$n = 37°$ (the measure of the first angle)

$n - 20 = 17°$ (the measure of the second angle)

$4n - 22 = 126°$ (the measure of the third angle)

First angle: **37°**
Second angle: **17°**
Third angle: **126°**

Check: $n + (n - 20) + (4n - 22) = 180$

$37 + (37 - 20) + (4 \cdot 37 - 22) = 180$

$37 + 17 + 126 = 180$

$180 = 180$

2. Two angles are supplementary. One angle is 16° more than three times the other. Find the measure of each angle.

Let n = the measure of the smaller angle (in degrees).

$3n + 16$ = the measure of the larger angle (in degrees)

$n + (3n + 16) = 180$

$4n + 16 = 180$

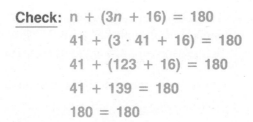

$4n = 164$

$n = 41°$ (measure of smaller angle)

$3n + 16 = 139°$ (measure of larger angle)

Smaller angle: **41°**
Larger angle: **139°**

Check: $n + (3n + 16) = 180$

$41 + (3 \cdot 41 + 16) = 180$

$41 + (123 + 16) = 180$

$41 + 139 = 180$

$180 = 180$

Be prepared for $w + 3w = 40$. It is correct because $w + 3w$ is one-half of the perimeter.

3. The length of a rectangle is three times its width. The perimeter is 80 inches. Find the dimensions.

Let w = the width of the rectangle (in inches).

$3w$ = length of rectangle (in inches)

$w + 3w + w + 3w = 80$

$8w = 80$

$w = 10$ inches (the width of the rectangle)

$3w = 30$ inches (the length of the rectangle)

Width: **10 inches**
Length: **30 inches**

Check: $w + 3w + w + 3w = 80$

$10 + 3(10) + 10 + 3(10) = 80$

$10 + 30 + 10 + 30 = 80$

$80 = 80$

4. The area of a square is 144 square inches. Its perimeter is equal to the perimeter of an equilateral triangle. What is the length of each side of the triangle?

Let A = the area of a square (in square inches), P = the perimeter of an equilateral triangle (in inches), s = the length of each side of the square (in inches), and n = the length of each side of the triangle (in inches).

$A = s^2$

$144 = s^2$

12 inches $= s$

$P = 4s$

$P = 4 \cdot 12$

$P = 3n$

$48 = 3n$

16 inches $= n$ (length of each side of the triangle)

Length of each side: **16 inches**

Check 1: $A = s^2$

$144 = 12^2$

$144 = 144$

Check 2: $P = 3n$

$48 = 3 \cdot 16$

$48 = 48$

5. The base of a rectangle is six inches more than its height. If the area of the rectangle is 160 square inches, find its base and height.

Even though -16 is a value of h, the height must be positive.

Let $h =$ height (in inches).

$h + 6 =$ base

$h(h + 6) = 160$

$h^2 + 6h = 160$

$h^2 + 6h - 160 = 0$

$(h + 16)(h - 10) = 0$

$h + 16 = 0$ or $h - 10 = 0$

$h = -16$ $h = 10$ inches (height)

$h + 6 = 16$ inches (base)

Height: **10 inches**
Base: **16 inches**

Check: $h(h + 6) = 160$

$10(10 + 6) = 160$

$10(16) = 160$

$160 = 160$

6. The screen for an overhead projector is a rectangle. What is the distance between opposite corners if the length is 80 inches and the width is 60 inches?

Let d = the distance between opposite corners (in inches).

$d^2 = 80^2 + 60^2$

$d^2 = 6,400 + 3,600$

$d^2 = 10,000$

$d = 100$ inches (distance between opposite corners)

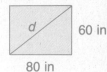

<u>**100 inches**</u>

Check: $d^2 = 80^2 + 60^2$

$100^2 = 80^2 + 60^2$

$10,000 = 6,400 + 3,600$

$10,000 = 10,000$

7. A housing developer's map or plat shows that a rectangular house lot is 100 feet wide and 150 feet long. After the area of the floor plan of the house is subtracted from the area of the lot, the difference is 4,600 square feet. What is the area of the floor plan of the house?

Let a = the area of the house (in square feet).

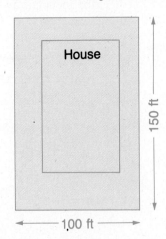

A = length × width

$A = (150)(100)$

$A = 15,000$ square feet (area of lot)

$A - a = 4,600$

$15,000 - a = 4,600$

$-a = -10,400$

$a = 10,400$ square feet (area of house)   <u>**10,400 square feet**</u>

Check 1: $A = (150)(100)$

$15{,}000 = 15{,}000$

Check 2: $A - a = 4{,}600$

$15{,}000 - 10{,}400 = 4{,}600$

$4{,}600 = 4{,}600$

Challenge

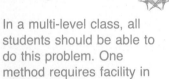

In a multi-level class, all students should be able to do this problem. One method requires facility in arithmetic. The other method requires facility in algebra.

8. A picture is surrounded by a rectangular frame. The uniform width of the frame is five inches. The area of the frame is two times the area of the picture. The length of the picture is 20 inches. Find the width of the picture if the area of the frame is 400 square inches.

Let $n =$ the width of the picture (in inches).

Let $a =$ the area of the picture (in square inches.)

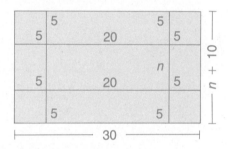

400 square inches = area of frame

$400 = 2a$

200 square inches = a (area of picture)

$20 \cdot n = 200$

$n = 10$ inches (width of picture)   <u>10 inches</u>

Check 1: $400 = 2a$

$400 = 2(200)$

$400 = 400$

Check 2: $20n = 200$

$20 \cdot 10 = 200$

$200 = 200$

Also,

$30(n + 10) - 20n = 400$

$30n + 300 - 20n = 400$

$10n = 100$

$n = 10$ inches (width of picture)

Check: $30(n + 10) - 20n = 400$

$30(10 + 10) - 20(10) = 400$

$30(20) - 200 = 400$

$600 - 200 = 400$

$400 = 400$

STUDY GUIDE 14

Coins

TERMS AND CONCEPTS

Introductory Precepts

Problems involving coins of different denominations are easily solved when the values of the coins are represented in the same unit of money. When the unit of money is cents, the value of three nickels in cents is 3(5) or 15 cents. The value of six dimes in cents is 6(10) or 60 cents. The value of five quarters in cents is 5(25) or 125 cents. The value of n nickels in cents is $n(5)$ or $5n$ cents. The value of d dimes in cents is $d(10)$ or $10d$ cents. The value of q quarters in cents is $q(25)$ or $25q$ cents. The value of x dollars in cents is $x(100)$ or $100x$ cents.

LEVELS OF COMPREHENSION

STEP 1 Read the problem.

STEP 2 Choose the variable(s).

STEP 3 Form the equation.

STEP 4 Solve the equation.

STEP 5 Check the equation.

MODEL PROBLEM 1

In Margo's piggy bank are nickels, dimes, and quarters. There are 15 more dimes than nickels and twice as many quarters as dimes. If the total is $25.25, how many coins of each denomination are there?

READ THE PROBLEM

After reading the problem, give answers to the following statements in the spaces provided.

Literal Level

There are 15 more ___dimes___ than ___nickels___. There are ___twice___ as many quarters as ___dimes___. The piggy bank held a total of ___$25.25___.

Interpretive Level

1. The denomination of coins about which the least is known is the

   nickel,   dime,   quarter   ___nickel___

2. If the number of nickels is represented by n, then the number of dimes is represented by

   $n - 15$, $15 - n$, $n + 15$ ___$n + 15$___

3. The value in cents of $(n + 15)$ dimes is

   $10(n - 15)$, $10(15 - n)$, $10(n + 15)$ ___$10(n + 15)$___

4. To represent the number of quarters, multiply the number of dimes by

   25,   2, $25q$ ___2___

Emphasize the importance of notation: 0.50¢ is one-half of a cent.

5. The value of the quarters in cents is

   $25(2)(n + 15)$, $25(15 - n)$, $25(n - 15)$ ___$25(2)(n + 15)$___

6. The total value of all coins in the piggy bank is

   25.25,   2,525 cents, $2,525   ___2,525 cents___

CHOOSE THE VARIABLE(S)

Let n = the number of nickels (the coin you know the least about).

Kind of coin	Number of coins	Value of each coin in cents	Total value in cents
Nickel	n	5	$5n$
Dime	$n + 15$	10	$10(n + 15)$
Quarter	$2(n + 15)$	25	$25(2)(n + 15)$

FORM THE EQUATION

Application Level

$5n + 10(n + 15) + 25(2)(n + 15) = 2,525$

SOLVE THE EQUATION

$5n + 10(n + 15) + 25(2)(n + 15) = 2{,}525$

$5n + 10n + 150 + 50(n + 15) = 2{,}525$

$15n + 150 + 50n + 750 = 2{,}525$

$\underline{65n + 900 = 2{,}525}$

$65n = 1{,}625$

$n = \underline{\quad 25 \quad}$ (number of nickels)

$n + 15 = \underline{\quad 40 \quad}$ (number of dimes)

$2(n + 15) = \underline{\quad 80 \quad}$ (number of quarters)

Nickels: **25**
Dimes: **40**
Quarters: **80**

CHECK THE EQUATION

$5n + 10(n + 15) + 25(2)(n + 15) = 2{,}525$

$5(25) + 10(25 + 15) + (25)(2)(25 + 15) = 2{,}525$

$5(25) + 10(40) + 25(80) = 2{,}525$

$125 + 400 + \underline{\quad 2{,}000 \quad} = 2{,}525$

$2{,}525 = 2{,}525$

ACTIVITY EXTENSION

If you had decided to let n = the number of dimes, then $\underline{\quad n - 15 \quad}$ would have represented the number of nickels and $2n$ would have represented the number of $\underline{\text{quarters}}$. The purpose of expressing the sum of the values of all the coins in terms of cents is to eliminate the $\underline{\text{decimal point}}$ from the equation, thus making the equation $\underline{\text{easier}}$ to solve.

MODEL PROBLEM 2

At the end of a basketball game, the ticket seller had receipts amounting to $740. The number of dimes was 100 more than the number of nickels. The number of quarters was 500 more than the number of dimes. The number of one-dollar bills was 300 less than the number of quarters. How many nickels, dimes, quarters, and one-dollar bills were there?

READ THE PROBLEM

After reading the problem, give the answers to the following statements in the spaces provided.

Literal Level

The coin about which you know the least is the ____nickel____. The number of dimes was __100__ more than the number of ____nickels____. The number of ____quarters____ was 500 more than the number of ____dimes____. The number of one-dollar bills was __300__ less than the number of quarters. The total value of the receipts from the game was ____$740____.

Interpretive Level

1. If n represents the number of nickels, then the value of the nickels is

$\dfrac{n}{5¢}$, $5n$ cents, $(5 - n)$ cents

____**5n cents**____

2. The number of dimes would be represented by

$100 - n$, $n - 100$, $n + 100$, $100 + m - n$

____**n + 100**____

3. The value of $(n + 100)$ dimes in cents is

$10(n + 10)$, $10(n + 100)$, $10(100 - n)$

____**10(n + 100)**____

4. The number of quarters would be represented by

$n + 100 + 500$, $600 - n$, $600n$

____**n + 100 + 500**____

5. The value of the number of quarters in cents is

$25(n + 100)$, $25(n + 600)$, $25(600 - n)$

____**25(n + 600)**____

6. The number of one-dollar bills is

$(n + 600) - 300$, $(n + 100) - 300$, $600n - 300$

____**(n + 600) − 300**____

7. The value of the $1 bills in cents would be

$100[(n + 100) - 300]$, $100[(n + 600) - 300]$,
$100(600n - 300)]$

____**100[(n + 600) − 300]**____

8. The total value of the receipts in cents is

740, $7,400$, $74,000$

____**74,000**____

CHOOSE THE VARIABLE(S)

Let n = the number of nickels.

Kind	Number	Value of each in cents	Total value in cents
Nickel	n	5	$5n$
Dime	$n + 100$	10	$10(n + 100)$
Quarter	$(n + 100) + 500$	25	$25[(n + 100) + 500]$
Dollar	$(n + 100 + 500) - 300$	100	$100[(n + 100 + 500) - 300]$

FORM THE EQUATION

Application Level

$5n + 10(n + 100) + 25[(n + 100) + 500] + 100[(n + 100 + 500) - 300] = \underline{74,000}$

SOLVE THE EQUATION

$5n + 10(n + 100) + 25[(n + 100) + 500] + 100[(n + 100 + 500) - 300] = 74,000$

$5n + 10n + 1,000 + 25(n + 600) + 100(n + 300) = 74,000$

$15n + 1,000 + 25n + 15,000 + 100n + 30,000 = 74,000$

$140n + 46,000 = 74,000$

$\dfrac{140n}{} = \dfrac{28,000}{}$

$n = \underline{200}$ (number of nickels)

$n + 100 = \underline{300}$ (number of dimes)

$(n + 100) + 500 = \underline{800}$ (number of quarters)

$(n + 100 + 500) - 300 = \underline{500}$ (number of one-dollar bills)

Nickels: **200**
Dimes: **300**
Quarters: **800**
One-dollar bills: **500**

CHECK THE EQUATION

$5n + 10(n + 100) + 25[(n + 100) + 500] + 100[(n + 100 + 500) - 300] = 74,000$

$5\underline{(200)} + 10(\underline{200} + 100) + 25[(\underline{200} + 100) + 500]$
$+ 100[(\underline{200} + 100 + 500) - 300] = 74,000$

$\underline{1,000} + 10(300) + 25\underline{(800)} + 100(500) = \underline{74,000}$

$1,000 + 3,000 + \underline{20,000} + 50,000 = 74,000$

$\underline{74,000} = 74,000$

ACTIVITY EXTENSION

Express the equation for the previous problem if the dollar is used as the unit of money.

$$\frac{1}{20}n + \frac{1}{10}(n + 100) + \frac{1}{4}[(n + 100) + 500] + 1\,[(n + 100 + 500)$$

$$- 300] = 740$$

MODEL PROBLEM 3

A bank messenger lost a bag of 700 coins worth $50. If the bag contained only nickels and dimes, how many of each coin were there? (Use two variables.)

READ THE PROBLEM

After reading the problem, give the answers to the following statements in the spaces provided.

Literal Level

The bank messenger _____lost_____ a bag of ___700___ coins having a value of ___$50___. Luckily, this time he was carrying only ___nickels___ and ___dimes___.

Interpretive Level

1. If n is the number of nickels and d is the number of dimes, then the number of coins is represented by

   $n - d, \qquad d - n, \qquad n + d$ 　　　　　$\underline{\quad n + d \quad}$

2. An equation relating to the total number of coins is

   $n - d = 700, \qquad d - n = 700, \qquad n + d = 700$

   　　　　　　　　　　　　　　　　　$\underline{\quad n + d = 700 \quad}$

3. The value of n nickels and d dimes in cents is

   $5n + 10d, \qquad 5d + 10n, \qquad (5 + 10)nd$ 　$\underline{\quad 5n + 10d \quad}$

4. The value of $50 in cents is 　　　　　　　　　　$\underline{\quad 5,000 \quad}$

   $50, \qquad 500, \qquad 5,000$

CHOOSE THE VARIABLE(S)

Let n = the number of nickels and d = the number of dimes.

Kind of coin	Number of coins	Value of each coin in cents	Total value in cents
Nickel	n	5	$5n$
Dime	d	10	$10d$

FORM THE EQUATIONS

Application Level

1. $n + d = 700$
2. $5n + 10d = 5{,}000$

SOLVE THE EQUATIONS

1. $n + d = 700$
2. $5n + 10d = 5{,}000$

$$-5n - 5d = -3{,}500$$

$$+5n + 10d = 5{,}000$$

$$5d = 1{,}500$$

$d = $ __300__ (number of dimes)

$n + d = $ __700__

$n = $ __400__ (number of nickels)

Dimes: **300**
Nickels: **400**

CHECK THE EQUATIONS

$n + d = 700$

$400 + $ __300__ $= 700$

__700__ $= 700$

$5n + 10d = 5{,}000$

$5(400) + 10(300) = 5{,}000$

$2{,}000 + $ __3{,}000__ $= 5{,}000$

__5{,}000__ $= 5{,}000$

ACTIVITY EXTENSION

Form the equation for Model Problem 3 using only one variable.

Students should have equal facility with both methods.

Method 1: Let $n = $ the number of nickels.

$700 - n = $ the number of dimes

$5n + 10(700 - n) = 5{,}000$

Method 2: Let d = the number of dimes.

$$\frac{700 - d}{} = \text{number of nickels}$$

$$10d + 5(700 - d) = 5,000$$

Both methods above give the same solution sets. In Method 1, you would find the number of ____nickels____ first. In Method 2, you would find the number of ____dimes____ first.

Name _____ Period _____

Teacher _____ Date _____ Grade _____

Coin Problems with Help

DIRECTIONS: Each of the following problems has been given a partial solution. Solve each problem by completing the given solution.

1. A young boy has six coins; he has two of each kind of coin ranging in value from a penny to a silver dollar. What is the value of the coins of each kind if the sum of their values is $3.82?

Values in terms of cents:

Let c = the value of a penny, and $2c$ = the value of two pennies.

$5c$ = the value of a nickel, and $10c$ = the value of two nickels

$\underline{10c}$ = the value of a dime, and $20c$ = the value of two dimes

$25c$ = the value of a quarter, and $\underline{50c}$ = the value of two quarters

$50c$ = the value of a half-dollar, and $\underline{100c}$ = the value of two half-dollars

$100c$ = the value of a dollar, and $200c$ = the value of two silver dollars

Form an equation:

$2c + 10c + 20c + 50c + 100c + 200c = \underline{382}$.

Solve the equation:

$382 = 382¢$ is correct since values were given in terms of cents.

$382c = 382¢$

$c = 1, 2c = 2¢$ (value of pennies)

$5c = 5, 10c = 10¢$ (value of nickels)

$\underline{10c = 10}$, $20c = 20¢$ (value of dimes)

$25c = 25, 50c = 50¢$ (value of quarters)

$50c = 50, 100c = 100¢$ (value of half-dollars)

$\underline{100c = 100}$, $200c = 200¢$ (value of silver dollars)

Pennies: **2¢**
Nickels: **10¢**
Dimes: **20¢**
Quarters: **50¢**
Half-dollars: **100¢**
Silver dollars: **200¢**

Check: $2c + 10c + 20c + 50c + 100c + 200c = 382$ (cents)

$$382c = 382$$

$$\frac{382 \cdot 1}{382} = 382$$

$$382 = 382 \text{ (cents)}$$

Is it really necessary to use algebra to solve this problem?   **No**

2. A bank teller received deposits of rolls of pennies, nickels, dimes, and quarters. The number of rolls of nickels was twice the number of rolls of pennies. The number of rolls of dimes was one more than the number of rolls of nickels. The number of rolls of quarters was twice the number of rolls of dimes. After giving these coins to the teller, a typewritten note was passed by the would-be customer indicating holdup. How much did the holdup artist net if the teller simply returned the wrapped money given to him by the holdup artist and stacks of worthless "dummy" money for weight?

   Nothing

3. If you had information that the would-be deposit in Problem 2 amounted to $188.50, how many rolls of each coin did the robber present?

   Let x = the number of rolls of pennies.

Kinds of rolls	Number of rolls	Value of each roll in cents	Total value in cents
Pennies	x	50	$50x$
Nickels	$2x$	200	$400x$
Dimes	$2x + 1$	500	$500(2x + 1)$
Quarters	$2(2x + 1)$	1,000	$1,000(4x + 2)$

$$50x + 400x + 500(2x + 1) + 1,000(4x + 2) = 18,850$$

$$50x + 400x + 1,000x + 500 + \underline{4,000x} + 2,000 = \underline{18,850}$$

$$5,450x + 2,500 = 18,850$$

$$5,450x = 16,350$$

$x = \underline{\ 3\ }$ (rolls of pennies)

$2x = \underline{\ 6\ }$ (rolls of nickels)

$2x + 1 = \underline{\ 7\ }$ (rolls of dimes)

$2(2x + 1) = \underline{\ 14\ }$ (rolls of quarters)

Pennies: **3 rolls**
Nickels: **6 rolls**
Dimes: **7 rolls**
Quarters: **14 rolls**

Check: $50x + 400x + 500(2x + 1) + 1{,}000(4x + 2) =$ ___18,850___

___50 · 3___ $+ 400 · 3 + 500 · (2 · 3 + 1) + 1{,}000(4 · 3 + 2) =$ ___18,850___

$150 +$ ___1,200___ $+ 500(7) + 1{,}000(14) =$ ___18,850___

___150___ $+ 1{,}200 + 3{,}500 + 14{,}000 =$ ___18,850___

$18{,}850 =$ ___18,850___

4. When Michelle opened her bank, she found $5.75 consisting of nickels, dimes, and quarters. There were as many nickels as dimes and four times as many quarters as there were nickels. How many coins of each kind were there? (Use one variable.)

Let $n =$ the number of nickels.

Kind	Number	Value in cents
Nickels	n	$5n$
Dimes	n	$10n$
Quarters	$4n$	$25(4n)$

$5n + 10n + 25(4n) = 575$

$5n + 10n + 100n =$ ___575___

___115n___ $= 575$

$n =$ ___5___ (numbers of nickels)

$n =$ ___5___ (number of dimes)

$4n =$ ___20___ (number of quarters)

Nickels: **5**
Dimes: **5**
Quarters: **20**

Check: $5n + 10n + 25(4n) = 575$

$5n + 10n + 100n = 575$

$5 ·$ ___5___ $+ 10 ·$ ___5___ $+ 100 ·$ ___5___ $= 575$

$25 + 50 + 500 = 575$

___575___ $= 575$

5. A lady's purse contained 12 coins consisting of quarters and dimes only. Their total value was $1.95. How many coins of each kind were there? (Use one variable.)

Let $q =$ the number of quarters.

Kind	Number	Value in cents
Quarters	q	$25q$
Dimes	$12 - q$	$10(12 - q)$

$$25q + 10(12 - q) = \underline{195}$$
$$25q + 120 - 10q = 195$$
$$\underline{15q + 120} = 195$$
$$\underline{15q} = \underline{75}$$
$$q = \underline{5} \text{ (number of quarters)}$$
$$12 - q = \underline{7} \text{ (number of dimes)}$$

Quarters: **5**
Dimes: **7**

Check: $25q + 10 \underline{\quad (12 - q) \quad} = 195$
$\qquad 25 \cdot 5 + 10\underline{\quad (12 - 5) \quad} = 195$
$\qquad 125 + 10(7) = 195$
$\qquad 125 + \underline{\quad 70 \quad} = 195$
$\qquad \underline{\quad 195 \quad} = 195$

6. Solve Problem 2 using two variables.

Let q = the number of quarters.

d = the number of dimes

Kind	Number	Value in cents
Quarters	q	$25q$
Dimes	d	$10d$

1. $q + d = 12$

2. $\underline{25q + 10d = 195}$

$\qquad -10q - 10d = -120$
$\qquad \underline{+25q + 10d = 195}$
$\qquad \underline{15q} \qquad = 75$
$q = \underline{\quad 5 \quad} \text{ (number of quarters)}$
$q + d = \underline{\quad 12 \quad}$
$5 + d = \underline{\quad 12 \quad}$
$d = \underline{\quad 7 \quad} \text{ (number of dimes)}$

Dimes: **7**
Quarters: **5**

Check: $q + d = 12$
$\qquad 7 + 5 = 12$
$\qquad 12 = 12$

7. Jane has x nickels and eight more quarters than she has nickels. The total value of her money is $5.00. How many of each coin does she have? (Use one variable.)

Let x = the number of nickels.

Kind	Number	Value in cents
Nickels	x	$5x$
Quarters	$x + 8$	$25(x + 8)$

$5x + \underline{25(x + 8)} = \underline{500}$

$5x + 25x + 200 = \underline{500}$

$\underline{30x + 200} = 500$

$30x = \underline{300}$

$x = \underline{10}$ (number of nickels)

$x + 8 = \underline{18}$ (number of quarters)

Nickels: **10**

Quarters: **18**

Check: $5x + \underline{25(x + 8)} = 500$

$5(10) + \underline{25(10 + 8)} = 500$

$50 + \underline{450} = 500$

$\underline{500} = 500$

8. A piggy bank was accidentally broken. Out fell nickels, dimes, and pennies. There were three times as many nickels as pennies and ten more dimes than pennies. How many of each coin were there if the total value was $1.78? (Use one variable.)

Let n = the number of pennies.

Kind	Number	Value in cents
Pennies	n	n
Nickels	$3n$	$5(3n)$
Dimes	$n + 10$	$10(n + 10)$

$\underline{n} + \underline{5(3n)} + 10(n + 10) = 178$

$\underline{n} + \underline{15n} + 10n + 100 = 178$

$26n + 100 = 178$

$\underline{26n} = \underline{78}$

$n = \underline{3}$ (number of pennies)

$3n = \underline{9}$ (number of nickels)

$n + 10 = \underline{13}$ (number of dimes)

Pennies: **3**

Nickels: **9**

Dimes: **13**

Check: $n + 5(3n) + 10(n + 10) = 178$

$3 + 5(3 \cdot \underline{}\overset{3}{}\underline{}) + 10(\underline{}\overset{3}{}\underline{} + 10) = 178$

$3 + \underline{}\overset{45}{}\underline{} + 130 = 178$

$\underline{}\overset{178}{}\underline{} = 178$

9. A bag of 800 coins is worth $50. If the bag contains only nickels and dimes, how many of each coin are there? (Use two variables.)

Let n = number of nickels.

d = number of dimes.

Kind	Number	Value in cents
Nickels	n	$5n$
Dimes	d	$10d$

1. $n + d = 800$

2. $5n + 10d = 5{,}000$

$\quad\quad -5n - 5d = -4{,}000$
$\quad\quad +5n + 10d = 5{,}000$

$\quad\quad\quad\quad\quad 5d = 1{,}000$

$d = \underline{}\overset{200}{}\underline{}$ (number of dimes)

$n + d = \underline{}\overset{800}{}\underline{}$

$n + 200 = 800$

$n = \underline{}\overset{600}{}\underline{}$ (number of nickels)

Dimes: **200**
Nickels: **600**

Check: $n + d = 800$

$600 + \underline{}\overset{200}{}\underline{} = 800$

$\underline{}\overset{800}{}\underline{} = 800$

Challenge

10. Mary deposited $11.80 in nickels, quarters, and dimes in her savings account. The number of dimes exceeded the number of nickels by 8, and the number of quarters was 20 less than the number of nickels. Find the number of each kind of coin she deposited. (Use one variable.)

Let n = the number of nickels.

Kind	Number	Value in cents
Nickels	n	$5n$
Dimes	$n + 8$	$10(n + 8)$
Quarters	$n - 20$	$25(n - 20)$

$5n + 10(n + 8) + 25(n - 20) = \underline{1{,}180}$

$5n + 10n + 80 + 25n - 500 = \underline{1{,}180}$

$40n - 420 = \underline{1{,}180}$

$\underline{40n} = 1{,}600$

$n = \underline{40}$ (number of nickels)

$n + 8 = \underline{48}$ (number of dimes)

$n - 20 = \underline{20}$ (number of quarters)

Nickels: **40**
Dimes: **48**
Quarters: **20**

Check: $5n + 10(n + 8) + 25(n - 20) = 1{,}180$

$5\underline{(40)} + 10(\underline{40} + 8) + 25(40 - 20) = 1{,}180$

$200 + 10(48) + 25(20) = 1{,}180$

$200 + 480 + 500 = 1{,}180$

$1{,}180 = \underline{1{,}180}$

Coin Problems

DIRECTIONS: Use the five levels of comprehension to solve each of the problems in the space provided. Write your answers in the blank to the right after each problem.

1. Mr. Gutierrez deposited $905 in his bank. The number of five-dollar bills was 10 more than the number of ten-dollar bills, and the number of one-dollar bills was 45 more than the number of five-dollar bills. How many bills of each type did he deposit?

   Let t = the number of ten-dollar bills.

Bills	Number	Value in dollars
Tens	t	$10t$
Fives	$t + 10$	$5(t + 10)$
Ones	$t + 10 + 45$	$1(t + 10 + 45)$

   $10t + 5(t + 10) + (t + 55) = 905$

   $10t + 5t + 50 + t + 55 = 905$

   $16t + 105 = 905$

   $16t = 800$

   $t = 50$ (number of ten-dollar bills)

   $t + 10 = 60$ (number of five-dollar bills)

   $t + 55 = 105$ (number of one-dollar bills)

   Ten-dollar bills: **50**
   Five-dollar bills: **60**
   One-dollar bills: **105**

   Check: $10t + 5(t + 10) + (t + 55) = 905$

   $10(50) + 5(50 + 10) + (50 + 55) = 905$

   $500 + 5(60) + 105 = 905$

   $500 + 300 + 105 = 905$

   $905 = 905$

2. A class contributed $8.50 in quarters and pennies to the Red Cross. In all, there were 82 coins. How many of each were there? (Use one variable.)

   Let n = the number of quarters.

Kind	Number	Value in cents
Quarters	n	$25n$
Pennies	$82 - n$	$(82 - n)$

$25n + (82 - n) = 850$

$24n + 82 = 850$

$24n = 768$

$n = 32$ (number of quarters)

$82 - n = 50$ (number of pennies)

Quarters: **32**

Pennies: **50**

Check: $25n + 82 - n = 850$

$\qquad\quad 25 \cdot 32 + 82 - 32 = 850$

$\qquad\quad 800 + 50 = 850$

$\qquad\quad 850 = 850$

3. Is it possible to have $24 in dimes and nickels and have four times as many nickels as dimes? (Use one variable.)

Let d = the number of dimes.

Kind	Number	Value in cents
Dimes	d	$10d$
Nickels	$4d$	$5(4d)$

$10d + 5(4d) = 2{,}400$

$10d + 20d = 2{,}400$

$30d = 2{,}400$

$d = 80$ (number of dimes)

$4d = 320$ (number of nickels)

Yes

Check: $10d + 5(4d) = 2{,}400$

$\qquad\quad 10 \cdot 80 + 5(4 \cdot 80) = 2{,}400$

$\qquad\quad 800 + 5(320) = 2{,}400$

$\qquad\quad 800 + 1{,}600 = 2{,}400$

4. Miss Rezaian cashed a check for $210 at a bank. She received one-dollar bills, five-dollar bills, and ten-dollar bills. The numbers of each kind of bill respectively represented three consecutive even integers. How many of each denomination did Miss Rezaian receive?

Let n = the number of one-dollar bills.

Kind of bill	Number	Value in dollars
$1	n	n
$5	$n + 2$	$5(n + 2)$
$10	$n + 4$	$10(n + 4)$

$n + 5(n + 2) + 10(n + 4) = 210$

$n + 5n + 10 + 10n + 40 = 210$

$16n + 50 = 210$

$16n = 160$

$n = 10$ (number of one-dollar bills)

$n + 2 = 12$ (number of five-dollar bills)

$(n + 4) = 14$ (number of ten-dollar bills)

One-dollar bills: **10**
Five-dollar bills: **12**
Ten-dollar bills: **14**

Check: $n + 5(n + 2) + 10(n + 4) = 210$

$10 + 5(10 + 2) + 10(10 + 4) = 210$

$10 + 5(12) + 10(14) = 210$

$10 + 60 + 140 = 210$

$210 = 210$

5. Irene has two bags of coins at the bank. The number of dimes is twice the number of nickels. If she has $80 in each of the two bags, how many coins of each type does she have? (Use two variables.)

Let n = the number of nickels.

d = the number of dimes

Kind	Number	Value in cents
Nickels	n	$5n$
Dimes	d	$10d$

Stress the role that substitution plays throughout mathematics.

1. $d = 2n$

2. $5n + 10d = 16,000$

$5n + 10(2n) = 16,000$

$5n + 20n = 16,000$

$25n = 16,000$

$n = 640$ (number of nickels)

$d = 2n = 1,280$ (number of dimes)

Nickels: **640**
Dimes: **1,280**

Check: $5n + 10d = 16,000$

$5(640) + 10(1,280) = 16,000$

$3,200 + 12,800 = 16,000$

$16,000 = 16,000$

6. A teacher cashed a check for $570. He asked for the money to be returned in five- and ten-dollar bills. The number of ten-dollar bills exceeded twice the number of five-dollar bills by 7. How many of each denomination did he receive? (Use two variables.)

Let f = the number of five-dollar bills.

t = the number of ten-dollar bills

Kind of bill	Number	Value in dollars
$5	f	$5f$
$10	t	$10t$

Use substitution again!

1. $t = 2f + 7$
2. $5f + 10t = 570$

$5f + 10t = 570$

$5f + 10(2f + 7) = 570$

$5f + 20f + 70 = 570$

$25f + 70 = 570$

$25f = 500$

$f = 20$ (number of five-dollar bills)

$t = 2f + 7$

$t = 2(20) + 7$

$t = 40 + 7$

$t = 47$ (number of ten-dollar bills)

Five-dollar bills: 20
Ten-dollar bills: 47

Check: $t = 2f + 7$

$47 = 2(20) + 7$

$47 = 40 + 7$

$47 = 47$

7. Students at your high school pitched coins into a wishing well for the benefit of charity. One hundred forty-four thousand pennies and $\frac{1}{72}$ as

many nickels were collected. The number of dimes was the same as the number of nickels. The number of quarters was $\frac{1}{20}$ of the number of dimes. The number of half dollars was $\frac{1}{10}$ as many as the number of quarters. The number of silver dollars was two less than the number of half dollars. How much money was donated by your high school? Give an arithmetic solution.

Coins	Number	Value (in dollars)
Pennies	144,000	$1,440
Nickels	2,000	100
Dimes	2,000	200
Quarters	100	25
Half dollars	10	5
Silver dollars	8	8
Total value		**$1,778**

$1,778

Challenge

8. Provide an algebraic solution to Problem 7.

Let h = the number of half dollars.

$h - 2$ = the number of silver dollars

$10h$ = the number of quarters

$2,000$ = the number of dimes

$2,000$ = the number of nickels

$144,000$ = the number of pennies

$10h = \frac{1}{20}(2,000)$

$10h = 100$

	Value (in dollars)
$h = 10$ (number of half dollars)	5
$h - 2 = 8$ (number of silver dollars)	8
$10h = 100$ (number of quarters)	25
$2,000$ = number of dimes	200
$2,000$ = number of nickels	100
$144,000$ = number of pennies	1,440

$1,778

Check: $10h = \frac{1}{20}(2,000)$

$10(10) = \frac{1}{20}(2,000)$

$100 = 100$

STUDY GUIDE 15

Investment

TERMS AND CONCEPTS

Introductory Precepts

Business problems usually involve investments. The amount of money invested or borrowed is called *principal*. Generally, one earns interest on money that is invested but one pays interest on money that is borrowed. The *simple interest* formula is $I = PRT$, where I stands for interest, P represents principal, R represents rate (measured as percent), and T represents time (measured in years). The amount of money at the end of a specific period of time can be found by adding interest earned for this period of time to the initial investment. The formula for this is $A = P + I$, where $A =$ the amount of money.

The interest earned on \$8,000 at a rate of 4 percent per annum (year) for three years is found by using the simple interest formula:

$$I = PRT$$
$$I = \$8,000 \times \left(\frac{4}{100}\right) \times 3$$
$$I = \$960$$

The amount at the end of three years is found by using this formula:

$$A = P + I$$
$$A = \$8,000 + \$960$$
$$A = \$8,960$$

LEVELS OF COMPREHENSION

STEP 1 Read the problem.

STEP 2 Choose the variable(s).

STEP 3 Form the equation.

STEP 4 Solve the equation.

STEP 5 Check the equation.

Solve by use of one variable.

MODEL PROBLEM 1

Mr. Rich invested $200,000, part at 8 percent and the rest at 20 percent. His annual income from these investments was $22,000. How much was invested at each rate?

READ THE PROBLEM

After reading the problem, give the answers to the following statements in the spaces provided.

Literal Level

Mr. Rich had a total investment of __$200,000__. Part of this investment earned __8 percent__. The other part earned __20 percent__. The annual income from these investments was __$22,000__.

Interpretive Level

1. As a decimal, eight percent is

   0.8,   0.80,   0.08,   none of these   __0.08__

2. As a decimal, 20 percent is

   20,   0.02,   0.20,   none of these   __0.20__

3. The length of time for each investment is

   one year, $\frac{1}{2}$ year,   two years,   none of these

   __one year__

4. If x dollars of the $200,000 is invested at 8 percent, then the interest for one year is expressed as

   0.80x dollars,   0.08x dollars,   0.008x dollars, none of these

   __0.08x dollars__

5. If the remainder of the $200,000 is invested at 20 percent, then the interest for one year is expressed as

   2($200,000 − x),   0.02($200,000 − x), 0.20($200,000 − x),   none of these   __0.20($200,000 − x)__

CHOOSE THE VARIABLE(S)

Let x = the investment yielding 8 percent per year (in dollars).

Complete this tabular arrangement to set up the problem.

Dollar investment	Yearly rate	Interest earned in one year
x	8 percent	0.08 (x)
200,000 − x	20 percent	0.20(200,000 − x)

FORM THE EQUATION

Application Level

$0.08(x) + 0.20(\$200{,}000 - x) = \$22{,}000$

SOLVE THE EQUATION

$0.08x + 0.20(\$200{,}000 - x) = \$22{,}000$

$0.08x + 40{,}000 - 0.20x = 22{,}000$

$-0.12x = -18{,}000$

$x = 150{,}000$ (investment at 8 percent)

$200{,}000 - x = 50{,}000$ (investment at 20 percent)

Eight percent: **$150,000**
Twenty percent: **$50,000**

CHECK THE EQUATION

$0.08(x) + 0.20(\$200{,}000 - x) = 22{,}000$

$0.08(\$150{,}000) + 0.20(\$200{,}000 - 150{,}000) = 22{,}000$

$12{,}000 + 0.20(\$50{,}000) = 22{,}000$

$12{,}000 + 10{,}000 = 22{,}000$

$22{,}000 = 22{,}000$

ACTIVITY EXTENSION

Solve by use of two variables.

Could Model Problem 1 have been solved using two variables and two equations?

Yes

MODEL PROBLEM 2

Mr. Rich invested $200,000, part at 8 percent and the rest at 20 percent. His annual income from these investments was $22,000. How much was invested at each rate?

READ THE PROBLEM

After reading the problem, give the answers to the following statements in the spaces provided.

Literal Level

The length of time for each investment is __one year__. One investment earned interest at __8 percent__. The other investment earned interest at __20 percent__. The variable representing the 8 percent investment __plus__ the variable representing the 20 percent investment have a sum of __$200,000__. The interest earned by the 8 percent investment plus the interest earned by the 20 percent investment have a __sum__ of $22,000 over a period of __one__ year.

CHOOSE THE VARIABLE(S)

Let x = the dollar investment at 8 percent per year (in dollars).

y = the dollar investment at 20 percent per year (in dollars)

Complete this tabular arrangement to set up the problem.

Interpretive Level

Dollar investment	Yearly rate	Interest earned in one year
x	8 percent	0.08x
y	20 percent	0.20y

FORM THE EQUATIONS

Application Level

1. $x + y = \$200,000$

2. $0.08x + 0.20y = \$22,000$

(If there are two variables, then there must be two equations.)

SOLVE THE EQUATIONS

1. $x + y = \$200,000$

2. $0.08x + 0.20y = \$22,000$

$$-0.20x - 0.20y = -40,000$$
$$+0.08x + 0.20y = 22,000$$

$$-0.12x = -18,000$$

$x = $ __150,000__ (investment at 8 percent)

$200,000 - x = $ __50,000__ (investment at 20 percent)

Eight percent: **$150,000**
Twenty percent: **$50,000**

CHECK THE EQUATION

$x + y = \$200{,}000$

$150{,}000 + \underline{50{,}000} = 200{,}000$

$200{,}000 = 200{,}000$

$0.08x + 0.20y = 22{,}000$

$\underline{0.08(150{,}000)} + 0.20(50{,}000) = 22{,}000$

$12{,}000 + \underline{10{,}000} = 22{,}000$

$\underline{22{,}000} = 22{,}000$

MODEL PROBLEM 3

Ms. Santiago invested \$100,000 at seven percent. How much more money does Ms. Santiago need to invest at five percent for the annual income from the two investments to be \$47,000?

READ THE PROBLEM

After reading the problem, give the answers to the following statements or questions in the spaces provided.

Literal Level

1. Ms. Santiago will earn __7 percent or 5 percent__ on one investment and __5 percent or 7 percent__ on another investment.

2. How much interest will the money invested at seven percent earn?

   __\$7,000__

3. How much interest will the money invested at five percent earn?

   __\$40,000__

4. Five percent as a decimal is

   0.50,   0.05,   0.005,   5,   none of these   __0.05__

5. The length of time for each investment is

   one year, $\frac{1}{2}$ year,   two years,   none of these   __one year__

6. If x dollars is invested at five percent, then the interest for one year is expressed as

   $5x$ dollars, $0.005x$ dollars, $0.05x$ dollars,   none of these

   __0.05x dollars__

276

Study Guide 15

CHOOSE THE VARIABLE(S)

Interpretive Level

Let y = the investment at 5 percent per year (in dollars).

Complete this tabular arrangement to set up the problem.

Dollar investment	Yearly rate	Interest earned in one year
$100,000	7 percent	0.07(100,000)
y	5 percent	0.05y

FORM THE EQUATION

Application Level

$0.07(\$100,000) + 0.05y = \$47,000$

SOLVE THE EQUATION

$0.07(\$100,000) + 0.05y = \$47,000$

$7,000 + 0.05y = 47,000$

$0.05y = \underline{\quad 40,000 \quad}$

$5y = 4,000,000$

$\underline{\quad y = 800,000 \quad}$ (invested at five percent)

Five percent: **$800,000**

CHECK THE EQUATION

$0.07(\$100,000) + \underline{\quad 0.05y \quad} = \$47,000$

$7,000 + 0.05(800,000) = 47,000$

$7,000 + \underline{\quad 40,000 \quad} = 47,000$

$47,000 = 47,000$

ACTIVITY EXTENSION

The simple interest rate of $\underline{\quad 5.22 \text{ percent} \quad}$ per annum yields interest of $47,000 on an investment of $900,000.

Name _____ Period _____

Teacher _____ Date _____ Grade _____

Investment Problems with Help

DIRECTIONS: Each of the following problems has been given a partial solution. Solve each problem by completing the given solution.

1. Mr. Sanchez changed from an investment of $40,000 bearing eight percent annual interest to an investment of $40,000 paying six percent annual interest. Find the difference of interests earned on the two investments over a period of one year.

   The eight percent investment:

   $I = PRT$

   $I = (\$40,000)(0.08)(1)$
   $I = \$3,200$
   _____ (interest earned on investment at eight percent in dollars)

   The six percent investment:
   $I = PRT$

   $I = (\$40,000)(0.06)(1)$

   $I = 2,400$ (interest earned on investment at six percent in dollars)

   Difference:
   $\$3,200 - \$2,400 = \$800$　　　　　　$\$800$

2. Dr. Brinkman invested $150,000 at an annual rate of one percent. Her husband earned $800 annual interest on an investment of $20,000. If the Brinkmans pooled their resources and invested $170,000 at six percent per annum the next year, how much more interest did they receive after making the change?

   Dr. Brinkman's earnings:

   $I = PRT$

   $I = \$150,000(0.01)(1)$
   $I = $ $\$1,500$ _____ (interest earned by Dr. Brinkman in dollars)

   Mr. Brinkman's earnings:
   $\$800$

   $\$1,500 + 800 = $ $\$2,300$ _____ (combined Brinkman interest)

   Interest earned at six percent:

   $I = PRT$

$I = 170{,}000(.06)(1)$ (dollars)

$I = \underline{\quad\$10{,}200\quad}$ (interest earned on investment at six percent in dollars)

Difference:

$\$10{,}200 - \$2{,}300 = \$7{,}900$ (dollars)

$\underline{\quad\$7{,}900\quad}$

3. Mrs. O'Connor gave each of her two children, Dan and Shannon, $30,000. Dan invested $30,000 in municipal bonds paying 10 percent annually. Shannon invested $20,000 in municipal bonds paying 12 percent interest annually and $10,000 in certificates of deposit with an annual yield of 5 percent. No risk is involved in any of the investments. Did Shannon or Dan make the better investment?

$I = PRT$

Son	Dollar investment	Yearly rate	Interest earned in one year
Dan	$30,000	10 percent	$3,000
Shannon	$20,000	12 percent	$2,400
	$10,000	5 percent	$500

$\$2{,}900$ total

$\$20{,}000 \times 0.12 = \underline{\quad\$2{,}400\quad}$

$\$30{,}000 \times 0.10 = \underline{\quad\$3{,}000\quad}$

$\$10{,}000 \times 0.05 = \underline{\quad\$500\quad}$

$\$3{,}000 - 2{,}900 = \underline{\quad\$100\quad}$

$\underline{\quad\text{Dan}\quad}$

4. During work one summer, Enrique and Maria saved $1,500 together. Their uncle borrowed the money for one year, paying 20 percent per year. How much interest did their uncle pay at the end of the year?

$I = PRT$

$\dfrac{(\$1{,}500)(0.20)(1)}{\$300}$

$\underline{\quad\$300\quad}$

5. A bride and groom received $10,000 as gifts from their parents and friends. They invested it in bonds paying 12 percent per year. They also had savings of $10,000. At what yearly rate of interest is their savings of $10,000 invested if they earn $2,600 in one year from their total investments?

Let $x =$ the rate of interest earned by savings investment (in percent).

Source of investment	Dollar investment	Yearly rate	Interest earned in one year
Wedding gifts	$10,000	12 percent	0.12($10,000)
Savings	$10,000	n	n($10,000)

$$0.12(\$10,000) + n(\$10,000) = \$2,600$$
$$1,200 + 10,000n = 2,600$$

$$10,000n = 1,400$$

$$n = \frac{1,400}{10,000} = \frac{14}{100} = 14 \text{ percent}$$

14 percent interest

Check: $0.12(\$10,000) + n(\$10,000) = \$2,600$
$$1,200 + \frac{0.14(10,000)}{} = 2,600$$
$$1,200 + \frac{1,400}{} = 2,600$$
$$2,600 = 2,600$$

6. Part of $30,000 was invested in a bank paying ten percent interest and part in a bank paying six percent interest. If the total income from both investments was $2,600 annually, how much was invested in the bank paying ten percent interest?

Let n = the investment at ten percent (in dollars).

$30,000 - n$ = investment at six percent (in dollars).

Kind of investment	Dollar investment	Yearly rate	Interest earned in one year
First part	n	10 percent	$0.10n$
Second part	$30,000 - n$	6 percent	$0.06(30,000 - n)$

$$0.10n + 0.06(\$30,000 - n) = \$2,600$$

$$10n + 180,000 - 6n = 260,000$$
$$4n = 80,000$$
$$n = 20,000 \text{ (investment at 10 percent)}$$
$$30,000 - n = 10,000 \text{ (investment at 6 percent)}$$

$20,000 invested at 10 percent

Check: $0.10n + 0.06(\$30,000 - n) = \$2,600$

$$\frac{0.10(20,000)}{2,000 + 600} + 0.06(30,000 - \$20,000) = 2,600$$

$$\underline{2,000 + 600} = 2,600$$

$$2,600 = 2,600$$

7. A lawyer invested a certain sum of money in municipal bonds paying 8 percent and twice as much in municipal bonds paying 12 percent. How much was invested in each if the yearly yield from both investments was $32,000?

Let $n =$ the investment at 8 percent (in dollars).

$2n =$ investment at 12 percent (in dollars)

Kind of investment	Dollar investment	Yearly rate	Interest earned in one year
First part	n	8 percent	$0.08n$
Second part	$2n$	12 percent	$0.12(2n)$

$$\underline{0.08n} + 0.12(2n) = \underline{\$32,000}$$

$$8n + 12(2n) = 3,200,000$$

$$8n + 24n = 3,200,000$$

$$32n = 3,200,000$$

$$\underline{n = \$100,000} \text{ (in dollars, investment at 8 percent)}$$

$$2n = 200,000 \text{ (in dollars, investment at 12 percent)}$$

Invested at 8 percent: **$100,000**
Invested at 12 percent: **$200,000**

Check: $0.08n + 0.12(2n) = \$32,000$

$$0.08(100,000) + 0.12[2(100,000)] = 32,000$$

$$8,000 + \frac{0.12(200,000)}{} = 32,000$$

$$8,000 + \underline{24,000} = 32,000$$

$$32,000 = \underline{32,000}$$

8. The same amount of interest is earned from two investments. One investment earns 12 percent while twice the amount invested at 12 percent earns 6 percent in another investment. Find the amount invested at each rate if the yearly yield from both investments was $7,200.

Let $n =$ the amount invested at 12 percent (in dollars).

$2n =$ amount invested at 6 percent (in dollars)

Investment	Principal (in dollars)	Yearly rate	Interest for one year
First	n	12 percent	0.12n
Second	2n	6 percent	0.06(2n)

$$0.12n + \underline{0.06(2n)} = \$7,200$$

$$12n + 6(2n) = 720,000$$

$$12n + \underline{12n} = 720,000$$

$$\underline{24n} = 720,000$$

$$n = \underline{\$30,000} \text{ (investment at 12 percent)}$$

$$2n = \$60,000 \text{ (investment at 6 percent)}$$

Invested at 12 percent: **$30,000**
Invested at 6 percent: **$60,000**

Check: $0.12n + 0.06(2n) = \$7,200$

$$\underline{0.12(30,000)} + 0.06(\$60,000) = \$7,200$$

$$3,600 + 3,600 = 7,200$$

$$\underline{7,200} = 7,200$$

9. A lot was sold for $60,000. In doing so, the owner gained 20 percent of the original price. How much did the owner originally pay for the lakefront property?

Let n = the original price of lot (in dollars).

$$\underline{0.20n} = \text{gain}$$

$$n + 0.20n = \$60,000$$

$$\underline{1.20n} = 60,000$$

$$n = \$50,000$$

$50,000

Check: $n + 0.20n = \$60,000$

$$\underline{50,000} + 0.20(50,000) = 60,000$$

$$50,000 + \underline{10,000} = 60,000$$

$$\underline{60,000} = 60,000$$

10. Ms. Phelp invested a sum of money in 10 percent bonds and three times as much in 20 percent bonds. The annual income received from these investments was $7,000. How much was invested in each type of bond?

Let n = the amount invested at 10 percent (in dollars).

$3n$ = the amount invested at 20 percent (in dollars)

Kind of investment	Dollar investment	Yearly rate	Interest earned in one year
First	n	10 percent	0.10n
Second	3n	20 percent	0.20(3n)

$\dfrac{0.10n + 0.20(3n)}{} = \$7,000$

$10n + 20(3n) = 700,000$

$10n + 60n = 700,000$

$\dfrac{70n}{} = 700,000$

$n = \underline{\$10,000}$ (investment at 10 percent)

$3n = \underline{\$30,000}$ (investment at 20 percent)

Invested at 10 percent: **$10,000**
Invested at 20 percent: **$30,000**

Check: $0.10n + \dfrac{0.20(3n)}{} = \$7,000$

$0.10(10,000) + 0.20(30,000) = \$7,000$

$1,000 + \dfrac{6,000}{} = 7,000$

$7,000 = 7,000$

Challenge

11. Mr. Bradley invested $200,000 at 10 percent. How much additional money must he invest at 4 percent in order for his total annual income to be $6\frac{2}{5}$ percent of his entire investment?

Let n = the amount invested at 4 percent (in dollars).

$200,000$ = the amount invested at 10 percent (in dollars)

$200,000 + n$ = the total amount invested (in dollars)

Kind of investment	Dollar investment	Yearly rate	Interest earned in one year
Initial	$200,000	10 percent	0.10(200,000)
Additional	n	4 percent	0.04(n)

$0.10(200,000) + \dfrac{0.04n}{} = 0.064(200,000 + n)$

$100(\$200,000) + \dfrac{40n}{} = 64(\$200,000 + n)$

$\$20,000,000 + 40n = \$12,800,000 + 64n$

$\dfrac{-24n}{} = -\$7,200,000$

$n = \dfrac{\$300,000}{}$ (investment at 4%) $\underline{\$300,000}$

Check: $0.10(\$200,000) + 0.04n = 0.064(\$200,000 + n)$

$20,000 + 0.04(300,000) = 0.064(200,000 + 300,000)$

$20,000 + 12,000 = 0.064(500,000)$

$32,000 = 32,000$

Investment Problems

DIRECTIONS: Use the five levels of comprehension to solve each of the problems in the space provided. Write your answers in the blank to the right after each problem.

1. A widow invested $90,000 at ten percent annual rate. How much must she invest at six percent in order for her annual income to be $1,000 per month?

   Let x = the amount to be invested at six percent (in dollars).

   $0.10(\$90,000) + 0.06x = \$12,000$

   $9,000 + 0.06x = 12,000$

   $0.06x = 3,000$

   $x = \$50,000$ (investment at six percent) $\underline{\$50,000}$

   Check: $0.10(\$90,000) + 0.06x = \$12,000$

   $\qquad 9,000 + 0.06(50,000) = 12,000$

   $\qquad 9,000 + 3,000 = 12,000$

   $\qquad 12,000 = 12,000$

2. Ms. Clements invested $80,000 at an annual rate of 12 percent and $200,000 at an annual rate of 10 percent. Miss Weidman invested $80,000 at an annual rate of 10 percent and $200,000 at an annual rate of 12 percent. Which lady earned more interest? What is the difference in amounts earned?

   $I = PRT$

Person	Dollar investment	Yearly rate	Interest earned in one year
Ms. Clements	$80,000	12%	$9,600
	$200,000	10%	$20,000
Miss Weidman	$80,000	10%	$8,000
	$200,000	12%	$24,000

   Check: Ms. Clements:

   $\qquad I = 0.12(\$80,000) + 0.10(\$200,000)$

   $\qquad I = 9,600 + 20,000 = \$29,600$

Miss Weidman:

I = 0.10($80,000) + 0.12($200,000)

I = 8,000 + 24,000 = $32,000

Difference: $32,000 − $29,600 = $2,400

Miss Weidman: **$2,400**

3. Will $25,000 invested at 10 percent and $50,000 invested at 15 percent return the same amount on an annual basis as $100,000 invested at 10 percent?

$I = PRT$

Dollar investment	Yearly rate	Interest earned in one year	
$25,000	10 percent	$2,500	} $10,000
$50,000	15 percent	$7,500	
$100,000	10 percent	$10,000	$10,000

Check: 0.10($25,000) + 0.15($50,000) = 0.10($110,000)

2,500 + 7,500 = 10,000

$10,000 = $10,000   Yes

4. Will $8,000 invested at 10 percent and $8,000 invested at 20 percent yield the same amount as $16,000 invested at 30 percent?

$I = PRT$

Dollar investment	Yearly rate	Interest earned in one year
$8,000	10 percent	$800
$8,000	20 percent	$1,600
$16,000	30 percent	$4,800

Check: 0.10($8,000) + 0.20($8,000)

= 800 + 1,600

= $2,400

0.30(16,000)

= 4,800

= $4,800

$2,400 < $4,800   No

5. Part of $20,000 was invested in bonds paying eight percent interest, and part in a mortgage paying five percent interest. How much was invested in each if the total annual income from both investments was $1,450?

Let x = the amount invested at eight percent (in dollars).

$20,000 - x$ = the amount invested at five percent (in dollars)

Kind of investment	Dollar investment	Yearly rate	Interest earned in one year
In bonds	x	8 percent	0.08x
In mortgage	$20,000 - x$	5 percent	0.05($20,000 - x$)

$0.08x + 0.05(\$20,000 - x) = \$1,450$

$8x + 100,000 - 5x = 145,000$

$3x + 100,000 = 145,000$

$3x = 45,000$

$x = \$15,000$ (investment at eight percent, in dollars)

$\$20,000 - x = \$5,000$ (investment at five percent, in dollars)

Investment at eight percent: $15,000
Investment at five percent: $5,000

Check: $0.08x + 0.05(\$20,000 - x) = \$1,450$

$8x + 5(20,000 - x) = 145,000$ (dollars)

$8(15,000) + 5(5,000) = 145,000$

$120,000 + 25,000 = 145,000$

$145,000 = 145,000$ (dollars)

6. A contractor invested a certain sum in a mortgage paying 15 percent and twice as much in a mortgage paying 20 percent. How much was invested in each if the yearly yield from both investments was $11,000?

Let n = the amount invested in mortgage paying 15 percent (in dollars).

$2n$ = the amount invested in mortgage paying 20 percent (in dollars)

Kind of investment	Dollar investment	Yearly rate	Interest earned in one year
Mortgage 1	n	15 percent	0.15n
Mortgage 2	$2n$	20 percent	0.20(2n)

$0.15n + 0.20(2n) = \$11{,}000$

$0.15n + 0.40n = 11{,}000$

$0.55n = 11{,}000$

$55n = 1{,}100{,}000$

$n = \$20{,}000$ (investment in mortgage 1)

$2n = \$40{,}000$ (investment in mortgage 2)

Investment in Mortgage	$20,000
Investment in Mortgage	$40,000

Check: $0.15n + 0.20(2n) = \$11{,}000$

$0.15n + 0.40n = 11{,}000$

$0.15(\$20{,}000) + 0.40(\$20{,}000) = 11{,}000$

$3{,}000 + 8{,}000 = 11{,}000$

$11{,}000 = 11{,}000$

7. A sum of money invested at 10 percent produces the same interest as an investment of $30,000 more than the previous sum at 4 percent. Find the amount invested at each rate.

Let n = the investment at ten percent (investment 1—in dollars)

$n + \$30{,}000$ = investment at four percent (investment 2—in dollars)

Kind of investment	Dollar investment	Yearly rate	Interest earned in one year
Investment 1	n	10 percent	$0.10n$
Investment 2	$n + \$30{,}000$	4 percent	$0.04(n + 30{,}000)$

$0.10n = 0.04(n + \$30{,}000)$

$10n = 4(n + 30{,}000)$

$10n = 4n + 120{,}000$

$6n = 120{,}000$

$n = \$20{,}000$ (investment at ten percent)

$n + \$30{,}000 = \$50{,}000$ (investment at four percent)

Investment at ten percent:	$20,000
Investment at four percent:	$50,000

Check: $0.10n = 0.04(n + \$30{,}000)$

$0.10(20{,}000) = 0.04(20{,}000 + 30{,}000)$

$2{,}000 = 0.04(50{,}000)$

$2{,}000 = 2{,}000$

8. A lot was sold for $180,000. In selling it, the owner lost ten percent of the amount he paid for the lot. How much was the original price of the lot?

Let x = the original price of the lot (in dollars).

$0.10x$ = the amount lost in the transaction (in dollars)

$x - 0.10x = \$180,000$

$0.90x = 180,000$

$x = 200,000$ (original price, in dollars)

Original price: $200,000

Check: $x - 0.10x = \$180,000$

$200,000 - 0.10(200,000) = 180,000$

$200,000 - 20,000 = 180,000$

$180,000 = 180,000$

9. Dorothy Goldman invested a sum of money in eight-percent bonds and twice as much in ten-percent bonds. Her annual income from these bonds was $5,600. How much was invested in each type of bond?

Let n = the amount invested at eight percent (investment 1—in dollars).

$2n$ = the amount invested at ten percent (investment 2—in dollars)

Type of bond	Dollar investment	Yearly rate	Interest earned in one year
Investment 1	n	8 percent	$0.08n$
Investment 2	$2n$	10 percent	$0.10(2n)$

$0.08n + 0.10(2n) = \$5,600$

$8n + 10(2n) = 560,000$

$8n + 20n = 560,000$

$28n = 560,000$

$n = 20,000$ (investment at eight percent, in dollars)

$2n = \$40,000$ (investment at ten percent, in dollars)

Investment at eight percent: $20,000
Investment at ten percent: $40,000

Check: $0.08n + 0.10(2n) = \$5,600$

$0.08(20,000) + 0.10(40,000) = 5,600$

$1,600 + 4,000 = 5,600$

$5,600 = 5,600$ (dollars)

10. When he retires, a major league ballplayer will receive a pension of $200,000 a year for life. How much money must he invest at ten percent before he retires to supplement his pension and thus receive $300,000 per year, to maintain his present lifestyle?

Let x = money to be invested at ten percent (in dollars).

$200,000 + 0.10(x) = $300,000

$0.10x = 100,000$

$x = $1,000,000$ <u>**$1,000,000**</u>

Check: $200,000 + 0.10x = $300,000

                $200,000 + 0.10(1,000,000) = 300,000

                $200,000 + 100,000 = 300,000

                $300,000 = 300,000

Challenge

11. Barbara Ishikawa invested $800,000 at ten percent. How much additional money must she invest at four percent in order that her total annual income will equal eight percent of her entire investment?

Let n = the investment at four percent needed in order to have a yearly yield of eight percent of her entire investment (in dollars).

Kind of investment	Dollar investment	Yearly rate	Interest earned in one year
Original	$800,000	10 percent	0.10($800,000)
Additional	n	4 percent	0.04n

$0.10($800,000) + 0.04(n) = 0.08($800,000 + n)$

$10(800,000) + 4n = 8(800,000 + n)$

$8,000,000 + 4n = 6,400,000 + 8n$

$-4n = -1,600,000$

$n = $400,000$ (investment at four percent, in dollars)

                <u>Investment at four percent: $400,000</u>

Check: $0.10($800,000) + 0.04n = 0.08($800,000 + n)$

          $0.10(800,000) + 0.04(400,000) = 0.08(800,000 + 400,000)$

          $80,000 + 16,000 = 64,000 + 32,000$

          $96,000 = 96,000$

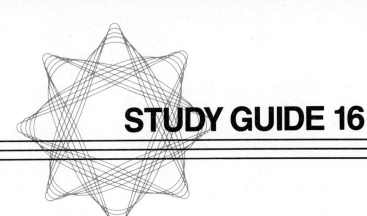

STUDY GUIDE 16

Work

TERMS AND CONCEPTS

Introductory Precepts

If it takes eight hours to complete a task by working at a steady rate, then the part of the work completed in one hour is $\frac{1}{8}$. After three hours of work, the part completed is $3 \cdot \left(\frac{1}{8}\right)$ or $\frac{3}{8}$ of the job. If it takes x hours to complete a job, then the part of the work completed in one hour is $\frac{1}{x}$, assuming there is no rate change. After x hours of work, the part completed is $x \cdot \left(\frac{1}{x}\right)$ or 1—the complete job! The fractional part of the job completed plus the fractional part of the job yet to be completed must always equal 1.

In the work problems of this study guide, unless otherwise stated, assume that the worker and the machine operate at a uniform rate.

LEVELS OF COMPREHENSION

STEP 1 Read the problem.

STEP 2 Choose the variable(s).

STEP 3 Form the equation.

STEP 4 Solve the equation.

STEP 5 Check the equation.

MODEL PROBLEM 1

John can paint a house in six hours. His sister Ellen can paint the same house in eight hours. How long would it take John and Ellen to paint the house if they work together?

READ THE PROBLEM

After reading the problem, give the answers to the following statements or questions in the spaces provided.

Literal Level

John can paint the house in _____six_____ hours. Ellen can paint the house in _____eight_____ hours. How many hours will it take John and Ellen to paint the house if they work _____together_____?

Interpretive Level

1. In one hour, John can complete what fractional part of the work?

   $\dfrac{1}{6}$, $\dfrac{6}{1}$, $\dfrac{1}{8}$, $\dfrac{8}{1}$,   none of these $\dfrac{1}{6}$

2. In one hour, Ellen can complete what fractional part of the work?

   $\dfrac{1}{6}$, $\dfrac{6}{1}$, $\dfrac{1}{8}$, $\dfrac{8}{1}$,   none of these $\dfrac{1}{8}$

3. In x hours, John can complete what fractional part of the work?

   $\dfrac{x}{8}$, $\dfrac{x}{6}$, $\dfrac{8}{x}$, $8x$,   none of these $\dfrac{x}{6}$

4. In x hours, Ellen can complete what fractional part of the work?

   $\dfrac{x}{8}$, $\dfrac{x}{6}$, $\dfrac{8}{x}$, $8x$,   none of these $\dfrac{x}{8}$

5. The fractional part that John completes in x hours plus the fractional part Ellen completes in x hours should equal:

   14, $\dfrac{1}{14}$, 1,   none of these 1

CHOOSE THE VARIABLE(S)

Let x = the number of hours it takes to paint the house if both John and Ellen work together.

Painter	Completes job	Part of job done in one hour	Part of job done in x hours
John	In 6 hours	$\dfrac{1}{6}$	$\dfrac{x}{6}$
Ellen	In 8 hours	$\dfrac{1}{8}$	$\dfrac{x}{8}$

Application Level

FORM THE EQUATION

$$\frac{x}{6} + \frac{x}{8} = 1$$

SOLVE THE EQUATION

$$\frac{x}{6} + \frac{x}{8} = 1$$

$$4x + 3x = 24$$

$$7x = 24$$

$$x = \underline{\quad 3\frac{3}{7} \quad} \text{ hours (working together)} \qquad \underline{3\frac{3}{7} \text{ hours}}$$

CHECK THE EQUATION

$$\frac{x}{6} + \frac{x}{8} = 1$$

$$\frac{\frac{24}{7}}{6} + \frac{\frac{24}{7}}{8} = 1$$

$$4\left(\frac{24}{7}\right) + 3\left(\frac{24}{7}\right) = 24$$

$$\left(\frac{96}{7}\right) + \left(\frac{72}{7}\right) = 24$$

$$\frac{168}{7} = 24$$

$$24 = 24$$

ACTIVITY EXTENSION

If Ellen worked faster than John, how would the total hours be changed?

It would be less than $3\frac{3}{7}$ hours.

MODEL PROBLEM 2

A farmer can thrash a field of wheat in 24 hours by using his combine. After he uses the combine for 16 hours, it breaks down. Using his old reaper and thrasher, he can harvest the field in 150 hours. After the combine broke down, the farmer finished the work by using the old equipment. How long did it take the farmer to finish the work he had started with the combine?

READ THE PROBLEM

After reading the problem, give the answers to the following statements or questions in the spaces provided.

Literal Level

The farmer can harvest the wheat using a combine in __24__ hours. The farmer can harvest the field using older equipment in __150__ hours. After __16__ hours, the combine breaks down. The farmer then decides to use the older equipment to __finish__ the job he had started with the __combine__. Find how many hours the __old-fashioned__ equipment was used.

Interpretive Level

1. In one hour with the combine, the farmer can complete what fractional part of the harvesting?

   $\frac{1}{24}$, $\frac{24}{1}$, $\frac{x}{24}$,   none of these   __$\frac{1}{24}$__

2. In 16 hours with the combine, the farmer can complete what fractional part of the harvesting?

   $\frac{24}{16}$, $\frac{16}{24}$, $\frac{1}{1}$,   none of these   __$\frac{16}{24}$__

3. In one hour with the old equipment, the farmer can complete what fractional part of the harvesting?

   $\frac{24}{25}$, $\frac{1}{150}$, $\frac{150}{1}$,   none of these   __$\frac{1}{150}$__

4. In x hours with the old machinery, the farmer can complete what fractional part of the harvesting?

   $\frac{x}{150}$, $\frac{x}{25}$, $x + 150$,   none of these   __$\frac{x}{150}$__

CHOOSE THE VARIABLE(S)

Let x = the number of hours that old equipment must be used.

Machinery	Hours to do job alone	Part of harvesting done in one hour	Part of job done in 16 hours	Part of job done in x hours
Combine	24 hr	$\dfrac{1}{24}$	$\dfrac{16}{24}$	—
Old equipment	150 hr	$\dfrac{1}{150}$	—	$\dfrac{x}{150}$

Application Level

FORM THE EQUATION

$$\frac{16}{24} + \frac{x}{150} = 1$$

SOLVE THE EQUATION

$$\frac{2}{3} + \frac{x}{150} = 1$$

$$\frac{x}{150} = \frac{1}{3}$$

$$3x = 150$$

$$x = \underline{\text{50 hours}} \quad \text{(number of hours that old equipment must be used)}$$

<u>50 hours</u>

CHECK THE EQUATION

$$\frac{16}{24} + \frac{x}{150} = 1$$

$$\frac{\frac{2}{3}}{} + \frac{50}{150} = 1$$

$$1 = 1$$

ACTIVITY EXTENSION

If the farmer had used the combine for 12 hours before it broke down, then he would have completed one-half of the work. If the old machinery working alone could harvest the field in 150 hours, how many hours would the farmer have to use this equipment to complete the last half of the harvesting?

<u>75 hours</u>

MODEL PROBLEM 3

A condominium builder is beginning a construction project that has a completion date of 240 days and requires that 100 workers work eight hours a day. After work has progressed for 180 days, 20 days are lost because of bad weather. How many more workers must be employed to work eight hours per day to complete the construction on schedule?

READ THE PROBLEM

After reading the problem, give the answers to the following statements or questions in the spaces provided.

Literal Level

Using 100 workers for eight hours a day, a condominium can be completed in __240__ days. __Twenty__ days are lost because of bad weather. How many more workers working eight hours a day must be employed in order to meet the completion __date (deadline)__? Each day, 100 workers working eight hours a day will expend __800__ labor-hours. If no further problems arise, the building will be complete after 240 days or __192,000__ labor-hours. During the inclement weather, __16,000__ labor-hours are lost. The condominium must be completed in __40 days__. If x = the number of extra workers to be hired, then for 40 days there will be __$(100 + x)(8)(40)$__ labor-hours expended.

CHOOSE THE VARIABLE(S)

Interpretive Level

Let x = the number of workers to be hired in order to meet deadline. Then
100 = the number of workers to be employed if there are no problems with completion date

__$100(8)$__ = the number of labor-hours expended each day

$100(8)(240)$ = the number of labor-hours required in order to complete work without problems

$100(8)(180)$ = the number of labor-hours expended prior to bad weather

$100(8)(20)$ = the number of labor-hours lost during bad weather

__$(100 + x)(8)(40)$__ = number of labor-hours expended after bad weather subsides

FORM THE EQUATION

Application Level

$100(8)(180) + (100 + x)(8)(40) = 100(8)(240)$

SOLVE THE EQUATION

$100(8)(180) + (100 + x)(8)(40) = 100(8)(240)$

$144,000 + 320(100 + x) = 192,000$

$144,000 + \underline{\quad 32,000 \quad} + 320x = 192,000$

$176,000 + 320x = 192,000$

$\underline{\quad 320x \quad} = 16,000$

$x = \underline{\quad 50 \quad}$ (men to be hired)

$\underline{\quad 50 \text{ men} \quad}$

CHECK THE EQUATION

$100(8)(180) + (100 + x)(8)(40) = 100(8)(240)$

$\underline{\quad 144,000 \quad} + 320(100 + 50) = 192,000$

$144,000 + 320(150) = 192,000$

$144,000 + \underline{\quad 48,000 \quad} = 192,000$

$\underline{\quad 192,000 \quad} = 192,000$

Model Problem 4 is an alternate solution for Model Problem 3.

MODEL PROBLEM 4

A condominium builder is beginning a construction project that has a completion date of 240 days using 100 workers eight hours a day. After work has progressed for 180 days, 20 days are lost because of bad weather. How many more workers must be employed to work eight hours per day to complete the construction on schedule?

READ THE PROBLEM

After reading the problem, give the answers to the following statements in the spaces provided.

Literal Level

The total labor-hours required to complete job is $\underline{100(8)(240)}$ $\underline{= 192,000}$. The total labor-hours expended through 180 days is $\underline{(100)(8)(180) = 144,000}$. The part completed by end of 180 days is

$\underline{\dfrac{144,000}{192,000} = \dfrac{3}{4}}$

CHOOSE THE VARIABLE(S)

Interpretive Level

One-fourth of the job needs to be completed. Let x = the number of workers to be hired in order to meet the deadline. Then the number of labor-hours done by entire crew in 40 days is $(100 + x)(8)(40)$.

Application Level

FORM THE EQUATION

$$\dfrac{3}{4} + \dfrac{(100 + x)(8)(40)}{192,000} = 1 \quad \text{or} \quad \dfrac{(100 + x)(8)(40)}{192,000} = \dfrac{1}{4}$$

SOLVE THE EQUATION

$$\dfrac{3}{4} + \dfrac{(100 + x)(8)(40)}{192,000} = 1 \quad \text{or} \quad \dfrac{(100 + x)(8)(40)}{192,000} = \dfrac{1}{4}$$

$$\dfrac{32,000 + 320x}{192,000} = \dfrac{1}{4}$$

$$128,000 + 1,280x = 192,000$$

$$1,280x = 64,000$$

$$x = 50 \text{ (workers to be hired)} \qquad \underline{\textbf{50 workers}}$$

CHECK THE EQUATION

$$\dfrac{3}{4} + \dfrac{(100 + x)(8)(40)}{192,000} = 1$$

$$\dfrac{3}{4} + \dfrac{(100 + 50)(320)}{192,000} = 1$$

$$\dfrac{3}{4} + \dfrac{(150)(320)}{192,000} = 1$$

$$\dfrac{3}{4} + \dfrac{48,000}{192,000} = 1$$

$$\dfrac{3}{4} + \dfrac{1}{4} = 1$$

$$1 = 1$$

Name _____ Period _____

Teacher _____ Date _____ Grade _____

Work Problems with Help

DIRECTIONS: Each of the following problems has been given a partial solution. Solve each problem by completing the given solution.

Arithmetic is all that is really required for problems 1 through 3. Forming equations and using schematics lend understanding to approach and readiness for problems 4 through 9.

1. After many years of probing for treasures lost long ago during a hurricane at sea, divers struck it rich. If eight workers could bring 25 gold bars to the surface each day, how many days did it take them to recover 1,000 gold bars? (Assume that the work proceeded at a uniform rate.)

   Let x = the number of days required to retrieve 1,000 gold bars.

   $25x = 1,000$

   $x =$ ___**40**___ days   ___**40 days**___

   Check: $25x = 1,000$

   $$\frac{25(40)}{} = 1,000$$

   $$1,000 = 1,000$$

2. A caterer can make 4,000 items in 20 hours for a party. After working for 10 hours, he cuts his hand. How many other caterers, each capable of making 1,000 items in ten hours, must be employed to complete the order within 20 hours?

   Let x = the number of additional caterers.

Workers	Number	Items	Time	Items completed in 10 hours
				$\left(\dfrac{10}{20}\right) \cdot (4,000)$
Original caterer	1	___4,000___	20 hr	or 2,000
Additional caterers	x	1,000	10 hr	1,000x

   $$\frac{1,000x}{} = \frac{2,000}{}$$

   $x =$ ___**2 caterers**___   ___**2 caterers**___

   Check: $1,000x = 2,000$

   $$1,000(2) = 2,000$$

   $$2,000 = 2,000$$

3. Martha and Laura work for a landscaping contractor. Martha can lay 500 square feet of sod in eight hours. Laura can lay 500 square feet of sod in 12 hours. The two women work together for two hours. Because of the threat of rain, they ask Anson to help them finish. How long should it take Anson to lay 500 square feet of sod if the three of them are to finish in one hour?

Let x = the number of hours required by Anson to lay 500 square feet of sod.

Worker	Time required for laying 500 square feet	Part finished in 1 hour	Part finished in 2 hours
Martha	8 hours	$\dfrac{1}{8}$	$\dfrac{2}{8}$
Laura	12 hours	$\dfrac{1}{12}$	$\dfrac{2}{12}$
Anson	x hours	$\dfrac{1}{x}$	—

$$\frac{1}{8} + \frac{2}{8} + \frac{1}{12} + \frac{2}{12} + \frac{1}{x} = 1$$

$$\frac{3}{8} + \frac{3}{12} + \frac{1}{x} = 1$$

$$\frac{\frac{5}{8}}{} + \frac{1}{x} = 1$$

$$\frac{\frac{1}{x}}{} = \frac{3}{8}$$

$$3x = 8$$

$x = \dfrac{\frac{8}{3}}{}$ (number of hours required by Anson to lay 500 square feet of sod)

$\dfrac{8}{3}$ **hours**

Check: $\dfrac{1}{8} + \dfrac{2}{8} + \dfrac{1}{12} + \dfrac{2}{12} + \dfrac{1}{x} = 1$

$$\frac{1}{8} + \frac{2}{8} + \frac{\frac{1}{12}}{} + \frac{2}{12} + \frac{1}{\frac{8}{3}} = 1$$

$$\frac{3}{8} + \frac{3}{12} + \frac{3}{8} = 1$$

$$\frac{6}{8} + \frac{\frac{1}{4}}{\underline{\hspace{1cm}}} = 1$$

$$\frac{6}{8} + \frac{2}{8} = 1$$

$$1 = 1$$

4. Chao-cheng can cut a lawn in 16 hours. Her brother can cut the lawn in eight hours. How long will it take Chao-cheng and her brother to cut the lawn working together?

Let x = the number of hours it will take to cut lawn if sister and brother work together.

Person	Working alone	Part done in one hour	Part done in x hours
Chao-cheng	16	$\frac{1}{16}$	$\frac{x}{16}$
Her brother	8	$\frac{1}{8}$	$\frac{x}{8}$

$$\left(\frac{x}{16}\right) + \left(\frac{x}{8}\right) = 1$$

$$32 \cdot \left(\frac{x}{16}\right) + 32 \cdot \left(\frac{x}{8}\right) = 32 \cdot 1$$

$$2x + 4x = 32$$

$$6x = 32$$

$$x = 5\frac{1}{3} \text{ hours (if sister and brother work together)}$$

$$5\frac{1}{3} \text{ hours} = 5.33 \text{ hours}$$

Check: $\left(\frac{x}{16}\right) + \left(\frac{x}{8}\right) = 1$

$$\left[\left(\frac{16}{3}\right) \div 16\right] + \left[\left(\frac{16}{3}\right) \div 8\right] = 1$$

$$\left(\frac{1}{3}\right) + \left(\frac{2}{3}\right) = 1$$

$$\frac{3}{3} = \frac{3}{3}$$

5. Al can paint a house in 20 days. Bob can paint the same house in 40 days. Carla can paint the same house in 15 days. How long will it take them to paint the house if they work together?

Let x = the number of hours it will take if all three work together.

Painter	Working alone	Part done in one hour	Part done in x hours
Al	20	$\frac{1}{20}$	$\frac{x}{20}$
Bob	40	$\frac{1}{40}$	$\frac{x}{40}$
Carla	15	$\frac{1}{15}$	$\frac{x}{15}$

$$\frac{x}{20} + \frac{x}{40} + \frac{x}{15} = 1$$

$$120 \cdot \frac{x}{20} + 120 \cdot \frac{x}{40} + 120 \cdot \frac{x}{15} = 120 \cdot 1$$

$$6x + 3x + 8x = 120$$

$$17x = 120$$

$$x = \underline{\phantom{7\frac{1}{17}}} \text{ hours (if all three work together)}$$
$$7\frac{1}{17}$$

$$7\frac{1}{17} \text{ hours} \cong 7.0588 \text{ hours}$$

Check: $\left(\frac{x}{20}\right) + \left(\frac{x}{40}\right) + \left(\frac{x}{15}\right) = 1$

$$\left[\left(\frac{120}{17}\right) \div 20\right] + \left[\left(\frac{120}{17}\right) \div 40\right)\right] + \left[\left(\frac{120}{17}\right) \div 15\right] = 1$$

$$\left[\left(\frac{120}{17}\right) \cdot \frac{1}{20}\right] + \left[\left(\frac{120}{17}\right) \cdot \frac{1}{40}\right] + \left[\left(\frac{120}{17}\right) \cdot \frac{1}{15}\right] = 1$$

$$\left(\frac{6}{17}\right) + \left(\frac{3}{17}\right) + \left(\frac{8}{17}\right) = 1$$

$$1 = 1$$

6. A printing press can finish an order in 72 hours. A slower press can finish the same order in 150 hours. After working alone for 32 hours, the faster press breaks down. How long will it take the slower press to finish the order?

Let x = the number of hours it will take the slower press to finish.

Machine	Working alone	Part done in one hour	Part done in 32 hours	Part done in x hours
Faster press	72	$\dfrac{1}{72}$	$\dfrac{32}{72}$	—
Slower press	150	$\dfrac{1}{150}$	—	$\dfrac{x}{150}$

$$\left(\frac{32}{72}\right) + \left(\frac{x}{150}\right) = 1$$

$$\left(\frac{4}{9}\right) + \left(\frac{x}{150}\right) = 1$$

$$\frac{x}{150} = \frac{5}{9}$$

$$9x = 750$$

$$x = 83\frac{1}{3}$$ hours (time of the slower press)

$$83\frac{1}{3} \text{ hours} \cong 83.33 \text{ hours}$$

Check: $\left(\dfrac{32}{72}\right) + \left(\dfrac{x}{150}\right) = 1$

$$\left(\frac{4}{9}\right) + \left[\left(\frac{750}{9}\right) \div 150\right] = 1$$

$$\left(\frac{4}{9}\right) + \left[\left(\frac{750}{9}\right) \cdot \left(\frac{1}{150}\right)\right] = 1$$

$$\left(\frac{4}{9}\right) + \left(\frac{5}{9}\right) = 1$$

$$1 = 1$$

7. By means of one pipe, a tub can be filled in 20 minutes. By means of another pipe, the same tub can be filled in 40 minutes. How long will it take to fill the tub if both pipes are used?

Let x = the number of minutes to fill the tub with both pipes.

Pipe	Minutes if working alone	Part done in one minute	Part done in x minutes
Faster pipe	20	$\dfrac{1}{20}$	$\dfrac{x}{20}$
Slower pipe	40	$\dfrac{1}{40}$	$\dfrac{x}{40}$

$$\left(\frac{x}{20}\right) + \frac{\dfrac{x}{40}}{} = 1$$

$$40 \cdot \left(\frac{x}{20}\right) + 40 \cdot \left(\frac{x}{40}\right) = 40 \cdot 1$$

$$2x + x = 40$$

$$3x = 40$$

$$x = 13\frac{1}{3}$$

minutes (number of minutes to fill the tub with both pipes)

$$13\frac{1}{3} \text{ minutes} \cong 13.33 \text{ minutes}$$

Check: $\left(\dfrac{x}{20}\right) + \left(\dfrac{x}{40}\right) = 1$

$$\left[\left(\frac{40}{3}\right) \div 20\right] + \left[\left(\frac{40}{3}\right) \div 40\right] = 1$$

$$\left(\frac{40}{3}\right) \cdot \left(\frac{1}{20}\right) + \left(\frac{40}{3}\right) \cdot \left(\frac{1}{40}\right) = 1$$

$$\left(\frac{2}{3}\right) + \left(\frac{1}{3}\right) = 1$$

$$1 = 1$$

8. Working together, Sam and Linda can build cabinets for a new house in eight days. Working alone, Linda can build the cabinets in 12 days. How long would it take Sam to complete the cabinets if he works alone?

Let x = the number of days for Sam to build the cabinets if he works alone.

Cabinetmaker	Time if alone (days)	Part done in one day	Part done if working together for one day
Linda	12	$\dfrac{1}{12}$	$\dfrac{1}{8}$
Sam	x	$\dfrac{1}{x}$	

$$\left(\frac{1}{12}\right) + \left(\frac{1}{x}\right) = \frac{1}{8}$$

$$24 \cdot \left(\frac{1}{12}\right) + 24 \cdot \left(\frac{1}{x}\right) = 24 \cdot \left(\frac{1}{8}\right)$$

$$2 + \left(\frac{24}{x}\right) = 3$$

$$\frac{24}{x} = 1$$

$$x = 24$$ _____ days (days for Sam to build cabinets if working alone)

<u>**24 days**</u>

Check: $$\left(\frac{1}{12}\right) + \left(\frac{1}{x}\right) = \frac{1}{8}$$

$$\left(\frac{1}{12}\right) + \left(\frac{1}{24}\right) = \frac{1}{8}$$

$$24 \cdot \left(\frac{1}{12}\right) + 24 \cdot \left(\frac{1}{24}\right) = 24 \cdot \left(\frac{1}{8}\right)$$

$$2 + 1 = 3$$

$$3 = 3$$

Challenge

Part filled in *x* minutes minus part emptied in *x* minutes is equal to 1 when tank is filled.

9. Pipe A can fill a gasoline storage tank in 30 minutes. Pipe B can fill the gasoline storage tank in 15 minutes. The tank has an undetected leak that will empty the tank in 60 minutes. If both pipes are used to fill the tank when empty, and the undetected leak is draining the tank, how long will it take to fill the tank?

Let x = the number of minutes it will take to fill the tank with both pipes if the tank leaks.

Filling	Time to fill completely (minutes)	Part filled in one minute	Part filled in x minutes
By pipe A	30	$\frac{1}{30}$	$\frac{x}{30}$
By pipe B	15	$\frac{1}{15}$	$\frac{x}{15}$
Draining	Time for leak to drain	Part drained in one minute	Part drained in x minutes
Leak	60	$\frac{1}{60}$	$\frac{x}{60}$

$$\left(\frac{x}{30}\right) + \left(\frac{x}{15}\right) - \left(\frac{x}{60}\right) = 1$$

$$60 \cdot \left(\frac{x}{30}\right) + 60 \cdot \left(\frac{x}{15}\right) - 60 \cdot \left(\frac{x}{60}\right) = 60 \cdot 1$$

$$2x + 4x - x = 60$$

$$5x = 60$$

$$\underline{\quad x = 12 \quad}$$ minutes (time it will take to fill the tank with both pipes if the tank leaks)

12 minutes

Check: $\left(\dfrac{x}{30}\right) + \left(\dfrac{x}{15}\right) - \left(\dfrac{x}{60}\right) = 1$

$$\left(\frac{12}{30}\right) + \left(\frac{12}{15}\right) - \left(\frac{12}{60}\right) = 1$$

$$\left(\frac{2}{5}\right) + \left(\frac{4}{5}\right) - \left(\frac{1}{5}\right) = 1$$

$$\left(\frac{6}{5}\right) - \left(\frac{1}{5}\right) = 1$$

$$\frac{5}{5} = 1$$

$$1 = 1$$

Name _____ Period _____

Teacher _____ Date _____ Grade _____

Work Problems

DIRECTIONS: Use the five levels of comprehension to solve each of the problems in the space provided. Write your answers in the blank to the right after each problem.

1. A moving company employee can pack 500 items of crystal in 12 hours. Another employee can pack the same 500 items of crystal in 16 hours. How long would it take the two employees to pack the 500 items if they work together? Would more help be needed if the packing is expected to be finished in less than six hours?

   Let x = the number of hours it takes to pack crystal working together.

Packer	Time to do packing alone	Part done in one hour	Part done in x hours
Packer A	12 hr	$\frac{1}{12}$	$\frac{x}{12}$
Packer B	16 hr	$\frac{1}{16}$	$\frac{x}{16}$

$$\left(\frac{x}{12}\right) + \left(\frac{x}{16}\right) = 1$$

$$48 \cdot \left(\frac{x}{12}\right) + 48 \cdot \left(\frac{x}{16}\right) = 48 \cdot 1$$

$$4x + 3x = 48$$

$$7x = 48$$

$$x = 6\frac{6}{7} \text{ hours (for two packers working together)}$$

$$6\frac{6}{7} \text{ hours} \cong 6.857 \text{ hours; Yes}$$
_____

Check: $\left(\frac{x}{12}\right) + \left(\frac{x}{16}\right) = 1$

$\left(6\frac{6}{7} \div 12\right) + \left(6\frac{6}{7} \div 16\right) = 1$

$$\left[\left(\frac{48}{7}\right) \div 12\right] + \left[\left(\frac{48}{7}\right) \div 16\right] = 1$$

$$\left[\left(\frac{48}{7}\right) \cdot \left(\frac{1}{12}\right)\right] + \left[\left(\frac{48}{7}\right) \cdot \left(\frac{1}{16}\right)\right] = 1$$

$$\left(\frac{4}{7}\right) + \left(\frac{3}{7}\right) = 1$$

$$\frac{7}{7} = 1$$

$$1 = 1$$

2. Henrietta and Jasmine have found work in a shoe factory. Using an old machine, Henrietta can pierce 1,000 holes in jogging shoes in five minutes. Jasmine uses a new machine and pierces 5,000 holes in similar jogging shoes in five minutes. The two machines each work for two hours. The slower machine develops a problem. If Jasmine and Henrietta must complete an order involving 744,000 holes, how many hours will be required for the new machine to finish?

Let x = the number of hours new machine must work alone to fill the order.

Machine	Holes	Time	Number in two hours	Number done together in two hours
Old machine	1,000	5 min	24(1,000)	144,000
New machine	5,000	5 min	24(5,000)	

$12x \cdot 5{,}000$ = number of holes completed in x hours (new)

$144{,}000 + 12x \cdot 5{,}000 = 744{,}000$

$60{,}000x = 600{,}000$

$x = 10$ hours (for new machine to finish)   10 hours

Check: $144{,}000 + 12x \cdot 5{,}000 = 744{,}000$

$144{,}000 + 12 \cdot 10 \cdot 5{,}000 = 744{,}000$

$144{,}000 + 600{,}000 = 744{,}000$

$744{,}000 = 744{,}000$

3. Mercedes and her mother can complete a typing assignment in two hours if they work together. Mercedes's mother can complete the job working alone in eight hours. How long would it take Mercedes working alone to complete the job?

Let x = the number of hours for Mercedes to do the work alone.

Person	Time to complete alone (hours)	Part done in one hour	Part done together in one hour
Mercedes	x hr	$\frac{1}{x}$	$\frac{1}{2}$
Mother	8 hr	$\frac{1}{8}$	

$$\left(\frac{1}{x}\right) + \left(\frac{1}{8}\right) = \frac{1}{2}$$

$$8x \cdot \left(\frac{1}{x}\right) + 8x \cdot \left(\frac{1}{8}\right) = 8x \cdot \left(\frac{1}{2}\right)$$

$$8 + x = 4x$$

$$8 = 3x$$

$$\frac{8}{3} \text{ hours} = x \text{ (for Mercedes to do the work alone)}$$

$$\frac{8}{3} \text{ hours} \cong 2.67 \text{ hours}$$

Check:
$$\left(\frac{1}{x}\right) + \left(\frac{1}{8}\right) = \frac{1}{2}$$
$$\left[1 \div \left(\frac{8}{3}\right)\right] + \left(\frac{1}{8}\right) = \frac{1}{2}$$
$$\left[1 \cdot \left(\frac{3}{8}\right)\right] + \left(\frac{1}{8}\right) = \frac{1}{2}$$
$$\left(\frac{3}{8}\right) + \left(\frac{1}{8}\right) = \frac{1}{2}$$
$$\frac{4}{8} = \frac{1}{2}$$
$$\frac{1}{2} = \frac{1}{2}$$

4. Tom and Jerry can build a fence in 15 hours if they work together. Tom can build the fence alone in 20 hours. He works ten hours and stops because of rain. When the rain stops, he calls Jerry to help him complete the job. How long did the two work together to finish the fence?

Let x = the number of hours if Tom and Jerry work together.

Fence builder	Time to complete job alone (hours)	Part done in one hour	Part done in ten hours
Tom	20 hr	$\dfrac{1}{20}$	$\dfrac{10}{20}$

Fence builders	Time to complete job working together	Part done in one hour	Part done in x hours
Tom and Jerry	15 hr	$\dfrac{1}{15}$	$\dfrac{x}{15}$

$$\left(\frac{1}{2}\right) + \left(\frac{x}{15}\right) = 1$$

$$\left(\frac{x}{15}\right) = \frac{1}{2}$$

$$2x = 15$$

$$x = 7\frac{1}{2} \text{ hours (Tom and Jerry work together)}$$

$$7\frac{1}{2} \text{ hours} = 7.5 \text{ hours}$$

Check:
$$\left(\frac{1}{2}\right) + \left(\frac{x}{15}\right) = 1$$

$$\left(\frac{1}{2}\right) + \left[\left(\frac{15}{2}\right) \div 15\right] = 1$$

$$\left(\frac{1}{2}\right) + \left[\left(\frac{15}{2}\right) \cdot \frac{1}{15}\right] = 1$$

$$\left(\frac{1}{2}\right) + \left(\frac{1}{2}\right) = 1$$

$$\frac{2}{2} = 1$$

$$1 = 1$$

5. Three pipes can fill a tank working together in x hours. Pipe A can fill the tank working alone in 10 hours, pipe B can fill the tank working alone in 12 hours, and pipe C can fill the tank working alone in 20 hours. How long would it take the three pipes to fill the tank if all are turned on at the same time?

Let x = the number of hours for the three pipes working together to fill the tank.

Pipe	Time to complete job alone (hours)	Part done in one hour	Part done in x hours
Pipe A	10 hr	$\frac{1}{10}$	$\frac{x}{10}$
Pipe B	12 hr	$\frac{1}{12}$	$\frac{x}{12}$
Pipe C	20 hr	$\frac{1}{20}$	$\frac{x}{20}$

$$\left(\frac{x}{10}\right) + \left(\frac{x}{12}\right) + \left(\frac{x}{20}\right) = 1$$

$$60 \cdot \left(\frac{x}{10}\right) + 60 \cdot \left(\frac{x}{12}\right) + 60 \cdot \left(\frac{x}{20}\right) = 60 \cdot 1$$

$$6x + 5x + 3x = 60$$

$$14x = 60$$

$$x = 4\frac{2}{7} \text{ hours (for the three pipes working together to fill tank)}$$

$$4\frac{2}{7} \text{ hours} \cong 4.286 \text{ hours}$$

Check: $$\left(\frac{x}{10}\right) + \left(\frac{x}{12}\right) + \left(\frac{x}{20}\right) = 1$$

$$\left[\left(\frac{30}{7}\right) \div 10\right] + \left[\left(\frac{30}{7}\right) \div 12\right] + \left[\left(\frac{30}{7}\right) \div 20\right] = 1$$

$$\left[\left(\frac{30}{7}\right) \cdot \left(\frac{1}{10}\right)\right] + \left[\left(\frac{30}{7}\right) \cdot \left(\frac{1}{12}\right)\right] + \left[\left(\frac{30}{7}\right) \cdot \left(\frac{1}{20}\right)\right] = 1$$

$$\left(\frac{3}{7}\right) + \left(\frac{5}{14}\right) + \left(\frac{3}{14}\right) = 1$$

$$\left(\frac{6}{14}\right) + \left(\frac{5}{14}\right) + \left(\frac{3}{14}\right) = 1$$

$$\frac{14}{14} = 1$$

$$1 = 1$$

6. Two mechanical harvesters can harvest a field of grain in 80 hours. The faster harvester can do it alone in 100 hours, and the slower can do it alone in 120 hours. Is this information inconsistent?

Let x = the number of hours it would take if both harvesters work together.

Harvester	Time to complete job alone (hours)	Part done in one hour	Part done in x hours
Faster	100 hr	$\dfrac{1}{100}$	$\dfrac{x}{100}$
Slower	120 hr	$\dfrac{1}{120}$	$\dfrac{x}{120}$

$$\left(\frac{x}{100}\right) + \left(\frac{x}{120}\right) = 1$$

$$6x + 5x = 600$$

$$11x = 600$$

$$x = \frac{600}{11} \text{ hours (working together)} \qquad \underline{\text{Yes}}$$

Check: $\dfrac{x}{100} + \dfrac{x}{120} = 1$ However, $\dfrac{80}{100} + \dfrac{80}{120} \neq 1$

$$\left(\frac{600}{11} \div 100\right) + \left(\frac{600}{11} \div 120\right) = 1$$

$$\frac{6}{11} + \frac{5}{11} = 1$$

$$1 = 1$$

Challenge

7. One crane can move 200 tons of steel in 40 hours. Another crane can move only 120 tons of steel in 40 hours. How long would it take the two cranes working together to move 500 tons of steel?

Let x = the number of hours if both cranes working together.

Crane	By itself can move	In	In one hour can move	Time to move 500 tons by itself	Part of job done in one hour	Part of job done in x hour
First	200 ton	40 hr	5 ton	100 hr	$\dfrac{1}{100}$	$\dfrac{x}{100}$
Second	120 ton	40 hr	3 ton	$\dfrac{500}{3}$ hr	$\dfrac{1}{\left(\frac{500}{3}\right)}$	$\dfrac{x}{\left(\frac{500}{3}\right)}$

$$\frac{x}{100} + \frac{x}{\frac{500}{3}} = 1$$

$$\frac{500}{3}\left(\frac{x}{100} + \frac{x}{\frac{500}{3}}\right) = \frac{500}{3}(1)$$

$$\frac{5x}{3} + x = \frac{500}{3}$$

$$5x + 3x = 500$$

$$8x = 500$$

$$x = \frac{500}{8} \text{ hours}$$

$$\frac{500}{8} \text{ hours}$$

Check: $\dfrac{x}{100} + \dfrac{x}{\frac{500}{3}} = 1$

$$\left(\frac{500}{8} \div 100\right) + \left(\frac{500}{8} \div \frac{500}{3}\right) = 1$$

$$\frac{5}{8} + \frac{3}{8} = 1$$

$$1 = 1$$

STUDY GUIDE 17

Solving Equations for One Variable in Terms of Other Variables

TERMS AND CONCEPTS

Introductory Precepts

A variable may be a letter or symbol that represents an unknown quantity. The primary purpose of solving a problem is to find that unknown quantity or variable. A constant such as a number in arithmetic never changes in value. An *equation* is an equality of two expressions. It is made up of two members, one on each side of the equality symbol.

Remember these major principles for solving any equation:

This study guide does not follow all the levels of comprehension. Since most students need extra help in this area, it is included as a bonus.

1. You may *add* the same quantity to both members of an equation.

2. You may *subtract* the same quantity from both members of an equation.

3. You may *multiply* both members of an equation by the same quantity.

4. You may *divide* both members of an equation by the same quantity.

Study the examples on the following pages to better understand the parallel that exists between solving an equation for the only variable present and solving an equation for a single variable when there is more than one variable present. Your goal is to work with the equation, performing operations to isolate one variable. Always remember to treat each member of the equation the same. You may use one equation as a pattern for the other.

As you study the examples, fill in the answer blank with the term (answer) necessary to form an equality. Be sure to check all work.

LEVELS OF COMPREHENSION

STEP 1 Read the problem.

STEP 2 Solve the equation.

STEP 3 Check the equation.

MODEL PROBLEM 1

The perimeter of a triangle can be found by using the formula $p = a + b + c$. Solve this equation for the value of b. Be sure to check the equation.

READ THE PROBLEM

After reading the problem, give the answers to the following statements in the spaces provided.

Literal Level

Interpretive Level

The variables in the equation are __p, a, b, c__. There are __no__ constants in the equation. To find the value of a single variable when there are four variables, it is necessary to __isolate__ this variable by using algebraic __principles__.

SOLVE THE EQUATION

Application Level

Solve for b.

$p = a + b + c$

$p + (-a) + \underline{(-c)} = a + b + c + \underline{(-a)} + (-c)$ \qquad $\underline{p - a - c = b}$

$\underline{p - a - c} = b$

CHECK THE EQUATION

$p = a + b + c$

$p = a + (p - a - c) + c$

$p = \underline{a + p - a - c + c}$

$p = p$

MODEL PROBLEM 2

The area of a triangle can be found by using the formula $A = \frac{1}{2} bh$. Solve this equation for h. Be sure to check the equation.

READ THE PROBLEM

After reading the problem, give the answers to the following statements in the spaces provided.

Literal Level

Interpretive Level

The variables in the equation are _____*A, b, h*_____. The only constant is

$\frac{1}{2}$ _____. To find the value of a single variable when there are three

variables, it is necessary to _____*isolate*_____ this variable by using

algebraic principles.

SOLVE THE EQUATION

Application Level

Solve for *h*.

$$A = \frac{1}{2} bh$$

$$\frac{2A}{} = \frac{1}{2} \cdot 2 \, bh$$

$$2A = \frac{bh}{}$$

$$2A \cdot \frac{\frac{1}{b}}{} = bh \cdot \frac{1}{b}$$

$$\frac{2A}{b} = h$$

$$\frac{\frac{2A}{b} = h}{}$$

CHECK THE EQUATION

$$A = \frac{1}{2} bh$$

$$A = \frac{1}{2} b \, \frac{\left(\frac{2A}{b}\right)}{}$$

$$A = A$$

MODEL PROBLEM 3

The perimeter of a rectangle can be found by using the formula $p = 2(t + w)$. Solve for *w*. Be sure to check the equation.

READ THE PROBLEM

After reading the problem, give the answer to the following statements in the spaces provided.

Literal Level

Interpretive Level

The variables in the equation are _____*p, t, w*_____. The number 2 is a

_____*constant*_____. To find the value of a single variable when there are

three variables, it is necessary to isolate this _____*variable*_____ by using

algebraic principles.

SOLVE THE EQUATION

Solve for w.

$p = 2(t + w)$

$p \cdot \underline{\dfrac{1}{2}} = 2(t + w) \cdot \dfrac{1}{2}$

$\dfrac{p}{2} = \underline{t + w}$

$\dfrac{p}{2} + (-t) = t + w + \underline{(-t)}$

$\underline{\dfrac{p}{2} - t} = w$

$\underline{\dfrac{p}{2} - t = w}$

CHECK THE EQUATION

$p = 2(t + w)$

$p = 2(t + \dfrac{p}{2} - t)$

$p = 2 \ \underline{\left(\dfrac{p}{2}\right)}$

$p = \underline{p}$

Model Problems 1, 2, and 3 required methods of solution that range from the simple to the complex. First, the addition or subtraction method was used, and this was followed by the multiplication or division method. Model Problem 3 involved using addition or subtraction as well as multiplication or division; this method is considered the most complex of the three categories.

In Parts A, B, and C of the Exercises below, supply the correct answers in the blanks that are provided. If you are successful, then you know the basics of solving an equation for a variable in terms of other variables.

EXERCISES

PART A

Solve for the designated variable by use of addition or subtraction.

1. Equation:

    $10 + b + 6 = 14$

    Solve for b:

    $10 + b + 6 + \underline{(-6)} = 14 + (-6)$

    $10 + b = 8$

    $b + 10 = 8$

$b + 10 + \underline{(-10)} = 8 + (-10)$

$b = -2$ $\underline{b = -2}$

Check: $10 + b + 6 = 14$

$10 + \underline{(-2)} + 6 = 14$

$14 = 14$

2. Equation:

$a + b + c = p$

Solve for b:

$a + b + c + \underline{(-c)} = p + (-c)$

$a + b = p + (-c)$

$b + a = p + (-c)$

$b + a + \underline{(-a)} = p + (-c) + (-a)$

$b = p + (-c) + (-a)$ $\underline{b = p + (-c) + (-a)}$

Check: $a + b + c = p$

$a + \underline{p + (-c) + (-a)} + c = p$

$a + (-a) + c + (-c) + p = p$

$p = p$

PART B

Solve for the designated variable by use of multiplication or division.

1. Equation:

$48 = \dfrac{1}{2} \cdot 10 \cdot h$

Solve for h:

$48 \underline{\ (2)\ } = \dfrac{1}{2} \cdot 10 \cdot h \cdot \underline{\ (2)\ }$

$96 = \dfrac{1}{2} \cdot 2 \cdot 10 \cdot h$

$96 = 10h$

$96 \div \underline{\ 10\ } = 10h \div \underline{\ 10\ }$

$9.6 = \dfrac{10}{10} \cdot h$

$9.6 = h$

$h = 9.6$ $\underline{h = 9.6}$

Check: $48 = \dfrac{1}{2} \cdot 10 \cdot h$

$$48 = \frac{1}{2} \cdot 10 \cdot \underline{(9.6)}$$

$$48 = 5(9.6)$$

$$48 = 48$$

2. Equation:

$$a = \frac{1}{2} bh$$

Solve for h:

$$a \underline{} = \frac{1}{2} \cdot b \cdot h \cdot \underline{(2)}$$

$$2a = \frac{1}{2} \cdot 2 \cdot b \cdot h$$

$$2a = bh$$

$$2a \div \underline{} = bh \div \underline{}$$

$$\frac{(2a)}{b} = \left(\frac{b}{b}\right) \cdot h$$

$$\frac{(2a)}{b} = h$$

$$h = \frac{(2a)}{b}$$

$$h = \frac{(2a)}{b}$$

Check: $a = \dfrac{1}{2} bh$

$$a = \frac{1}{2} b \underline{\left(\frac{2a}{b}\right)}$$

$$a = \frac{2}{2} \cdot \frac{b}{b} \cdot a$$

$$a = 1 \cdot 1 \cdot a$$

$$a = a$$

PART C

Solve for the designated variable by use of addition or subtraction and multiplication or division.

1. Equation:

$$600 = \frac{1}{2} \cdot 10 \cdot (b + 20)$$

Solve for *b:*

$$\frac{2}{} (600) = \frac{2}{} \cdot \frac{1}{2} \cdot 10(b + 20)$$

$1,200 = 10(b + 20)$

$1,200 = 10b + 200$

$$1,200 + \frac{(-200)}{} = 10b + 200 + \frac{(-200)}{}$$

$1,000 = 10b$

$$1,000 \div \frac{10}{} = 10b \div \frac{10}{}$$

$100 = b$

$$\underline{100 = b}$$

Check: $600 = \frac{1}{2} \cdot 10 \cdot (b + 20)$

$$600 = \frac{1}{2} \cdot 10(100 + 20)$$

$$600 = 5\,\underline{(120)}$$

$$600 = 600$$

2. Equation:

$$A = \left(\frac{1}{2}\right)h(b + z)$$

Solve for *b:*

$$\frac{2}{} \cdot A = \frac{2}{} \cdot \frac{1}{2} \cdot h(b + z)$$

$2A = h(b + z)$

$2A = hb + hz$

$$2A + \frac{(-hz)}{} = hb + hz + \frac{(-hz)}{}$$

$2A + (-hz) = hb$

$$\frac{2A + (-hz)}{h} = \frac{hb}{h}$$

$$\frac{2A - hz}{h} = b$$

$$\underline{\frac{2A - hz}{h} = b}$$

Check: $A = \left(\frac{1}{2}\right)h\,(b + z)$

$$A = \left(\frac{1}{2}\right)h\left(\frac{2A - hz}{h} + z\right)$$

$$A = \left(\frac{1}{2}\right)h\left(\frac{2A - hz}{h} + \frac{hz}{h}\right)$$

$$A = \left(\frac{h}{2}\right)\left(\frac{2A - hz + hz}{h}\right)$$

$$A = \left(\frac{h}{2}\right) \cdot \left(\frac{2A}{h}\right)$$

$$A = \frac{2}{2} \cdot \frac{h}{h} \cdot A$$

$$A = A$$

Solving Equations for One Variable in Terms of Other Variables: Problems with Help

DIRECTIONS: Each of the following problems has been given a partial solution. Solve each problem by completing the given solution.

1. Equation:

$5 + n = b$

Solve for *n*:

$5 + n + (-5) = b + (-5)$

$\underline{5 + (-5) + n = b + (-5)}$

$\underline{0} + n = b + (-5)$

$\underline{n = b + (-5)}$ $\underline{n = b + (-5)}$

Check: $5 + n = b$

$5 + [b + (-5)] = b$

$5 + [(-5) + b] = b$

$[5 + (-5)] + b = b$

$\underline{0 + b = b}$

$\underline{b = b}$

2. Equation:

$6x + 2 = m$

Solve for *x*:

$6x + 2 + (-2) = m + (-2)$

$\underline{6x + 0} = m + -2$

$6x = \underline{m + -2}$

$\frac{1}{6} \cdot 6x = \frac{1}{6} \cdot (m + -2)$

$x = \frac{1}{6}m + \underline{\left(-\frac{2}{6}\right)}$

$x = \frac{1}{6}m + \underline{\left(-\frac{1}{3}\right)}$ $\underline{x = \frac{1m}{6} + \left(-\frac{1}{3}\right)}$

Check: $6x + 2 = m$

$$6\left[\frac{1m}{6} + \left(-\frac{1}{3}\right)\right] + 2 = m$$

$$6 \cdot \frac{1m}{6} + 6 \cdot \left(-\frac{1}{3}\right) + 2 = m$$

$$\frac{6m}{6} + (-2) + 2 = m$$

$$m = m$$

3. Equation:

$p = 3s$

Solve for s:

$$\frac{1}{3} \cdot p = \frac{1}{3} \cdot 3s$$

$$\frac{p}{3} = s$$

_____

Check: $p = 3s$

$$p = \frac{3\left(\dfrac{p}{3}\right)}{}$$

$$p = \frac{p}{}$$

$s = \dfrac{p}{3}$

_____

4. Equation:

$$V = \frac{4}{3}\pi r^3$$

Solve for r^3:

$$\frac{3}{4} \cdot V = \frac{3}{4} \cdot \underline{\frac{4}{3}} \cdot \pi r^3$$

$$\frac{\dfrac{3V}{4}}{} = \pi r^3$$

$$\frac{3V}{4\pi} = r^3$$

$r^3 = \dfrac{3V}{4\pi}$

_____

Check: $V = \dfrac{4}{3}\pi r^3$

$$V = \frac{4}{3}\pi \cdot \frac{3V}{4\pi}$$

$$V = V$$

5. Equation:

$A = bh$

Solve for *b:*

$$A \cdot \frac{1}{h} = b \cdot h \cdot \frac{1}{h}$$

$$\frac{A}{h} = b$$

$$b = \frac{A}{h}$$

Check: $A = bh$

$$A = \frac{A}{h} \cdot h$$

$$A = \frac{\frac{h}{h} \cdot A}{}$$

$$A = \underline{A}$$

6. Equation:

$$y = \frac{1}{x} + b$$

Solve for *x:*

$$y \cdot x = \left(\frac{1}{x} + b\right) \cdot x$$

$$yx = \left(\frac{x}{x}\right) + bx$$

$$yx = 1 + bx$$

$$yx + (-bx) = 1 + bx + (-bx)$$

$$yx + (-bx) = 1$$

$$x[y + (-b)] = 1$$

$$\frac{x[y + (-b)]}{[y + (-b)]} = \frac{1}{[y + (-b)]}$$

$$x = \frac{1}{y + (-b)}$$

$$x = \frac{1}{y + -b}$$

Introduce the complex fraction in which either numerator or denominator is a fraction.

Check: $y = \frac{1}{x} + b$

$$y = \frac{1}{\frac{1}{y + (-b)}} + b$$

$$y = \underline{y + (-b) + b}$$

$$y = \underline{y}$$

Challenge

This is included because
of its importance in sci-
ence.

7. Equation:

$$F = \frac{9C}{5} + 32$$

Solve for C:

$$\underline{\frac{5}{9}} \cdot F = \underline{\frac{5}{9}} \left(\frac{9C}{5} + 32 \right)$$

$$\frac{5F}{9} = \frac{5}{9} \cdot \frac{9C}{5} + \frac{5}{9} \cdot 32$$

$$\frac{5F}{9} = \underline{\quad C \quad} + \frac{5}{9} \cdot 32$$

$$\frac{5F}{9} - \frac{5}{9} \cdot 32 = C + \frac{5}{9} \cdot 32 - \frac{5}{9} \cdot 32$$

$$\frac{5}{9} \underline{\quad (F - 32) \quad} = C$$

$$C = \frac{5}{9}(F - 32)$$

Check: $F = \dfrac{9C}{5} + 32$

$$F = \frac{9}{5} \left[\frac{5}{9}(F - 32) \right] + \underline{\quad 32 \quad}$$

$$F = \underline{\quad F \quad} - 32 + 32$$

$$F = \underline{\quad F \quad}$$

Solving Equations for One Variable in Terms of Other Variables: Problems

DIRECTIONS: Solve each of the equations for the indicated variable in the space provided. Write your answers in the blank to the right after each problem.

1. Equation:

$$zx + c = 1$$

Solve for x:

$$zx + c + (-c) = 1 + (-c)$$

$$zx = 1 + (-c)$$

$$\frac{1}{z} \cdot zx = \frac{1}{z}[1 + (-c)]$$

$$x = \frac{1}{z} + \left(-\frac{c}{z}\right)$$

$$x = \frac{1}{z} - \frac{c}{z}, \text{ or } \frac{1-c}{z}$$

or

$$x = \frac{1}{z} - \frac{c}{z}$$

$$x = \frac{1-c}{z}$$

_____

Check: $zx + c = 1$

$$z\left(\frac{1}{z} + -\frac{c}{z}\right) + c = 1$$

$$z\left(\frac{1}{z}\right) + z\left(\frac{-c}{z}\right) + c = 1$$

$$1 + \frac{z}{z} \cdot (-c) + c = 1$$

$$1 + 1 \cdot (-c) + c = 1$$

$$1 = 1$$

2. Equation:

$$ax + y = c$$

Solve for y:

$$ax + y + (-ax) = c + (-ax)$$

$$y + ax + (-ax) = c + (-ax)$$

$$y = c + (-ax)$$

$$y = c + (-ax)$$

_____

Check: $ax + y = c$

$ax + [c + (-ax)] = c$

$ax + c + (-ax) = c$

$ax + (-ax) + c = c$

$c = c$

3. Equation:

$$A = \frac{1}{2} bh$$

Solve for b:

$$A(2) = \frac{1}{2} \cdot b \cdot h \cdot 2$$

$$2A = \frac{1}{2} \cdot 2 \cdot b \cdot h$$

$$2A = \frac{2}{2} \cdot b \cdot h$$

$$2A = 1 \cdot b \cdot h$$

$$2A = bh$$

$$\frac{2A}{h} = 1 \cdot b$$

$$b = \frac{2A}{h}$$

$$b = \frac{2A}{h}$$

Check: $A = \frac{1}{2} bh$

$$A = \frac{1}{2}\left(\frac{2A}{h}\right)h$$

$$A = \frac{1}{2} \cdot \frac{2A}{h} \cdot h$$

$$A = A$$

4. Equation:

$$\frac{1}{x} + \frac{1}{y} = z$$

Solve for x:

$$xy \cdot \frac{1}{x} + xy \cdot \frac{1}{y} = xy \cdot z$$

$$\frac{xy}{x} + \frac{xy}{y} = xyz$$

$$y + x = xyz$$

$$y + x + (-y) = xyz + (-y)$$

$$x = xyz + (-y)$$

$$x + (-xyz) = xyz + (-y) + (-xyz)$$

$$x + (-xyz) = -y + 0$$

$$x[1 + (-yz)] = -y$$

$$\frac{x[1 + (-yz)]}{[1 + (-yz)]} = \frac{-y}{[1 + (-yz)]}$$

$$x = \frac{-y}{1 + (-yz)} \qquad \qquad \underline{x = \frac{-y}{1 + (-yz)}}$$

Check: $\dfrac{1}{x} + \dfrac{1}{y} = z$

$$\left[1 \div \frac{-y}{1 + (-yz)}\right] + \frac{1}{y} = z$$

$$\frac{1 + -(yz)}{-y} + \frac{1}{y} = z$$

$$-\frac{1}{y} + z + \frac{1}{y} = z$$

$$z = z$$

Challenge **5.** Equation:

This is included because of its importance in science.

$$C = \frac{5}{9}(F - 32)$$

Solve for F:

$$\frac{9}{5} \cdot C = \frac{9}{5} \cdot \frac{5}{9}(F - 32)$$

$$\frac{9C}{5} = F - 32$$

$$\frac{9C}{5} + 32 = F \qquad \qquad \underline{F = \frac{9C}{5} + 32}$$

Check: $C = \dfrac{5}{9}(F - 32)$

$$C = \frac{5}{9}\left(\frac{9C}{5} + 32 - 32\right)$$

$$C = \frac{5}{9} \cdot \frac{9C}{5}$$

$$C = C$$